D0235916

SCIENCE AND
TECHNOLOGY (ST)

APPLIED SCIENCE
AND TECHNOLOGY (AST)

OBSERVATORY

THE HUMAN
ORGANISM

STUDENT BOOK
First Year of Secondary Cycle Two

J. Robert Lalonde
Series Editor

Marie-Danielle Cyr
Jean-Sébastien Verreault

ÉDITIONS DU RENOUVEAU PÉDAGOGIQUE INC.

5757, RUE CYPIHOT
SAINT-LAURENT (QUÉBEC)
H4S 1R3

TÉLÉPHONE : (514) 334-2690
TÉLÉCOPIEUR : (514) 334-4720
erpidlm@erpi.com

English Edition

Managing editor
Yzabelle Martineau

Translation
Freeman Translation
Kelli Ann Ferrigan

Project editor and copy editor
Elizabeth Lewis

Proofreader
My-Trang Nguyen

Photo research and permissions
Marie-Chantal Masson

Art director
Hélène Cousineau

Graphic design coordinator
Sylvie Piotte

Electronic publishing
Mardigrafe inc.

Cartography
Dimension DPR

Consultants

Samira Cohen Spain, science and technology teacher,
New Frontiers School Board

Danielle Hamel, science and technology teacher,
Eastern Townships School Board

Alison Hurst, science and technology teacher,
Sir Wilfrid Laurier School Board

Mary Lum, science and technology teacher,
New Frontiers School Board

Gilles Roussin, science and technology teacher,
West Island College

Valérie Vien, science and technology teacher,
West Island College

Original French Edition

Managing editor
Monique Boucher

Project editors and copy editors
Marielle Champagne
Carole Lambert
Hélène Pelletier
Sylvie Racine

Copy editor
Luc Asselin

Proofreader
Pierre-Yves L'Heureux

Photo research and permissions
Marie-Chantal Masson

Art director
Hélène Cousineau

Graphic design coordinator
Sylvie Piotte

Cover design
Claire Senneville

Graphic design
Valérie Deltour
Frédérique Bouvier

Electronic publishing
Valérie Deltour

Illustrations
Michel Rouleau

Cartography
Dimension DPR

Writers
Hélène Crevier (INFO features)
Dominique Forget (newspaper article adaptations)
Danielle Ouellet (FOLLOW-UP features)

Consultants

Annie Châteauneuf, science and technology teacher,
Polyvalente Chanoine-Armand-Racicot, Commission scolaire
des Hautes-Rivières
Chantale Dionne, science and technology teacher, Polyvalente
de Jonquière, Commission scolaire de la Jonquière

Science content reviewers

Luce Boulanger, clinical biochemist

Josée Brisson, chemist and professor at Université Laval

Normand Brunet, biologist and assistant professor
at Institut des sciences de l'environnement, UQAM

Éric Duchemin, biologist, geologist, chemist
and specialist in environmental science

Richard Gagnon, physicist

Richard Mathieu, biologist and teacher at Cégep
de Drummondville

Guy Olivier, engineer and professor at École
Polytechnique de Montréal

Bruno Tremblay, climatologist and assistant professor
in the Department of Atmospheric and Oceanic Sciences,
McGill University

Registration of copyright – Bibliothèque et Archives nationales du Québec, 2009
Registration of copyright – Library and Archives Canada, 2009

Printed in Canada   1234567890 HLN 09
ISBN 978-2-7613-2746-6   11072 ABCD PSM12

These programs are funded by Québec's Ministère de l'Éducation, du Loisir et du Sport, through contributions from the Canada-Québec Agreement on Minority-Language Education and Second-Language Instruction.

TABLE OF CONTENTS

This manuel covers the programs Science and Technology (ST) and Applications of Science and Technology (AST). Several parts of the manual are particular to one or the other program, as indicated by the colour bars (see pages VII and VIII).

ST only

AST only

CHAPTER 3

THE HUMAN ORGANISM AND THE BEHAVIOUR OF FLUIDS 65

CHAPTER 4

THE HUMAN ORGANISM AND
THE PERCEPTION OF LIGHT AND SOUND 91

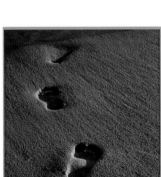

CHAPTER 12

THE HUMAN ORGANISM AND TECHNOLOGY IN ACTION

OBSERVATORY

AT A GLANCE

OPENING PAGE
OF AN AREA

The title of the area

A brief presentation of the area

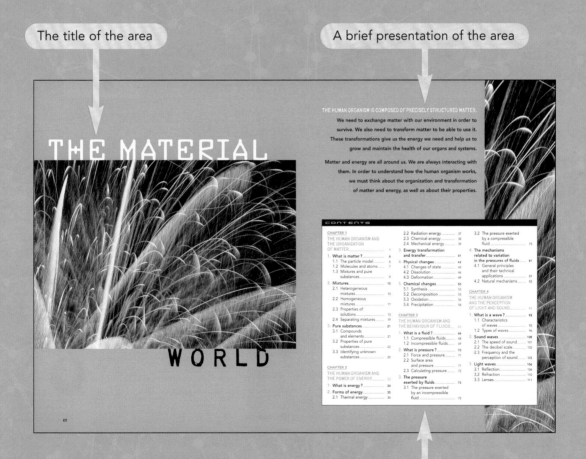

THE MATERIAL

WORLD

THE HUMAN ORGANISM IS COMPOSED OF PRECISELY STRUCTURED MATTER.
We need to exchange matter with our environment in order to
survive. We also need to transform matter to be able to use it.
These transformations give us the energy we need and help us to
grow and maintain the health of our organs and systems.

Matter and energy are all around us. We are always interacting with
them. In order to understand how the human organism works,
we must think about the organization and transformation
of matter and energy, as well as about their properties.

The contents of the chapter in the area

CHAPTER FEATURES

The **Introduction** establishes concrete links between the chapter content and the human organism, the program theme for the first year of Secondary Cycle Two.

The **Timeline** lists discoveries and inventions linked to concepts introduced in the chapter from the beginning of human history until present day.

The **Cycle One** pictogram identifies concepts studied in Secondary Cycle One.

Etymology notes provide a better understanding of more abstract or complex words.

Definitions of program concepts are in colour and reviewed in the Glossary.

1.24 In order to get these jeans really clean, we need to choose a solvent in which the stains are the most soluble.

1.25 Sugar dissolves faster and in larger amounts in hot cocoa than in cold milk. The solubility of sugar increases as its temperature increases.

1.26 An open bottle of soda pop releases increasing amounts of carbon dioxide as its temperature increases.

Photos are often used to support the text.

 SEPARATING MIXTURES

Mixtures exist everywhere in nature; in fact, there are practically no pure substances in nature. We have to apply purification techniques to obtain pure substances. Many techniques are physical separations, that is, they separate the constituents of a mixture without changing their nature (Figure 1.27, next page). When it is impossible to physically separate a substance any further, then we have a pure substance.

Here are a few examples of cases where we commonly separate the constituents of a mixture:

● to make water safe for drinking, we remove any impurities and **PATHOGENS** that may be present.

● to obtain gas, diesel fuel, tar, furnace oil and so on, we process oil, separating it into its various constituents.

● to obtain many of the metals that we use in manufacturing (such as gold, silver and copper), we purify their ore, that is, remove the rock that makes up part of the various minerals.

Sometimes, we need to use more than one separation technique in order to obtain the substance(s) we want. For example, in a water filtration plant, we use the processes of both decantation and filtration (next page) to make water safe for drinking. In spite of this, the water is still not 100 percent pure. If we wanted to purify the water completely, we would need to use a distillation process.

WHAT TO CHOOSE ?
In Canada, bottled water, like tap water, is strictly regulated. According to Health Canada guidelines, neither variety poses a health risk and the choice of one or the other is a matter of personal preference.

HOW TO SEPARATE A MIXTURE

THE ORGANIZATION OF MATTER 19

The **Info brief** feature recounts examples of the amazing phenomena that occur in everyday life that can help students relate to the world around them. When present, the pictogram indicates the existence of an activity handout for distribution among the students.

This pictogram refers to the **Toolbox,** which refers to skills that the student must know in order to deal with chapter content, conduct an experiment or carry out a technical activity.

Words in the text written in small **CAPITALS** are defined in the Glossary.

These pictograms are reminders that there are **LABS** (science laboratories) or **TECH** (technological laboratories) related to the content at hand.

Illustrations and **Tables** support the students' understanding of concepts.

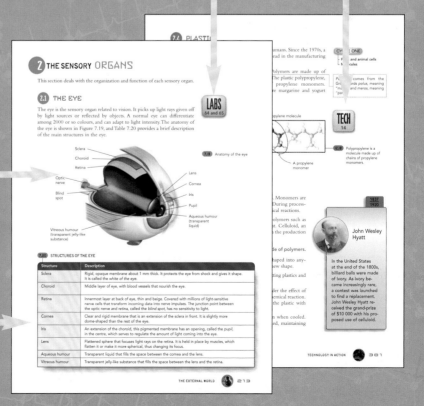

2 THE SENSORY ORGANS

This section deals with the organization and function of each sensory organ.

2.1 THE EYE

The eye is the sensory organ related to vision. It picks up light rays given off by light sources or reflected by objects. A normal eye can differentiate among 2000 or so colours, and can adapt to light intensity. The anatomy of the eye is shown in Figure 7.19, and Table 7.20 provides a brief description of the main structures in the eye.

7.19 Anatomy of the eye

Sclera
Choroid
Retina
Optic nerve
Blind spot
Lens
Cornea
Iris
Pupil
Aqueous humour (transparent liquid)
Vitreous humour (transparent jelly-like substance)

7.20 STRUCTURES OF THE EYE

Structure	Description
Sclera	Rigid, opaque membrane about 1 mm thick. It protects the eye from shock and gives it shape. It is called the white of the eye.
Choroid	Middle layer of eye, with blood vessels that nourish the eye.
Retina	Innermost layer at back of eye, thin and beige. Covered with millions of light-sensitive nerve cells that transform incoming data into nerve impulses. The junction point between the optic nerve and retina, called the blind spot, has no sensitivity to light.
Cornea	Clear and rigid membrane that is an extension of the sclera in front. It is slightly more dome-shaped than the rest of the eye.
Iris	An extension of the choroid, this pigmented membrane has an opening, called the pupil, in the centre, which serves to regulate the amount of light coming into the eye.
Lens	Flattened sphere that focuses light rays on the retina. It is held in place by muscles, which flatten it or make it more spherical, thus changing its focus.
Aqueous humour	Transparent liquid that fills the space between the cornea and the lens.
Vitreous humour	Transparent jelly-like substance that fills the space between the lens and the retina.

THE EXTERNAL WORLD 213

7.4 PLASTIC

...umans. Since the 1970s, a ...ead in the manufacturing

...olymers are made up of ...The plastic polypropylene, ... propylene monomers, ...re margarine and yogurt

CYCLE ONE
● P...t and animal cells
● M...molecules

P...comes from the Gr...ords polis, meaning "m...and meros, meaning "par..."

LABS 64 and 65

...opylene molecule

TECH 14

7.26 Polypropylene is a molecule made up of chains of propylene monomers.

A propylene monomer

... Monomers are ...During process-...cal reactions.

...olymers such as ...t. Celluloid is ...the production

...de of polymers.

...haped into any-...w shape.

...ting plastics and

...der the effect of ...emical reaction. ...the plastic with

...n when cooled. ...d, maintaining

1837 1920
John Wesley Hyatt

In the United States at the end of the 1800s, billiard balls were made of ivory. As ivory became increasingly rare, a contest was launched to find a replacement. John Wesley Hyatt received the grand-prize of $10 000 with his proposed use of celluloid.

TECHNOLOGY IN ACTION 381

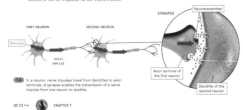

Brief **Biographies** underscore the contributions made by many different people to important advancements in the field of science or technology.

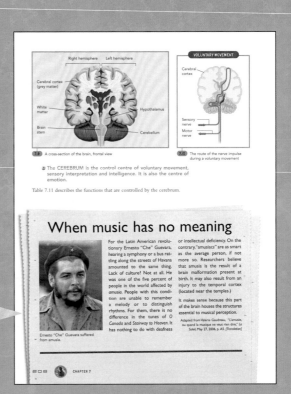

Summaries of actual newspaper and magazine **Articles** set concepts covered in the chapter within the context of current events.

Connections emphasize the links between the concepts covered in the chapter and the disciplines of mathematics, history or physical education.

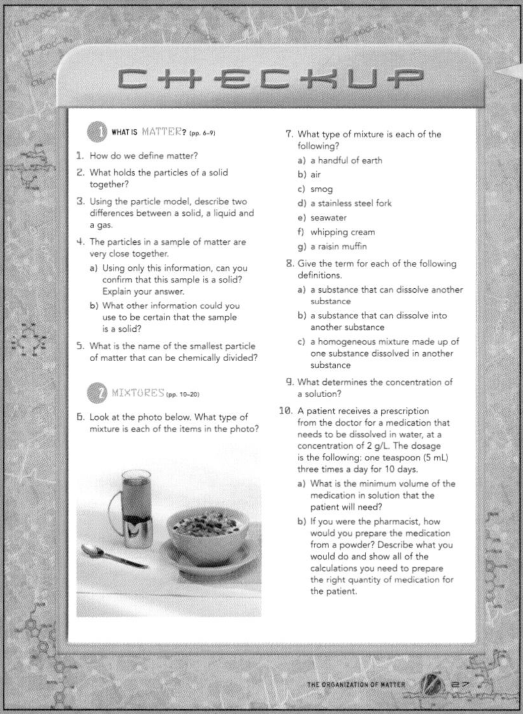

CHECKUP

1 WHAT IS MATTER? (pp. 6–9)

1. How do we define matter?
2. What holds the particles of a solid together?
3. Using the particle model, describe two differences between a solid, a liquid and a gas.
4. The particles in a sample of matter are very close together.
   a) Using only this information, can you confirm that this sample is a solid? Explain your answer.
   b) What other information could you use to be certain that the sample is a solid?
5. What is the name of the smallest particle of matter that can be chemically divided?

2 MIXTURES (pp. 10–20)

6. Look at the photo below. What type of mixture is each of the items in the photo?
7. What type of mixture is each of the following?
   a) a handful of earth
   b) air
   c) smog
   d) a stainless steel fork
   e) seawater
   f) whipping cream
   g) a raisin muffin
8. Give the term for each of the following definitions.
   a) a substance that can dissolve another substance
   b) a substance that can dissolve into another substance
   c) a homogeneous mixture made up of one substance dissolved in another substance
9. What determines the concentration of a solution?
10. A patient receives a prescription from the doctor for a medication that needs to be dissolved in water, at a concentration of 2 g/L. The dosage is the following: one teaspoon (5 mL) three times a day for 10 days.
    a) What is the minimum volume of the medication in solution that the patient will need?
    b) If you were the pharmacist, how would you prepare the medication from a powder? Describe what you would do and show all of the calculations you need to prepare the right quantity of medication for the patient.

THE ORGANIZATION OF MATTER 27

Checkup contains questions on the chapter as a whole and concludes with the construction of a Concept map.

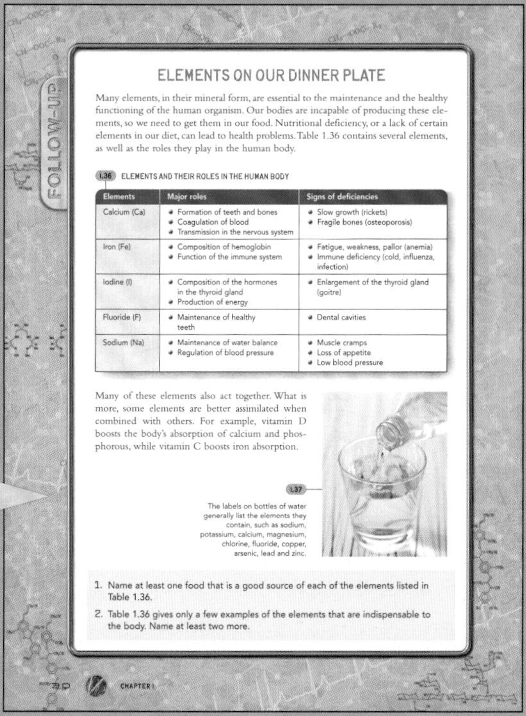

FOLLOW-UP

ELEMENTS ON OUR DINNER PLATE

Many elements, in their mineral form, are essential to the maintenance and the healthy functioning of the human organism. Our bodies are incapable of producing these elements, so we need to get them in our food. Nutritional deficiency, or a lack of certain elements in our diet, can lead to health problems. Table 1.36 contains several elements, as well as the roles they play in the human body.

1.36 ELEMENTS AND THEIR ROLES IN THE HUMAN BODY

Elements	Major roles	Signs of deficiencies
Calcium (Ca)	• Formation of teeth and bones • Coagulation of blood • Transmission in the nervous system	• Slow growth (rickets) • Fragile bones (osteoporosis)
Iron (Fe)	• Composition of hemoglobin • Function of the immune system	• Fatigue, weakness, pallor (anemia) • Immune deficiency (cold, influenza, infection)
Iodine (I)	• Composition of the hormones in the thyroid gland • Production of energy	• Enlargement of the thyroid gland (goitre)
Fluoride (F)	• Maintenance of healthy teeth	• Dental cavities
Sodium (Na)	• Maintenance of water balance • Regulation of blood pressure	• Muscle cramps • Loss of appetite • Low blood pressure

Many of these elements also act together. What is more, some elements are better assimilated when combined with others. For example, vitamin D boosts the body's absorption of calcium and phosphorous, while vitamin C boosts iron absorption.

1.37 The labels on bottles of water generally list the elements they contain, such as sodium, potassium, calcium, magnesium, chlorine, fluoride, copper, arsenic, lead and zinc.

1. Name at least one food that is a good source of each of the elements listed in Table 1.36.
2. Table 1.36 gives only a few examples of the elements that are indispensable to the body. Name at least two more.

30 CHAPTER 1

Follow-up provides analysis of various problems related to human health.

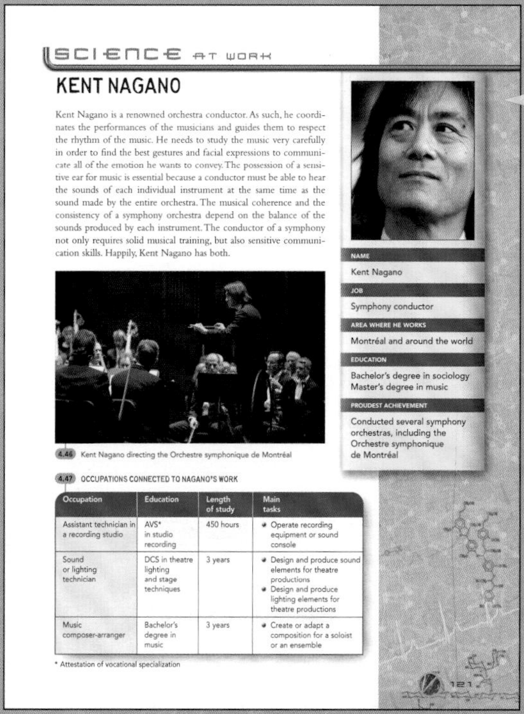

SCIENCE AT WORK

KENT NAGANO

Kent Nagano is a renowned orchestra conductor. As such, he coordinates the performances of the musicians and guides them to respect the rhythm of the music. He needs to study the music very carefully in order to find the best gestures and facial expressions to communicate all of the emotion he wants to convey. The possession of a sensitive ear for music is essential because a conductor must be able to hear the sounds of each individual instrument at the same time as the sound made by the entire orchestra. The musical coherence and the consistency of a symphony orchestra depend on the balance of the sounds produced by each instrument. The conductor of a symphony not only requires solid musical training, but also sensitive communication skills. Happily, Kent Nagano has both.

4.46 Kent Nagano directing the Orchestre symphonique de Montréal

NAME
Kent Nagano

JOB
Symphony conductor

AREA WHERE HE WORKS
Montréal and around the world

EDUCATION
Bachelor's degree in sociology
Master's degree in music

PROUDEST ACHIEVEMENT
Conducted several symphony orchestras, including the Orchestre symphonique de Montréal

4.47 OCCUPATIONS CONNECTED TO NAGANO'S WORK

Occupation	Education	Length of study	Main tasks
Assistant technician in a recording studio	AVS* in studio recording	450 hours	• Operate recording equipment or sound console
Sound or lighting technician	DCS in theatre lighting and stage techniques	3 years	• Design and produce sound elements for theatre productions • Design and produce lighting elements for theatre productions
Music composer-arranger	Bachelor's degree in music	3 years	• Create or adapt a composition for a soloist or an ensemble

* Attestation of vocational specialization

121

Science at work highlights inspiring individuals and the trades or professions associated with their particular field of work.

APPENDIXES

The appendixes contain reference tables used in the study of various concepts. A periodic table of elements is included on the inside back cover of the textbook.

APPENDIX I

PROPERTIES OF COMMON SUBSTANCES

SUBSTANCES IN GASEOUS PHASE AT 20°

Substance (chemical formula)	Description	Characteristics and applications	Dangers and precautions	MP (°C)	BP (°C)	(g/mL at 20°C)	Solubility in water at 20°C	Chemical properties
Ammonia (NH₃)	Colourless Characteristic odour	Manufacture of cleaning products and fertilizers Refrigeration	Highly toxic, irritating and corrosive Can cause burns	-78	-33	0.000 75	531	Forms white smoke with hydrogen chloride Extinguishes flame Neutral litmus paper turns blue
Carbon dioxide (CO₂)	Colourless Odourless Does not exist in liquid form	Product of combustion Soft drinks Dry ice (solid form)	Causes greenhouse effect	-79²	N/A	0.001 98	1.6	Extinguishes flame Turns limewater cloudy Neutral litmus paper turns red
Carbon monoxide (CO)	Colourless Odourless	By-product of incomplete combustion	Deadly if inhaled Flammable	-207	-192	0.001 25	0.26	Produces bright-blue flame
Chlorine (Cl₂)	Greenish-yellow Suffocating odour	Ingredient of disinfectants Treatment of drinking water Bleaching agent	Highly toxic Irritating to respiratory tract, eyes and skin	-102	-35	0.002 94	7.3	Reignites an incandescent ember
Helium (He)	Colourless Odourless	Inflating balloons Cryogenics Welding Refrigeration	Generally non-toxic, but can cause asphyxia if inhaled in large quantity	-272	-269	0.000 18	0.0017	Inert (does not react) Extinguishes flame
Hydrogen (H₂)	Colourless Odourless	Production of various substances (ammonia, hydrogenated vegetable oil) Rocket fuel	Explosive when near a flame Can cause asphyxia	-259	-253	0.000 09	0.002	Explodes when exposed to burning wood splint

416   APPENDIX I

GLOSSARY

The **Glossary** includes terms essential to the comprehension of concepts.

Definitions can also be found on the pages indicated in bold.

A

Absolute dating: method used to determine the age of fossils in years (p. 325)

Absorption: passage of nutrients from the digestive tract into the blood or lymph (p. 171)

Alloy: result of mixing a metal with one or more metallic or non-metallic substances (p. 379)

Alternating current (AC): an electric current in which electrons flow in a back-and-forth motion (p. 400)

Amplitude (of a wave): maximum distance travelled by a particle in a medium compared to its position at equilibrium (p. 94)

Antibody: substance secreted by white blood cells to neutralize invaders (p. 189)

Antigen: substance recognized as foreign by the body and that triggers the body's white blood cells to produce antibodies (p. 189)

Artery: blood vessel that carries blood from the heart to other parts of the body (p. 183)

Assembly process: series of operations in which various parts are put together to produce a technical object (p. 407)

Assisted reproduction: all medical procedures used to help women become pregnant (p. 258)

Asteroid: celestial body of irregular shape, in orbit around the Sun (p. 283)

Astronomical unit (AU): unit of measurement equal to about 150 million km, the average distance between Earth and the Sun (p. 281)

Atmospheric pressure: pressure exerted by the atmosphere (p. 79)

Atom: smallest particle of matter; it cannot be divided by chemical means (pp. 8, 36)

B

Bacteria: unicellular organisms without nuclei (p. 236)

Basic lines: lines whose appearance and meaning are determined by international agreements (p. 338)

Basic mechanical function: role played by a component or a group of components in the function or assembly of a technical object (p. 383)

Biotechnology: collection of technologies that are applied to living organisms or substances derived from living organisms in order to meet a need or a want (p. 236)

Blood compatibility: fact that one person can receive blood from another person (p. 181)

Blood transfusion: injection of blood into a person (p. 180)

Bone: hard solid organ that forms part of the skeleton (p. 222)

Brain: parts of the central nervous system located in the cranium (p. 206)

Brain stem: control centre of internal stimuli as well as of involuntary movement (p. 211)

C

Capillary: blood vessel with a small diameter and very thin walls in which exchanges between the blood and the cells of organs occur (p. 183)

Celestial body: any natural objects in the Universe; synonym of celestial object (p. 283)

Cell: basic unit of life (p. 126)

Cell culture: laboratory technique that involves growing or culturing cells outside of their natural environment (p. 240)

Cell division: process that is essential to the production of new cells for the purpose of growth, tissue repair and sexual reproduction (p. 131)

Cellular respiration: process essential to life by which a cell produces energy through nutrient combustion, such as glucose (pp. 39, 172)

Centrifugation: process that accelerates and amplifies the separation of components of a mixture using a centrifuge, a high-speed rotating machine (pp. 20, 177)

Cerebellum: centre of balance and movement coordination (p. 210)

Cerebrum: control centre of voluntary movement, sensory interpretation and intelligence. It is also the centre of emotion (p. 208)

Characteristic property: property that helps us identify a pure substance or the group to which the pure substance belongs (p. 23)

Chemical change: change that transforms the nature and characteristic properties of matter (p. 50)

Chemical energy: energy stored in the bonds of a molecule (p. 38)

Chemical transformation (in digestive tract): process that breaks down the complex molecules of food into simpler molecules. These changes occur with the help of secretions from the digestive glands (p. 170)

432   GLOSSARY

INDEX

The **Index** lists all keywords and the pages where they appear.

XIV

THE MATERIAL

WORLD

THE HUMAN ORGANISM IS COMPOSED OF PRECISELY STRUCTURED MATTER.
We need to exchange matter with our environment in order to survive. We also need to transform matter to be able to use it. These transformations give us the energy we need and help us to grow and maintain the health of our organs and systems.

Matter and energy are all around us. We are always interacting with them. In order to understand how the human organism works, we must think about the organization and transformation of matter and energy, as well as about their properties.

CONTENTS

1986 — Discovery of fullerenes, a family of molecules shaped like soccerballs

1944 — Development of paper chromatography

1898 — Discovery of radium and polonium, the first radioactive elements

1869 — Publication of first version of current periodic table

1860 — Distinction made between atoms and molecules

1827 — Brownian motion of particles observed

1807 — Dalton's atomic theory

1781 — Discovery that water is not an element

1754 — Discovery of chemical composition of carbon dioxide

1661 — Concept of chemical elements

1619 — Discovery of carbon dioxide

CIRCA -400 — Emergence of idea that matter is composed of atoms; at first rejected, only to reappear in the 19th century

CIRCA -450 — Emergence of idea that all matter is composed of four elements: air, water, earth and fire

THE HUMAN ORGANISM

AND THE ORGANIZATION OF MATTER

Everything that makes up the human body—skin, bones, muscles, blood—is matter, just as everything around us is matter, from the air we breathe to the food we eat and the objects we use. But how do we tell the difference between the air we breathe, the water we drink and the earth we walk on? How many different kinds of matter are there? What can we learn by studying them? Since we depend entirely on matter, we are better off learning how it is organized, so we can benefit from its properties.

1 WHAT IS MATTER?

The air we breathe, the water and food we consume and the materials we use are all made of matter. We ourselves are made of matter. Basically, anything that takes up space and has mass is matter.

> ▶ MATTER is anything that has volume and mass.

CYCLE ONE
- Volume
- Mass
- States of matter
- Atom
- Molecule

1.1 THE PARTICLE MODEL

The particle model is a tool that can help us learn more about matter.

A model is a simplified version of reality. It helps us make an abstract or difficult-to-observe phenomenon, process or system more tangible. In science, a model also helps us understand observed behaviours by comparing how they relate to one another. It also helps us to predict new behaviours. Although every model has its limits, a good working model can always be modified and perfected.

The particle model is an example of a scientific model. It draws on the idea that matter is not continuous, but is instead made up of particles. More specifically, the model is based on the following statements:

Particle comes from the Latin word *particula*, meaning "little bit or part."

- Matter is made up of particles that are extremely small.
- These particles are in constant movement.
- When the temperature increases, the movement of these particles increases.
- The particles may be held together by forces of attraction.

> ▶ The PARTICLE MODEL is a scientific model based on the idea that matter is made up of small particles.

In this book, this model is used to explain different phenomena related to matter.

Robert Brown

1773
1858

In 1827, this Scottish botanist discovered that particles of a material in suspension in a liquid or in a gas are in constant motion. Today, this is called *Brownian motion*.

PHASES OF MATTER

The particle model helps us examine three different types of matter: sugar, water and oxygen (Figures 1.1–1.3). The illustrations show the three phases that matter generally assumes: solid, liquid or gas. The model helps us understand how the particles in each of these phases are organized as well as how they behave.

Solid phase

The particles in a solid are very close to each other because they are bound by strong forces of attraction. In Figure 1.1, we can see that the sugar particles appear to be very organized. The particles in a solid have very little freedom to move around. They can only vibrate in one spot. This gives the solid a definite structure and shape, which is why a solid generally does not need to be in a container in order to hold its shape and volume.

Liquid phase

In a liquid, the particles are also very close together. They are, however, bound by forces that are weaker than those in solids. In Figure 1.2, we can see that the water particles are fairly disorganized. They have more freedom to move than in solids, and can slide over each other. Liquids have a definite volume but an indefinite form, which means they assume the shape of the container they are in, but lose their shape when they are poured out.

Gaseous phase

The particles of a gas are very far apart; they are not bound by forces of attraction. In Figure 1.3, we can see that there is lots of space between the particles and thus ample freedom of movement. They take up all the space they are given. Gases do not have definite shape or volume. If we open a container of gas, some of the gas will naturally escape.

1.2 MOLECULES AND ATOMS

The particle model stipulates that matter is made up of particles. To find out why the particles of different substances are not the same, and to learn more about the nature of the particles that make up matter, we need to use another scientific model, called the *atomic model* of matter.

The atomic model is based on experiments that were performed over the last century. Thanks to the knowledge that these experiments have revealed, we now know that the particles that make up matter are either molecules or atoms.

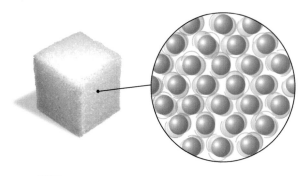
1.1 Particles of solid sugar

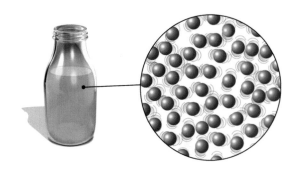
1.2 Particles of liquid water

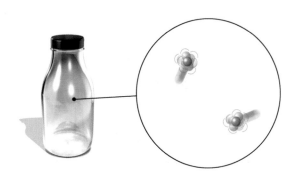
1.3 Particles of oxygen gas

An atom is the smallest, indivisible unit of matter that exists. Take for example a piece of graphite (a pencil lead). If we grind it, we get carbon powder. If it was possible to separate the grains of powder until we had the smallest possible particles of carbon, we would have carbon atoms.

Atom comes from the Greek word *atomos*, meaning "indivisible."

▶ An ATOM is the smallest particle of matter. It cannot be divided by chemical means.

In nature, atoms are rarely all alone. Usually they are chemically bound to other atoms forming molecules. Most of the particles that make up the countless natural substances in our world are actually molecules, that is, groups of atoms held together by chemical bonds.

1.4 When we grind a piece of graphite, we get carbon powder. Each of the individual grains of powder contains billions of carbon atoms. An atom, therefore, is extremely small.

▶ A MOLECULE is a group of two or more atoms held together by chemical bonds.

If we return to the three substances shown in Figures 1.1 to 1.3 (sugar, water and oxygen), we can see that their smallest particles are molecules and atoms.

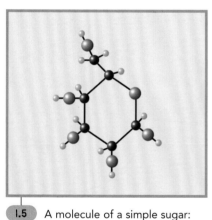

1.5 A molecule of a simple sugar: glucose

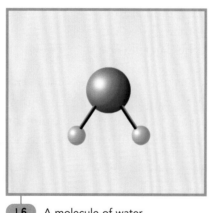

1.6 A molecule of water

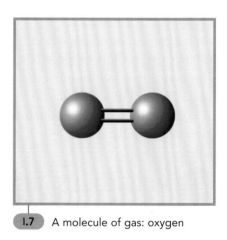

1.7 A molecule of gas: oxygen

A glucose molecule is made up of three types of atoms: carbon (black), hydrogen (white) and oxygen (red). The black lines between the atoms represent the chemical bonds that hold the atoms together. The water molecule is made up of two hydrogen atoms and one oxygen atom. Lastly, the oxygen molecule contains only one kind of atom: oxygen.

All existing matter is formed with a relatively small number of different kinds of atoms (about one hundred). Basically, it works like a construction set: we just have to organize atoms in the right combinations and we can build all the molecules on Earth.

Now you can see them!

Just a few decades ago, a microscope powerful enough to allow us to see atoms would have been an impossibility. Now however, thanks to the work carried out in Zurich in 1981 by German engineer Gerd Binnig and his Swiss colleague Heinrich Rohrer, it is possible. Their secret? They use a scanning tunnelling microscope (stm), which makes use of a natural physical phenomenon called "quantum tunnelling."

The principle behind the instrument is relatively simple. Take the very fine conducting tip of an stm and place it extremely close to the object to be examined (at a distance of about 100 000 times less than the width of a hair). Then apply an electrical charge to the tip. Electrons move through the virtual "tunnel" thus established between the two surfaces, creating a low electrical current. The closer the tip gets to the surface of the sample, the stronger the cur-

This picture shows a pile of gold atoms (shown in yellow, orange and red) on the surface of carbon atoms (shown in green). The colours were added to make the atoms more visible.

rent. By measuring the strength of the current, scientists are able to detect the bumps on the object's surface that are formed by the atoms.

This instrument earned its inventors the Nobel prize for physics in 1986.

Adapted from Henri-Pierre Penel, "Le microscope à effet tunnel," *Science et vie*, December 2003, pp. 168-170. *[Translation]*

1.3 MIXTURES AND PURE SUBSTANCES

Atoms can bind chemically to other atoms to form molecules. Atoms and molecules can also be mixed together without forming chemical bonds. When a substance contains at least two types of particles (atoms or molecules), we call it a *mixture*. When all the particles in a substance are identical, we consider it a *pure substance*.

- ▶ A MIXTURE consists of at least two different substances, that is, it contains at least two types of particles.

- ▶ A PURE SUBSTANCE consists of one substance, that is, it contains only one type of particle.

Figure 1.8 provides an overview of the organization of matter. It is described in more detail in the following pages.

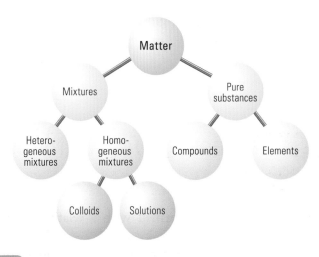

1.8 Organization of matter

2 MIXTURES

Mixtures can be divided into two types: heterogeneous mixtures and homogeneous mixtures.

Take a look at Figure 1.9. Which mixtures are heterogeneous? Which ones are homogeneous?

CYCLE ONE
- The separation of mixtures
- Mixtures
- Solutions

SOUP

APPLE JUICE

MAYONNAISE

TEN-KARAT GOLD RING

GRANITE

MILK

1.9 Examples of mixtures

2.1 HETEROGENEOUS MIXTURES

The soup and the granite in Figure 1.9 are obviously mixtures, because we can see with our eyes what they are made of. Their constituents are not uniformly mixed. We call them heterogeneous mixtures.

> ▶ A HETEROGENEOUS MIXTURE is made up of at least two substances that can be distinguished with the naked eye.

Heterogeneous comes from the Greek words *heteros*, meaning "different," and *genos*, meaning "kind, gender, race."

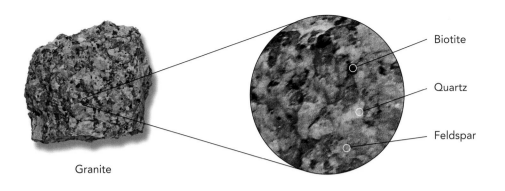

Granite

 1.10 In a chunk of granite, we can see grains of biotite (black), quartz (white) and feldspar (pink). Thus, granite is a heterogeneous mixture.

Biotite

Quartz

Feldspar

2.2 HOMOGENEOUS MIXTURES

Let's look at Figure 1.9 again. The apple juice, mayonnaise, gold ring and milk are less obviously mixtures. Their various constituents cannot be seen with the naked eye. Their constituents are uniformly combined and therefore they are called *homogeneous* *mixtures*.

Homogeneous comes from the Greek words *homos*, meaning "same," and *genos*, meaning "kind, gender, race."

▶ A HOMOGENEOUS MIXTURE is made up of at least two substances that cannot be distinguished with the naked eye.

COLLOIDS

By using an optical instrument more precise than the human eye (for example, a magnifying glass or a microscope), we can see that milk (Figure 1.12) and mayonnaise are made up of drops of fat in suspension. These mixtures contain at least two different liquids (one being suspended fat and the other, a substance made up primarily of water). This type of mixture is called a *colloid*. A colloid is generally opaque.

▶ A COLLOID is a homogeneous mixture in which at least two different substances can be distinguished under a magnifying instrument.

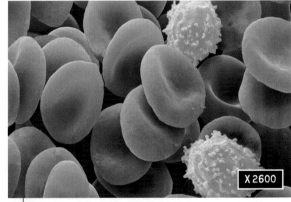

X 2600

1.11 Blood is a colloid. When looked at through a microscope, we can distinguish red and white cells floating in a yellowish substance, which is called *plasma*.

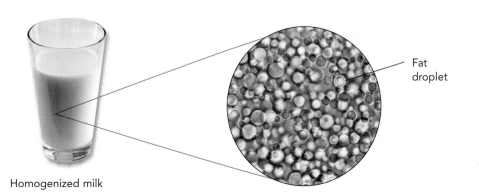

Homogenized milk

Fat droplet

1.12 Homogenized milk is a colloid. When we look at it through a microscope, we can distinguish two types of substances: droplets of fat and skim milk.

LAB 1

When it is impossible to distinguish the constituent parts of a mixture, even through a microscope, the mixture is called a *solution*. A solution is generally transparent.

▶ A SOLUTION is a homogeneous mixture in which it is impossible to distinguish its constituent parts, even under a magnifying instrument.

In Figure 1.9, the apple juice is made up of sugar and other aromatic substances, which are dissolved in water, and the 10-karat gold ring is made up of copper and silver dissolved in gold. The apple juice and the gold ring are examples of solutions.

Apple juice

1.13 Apple juice is a solution. When we look at it through a microscope, we can't distinguish its constituent parts.

In a solution, the substance that seems to disappear into the other substance is called the *solute*. Usually there is less of this substance. The substance into which the solute has dissolved is called the *solvent*. There is generally more solvent than solute.

▶ A SOLUTE is a substance that dissolves in another substance.

▶ A SOLVENT is a substance that can dissolve a solute.

On the next page, Table 1.15 shows various examples of solutions grouped according to their phase, that is, according to whether they are a solid, liquid or gas. Note that it is the phase of the solvent that determines the phase of the solution.

When the solvent is a metal, the result is called an *alloy*. The 10-karat gold ring from Figure 1.9 is an example of an alloy.

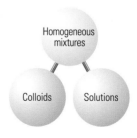

1.14 Types of homogeneous mixtures

There are many examples of solutions in the human body. Saliva, sweat, tears and urine are all common solutions in the body. They also share a common solvent: water.

Phases of solution components (Solute + solvent → solution)	Solutes	Solvent	Solution
Gas + gas → gas	Oxygen, carbon dioxide, water vapour, argon, etc.	Nitrogen	Air
Gas + liquid → liquid	Carbon dioxide	Water	Carbonated water
Liquid + liquid → liquid	Alcohol, aromatic substances	Water	Wine
Solid + liquid → liquid	Salt	Water	Salt water
Solid + solid → solid	Carbon	Iron	Steel

2.3 PROPERTIES OF SOLUTIONS

LABS
2–7

A solution's properties are what distinguish it from other solutions. Here we will take a look at three important properties: concentration, dilution and solubility.

CONCENTRATION

The proportions of solute and solvent are different from one solution to another. The quantity of solute in a volume of solution indicates the concentration of the solution.

> ▶ The **CONCENTRATION** of a solution corresponds to the quantity of dissolved solute in a given quantity of solution.

A solution's concentration can be expressed in a variety of ways, such as:

- number of grams of solute per litre of solution (g/L)
- number of grams of solute per 100 mL of solution (percent mass/volume or %m/V)
- number of millilitres of solute per 100 mL of solution (percent volume/volume or %V/V)
- number of grams of solute per 100 g of solution (percent mass/mass or %m/m)

For example, a bottle of water contains 45 mg of calcium per litre of water (.045 g/L), and a bottle of vinegar, with a concentration of 5%V/V, contains 5 mL acetic acid for 100 mL vinegar.

We can calculate the concentration of a solution in g/L, using the following formula:

$$C = \frac{m}{V}$$

where C is the concentration (in g/L)
m is the mass of the solute (in g)
V is the volume of the solution (in L)

WHAT'S TRUE?
What's the difference between fruit juice, fruit drink, fruit cocktail, fruit punch and fruit nectar? Only containers labelled "fruit juice" contain 100 percent real juice. All the others contain juice diluted in water, and additives, of which sugar is the principal one.

HOW TO PREPARE
A SOLUTION

HOW TO SOLVE A
MATHEMATICAL PROBLEM

Let's take, for example, 2 L of a saltwater solution containing 5 g of salt. What is the concentration of this solution?

$$C = \frac{m}{V} = \frac{5\text{ g}}{2\text{ L}} = \frac{2.5\text{ g}}{1\text{ L}}$$

The concentration of the solution is 2.5 g/L.

It is often useful to know the concentration of a solution. For example, companies that make energy drinks study the concentration of various substances dissolved in the human body to create drinks that not only rehydrate the body, but also contain the quantity of salt and sugar that the body needs to recover quickly from an intense workout.

1.16   If the police suspect a driver of drinking and driving, they administer a Breathalyzer test to measure the level of alcohol in his or her blood.

  CONNECTIONS ᴍᴀᴛʜᴇᴍᴀᴛɪᴄꜱ

Linear functions and proportions

A linear function is an algebraic relationship defined in the set of real numbers. It can be defined by an equation, such as $y = ax$ where a is the constant.

As with all functions in the set of real numbers, the linear function can be represented on a Cartesian graph. The result is a straight line, which begins at the starting point of the two axes, (0, 0). The straight line is made up of all the points whose coordinates (x, y) make up the function.

The slope of the line is equal to the value of the constant. When the constant is positive, as in the diagram on the left, the line has a positive slope. When the constant equals zero, the line is horizontal and parallels the x axis. When the constant is negative, the line has a negative slope.

To find a in the algebraic equation that defines the linear function, we get $a = y / x$. The relationship between the value of y and the corresponding value of x is always equal to the constant. As a result, all y / x relationships are equal: they are proportional.

If we use the data from the diagram, we find that:

$$a = \frac{2.5}{1} = \frac{5}{2} = \frac{7.5}{3} = \ldots = 2.5\text{ g/L}$$

This proportion can be used to calculate the concentration of a solution, among other things. It would then be expressed as $C = \frac{m}{V}$.

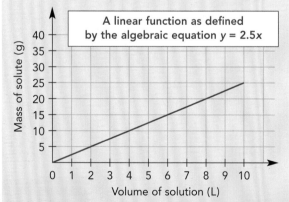

A linear function as defined by the algebraic equation y = 2.5x

Mass of solute (g)

Volume of solution (L)

This line shows the mass of solute present in different volumes of a solution with a concentration of 2.5 g/L.

THE DEMISE OF THE PENNY?

Adapted from Gabrielle Duchaine-Baillargeon, "La fin des 'cennes noires'?" *L'Actualité* 31, 13 (September 1, 2006), p.16. *[Translation]*

In the United States, the future of both the penny and the nickel looks grim: the cost to produce these coins is more than their worth on the market. The U.S. government spends 1.23 ¢ to make each penny and 5.73 ¢ to make each nickel. These high costs are due to increases in the price of zinc and copper, two precious metals used in the production of coins.

In Canada, we have decreased the concentration of precious metals in our coins. Our penny, which was once made almost entirely of copper, is now a steel coin plated with copper. In the five-cent coin, steel has replaced nickel. Because Canada is one of the world's leading producers of iron, the main ingredient in steel, the use of this alloy is cost-effective. Today, it costs just 0.008 ¢ to produce a penny on this side of the border.

Canada has lowered the concentration of precious metals in its coins.

DILUTION

We often need to change the concentration of a solution. To increase the concentration of a solution, it is simpler to add solute than to remove solvent. On the other hand, if we want to decrease the concentration of a solution—that is, to dilute it—we add more solvent (as it is generally not possible to remove the solute).

Let's look at a few examples where we need to change the concentration of a solution. To make juice from frozen concentrate, we need to add water. In other words, we dilute the frozen concentrate. When our soup is not salty enough, we add salt, thus increasing the soup's concentration of salt.

In a laboratory, when preparing a solution with a precise concentration, we can use either pure substances or concentrated mixtures. In the first case, the technique is called *dissolution* (Chapter 2, page 46) and in the second case, the technique is called *dilution*.

> ▶ **DILUTION** is a laboratory technique that involves decreasing the concentration of a solution by adding solvent.

1.17 When preparing medication, pharmacists often have to dilute the medication in order to obtain the exact dosage indicated on the prescription.

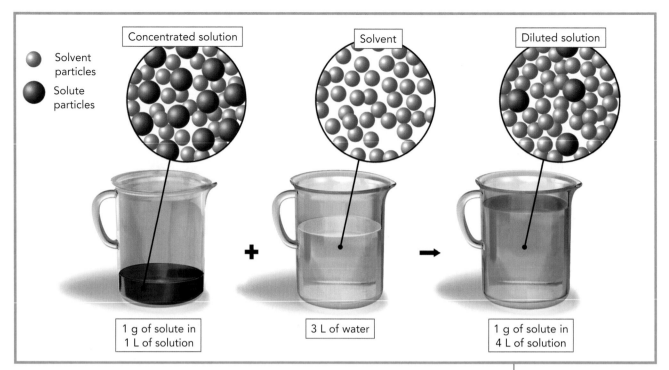

| Concentrated solution | Solvent | Diluted solution |

Solvent particles

Solute particles

1 g of solute in 1 L of solution

3 L of water

1 g of solute in 4 L of solution

1.18 The addition of a solvent to a solution decreases its concentration, that is, it dilutes the solution.

Let's look at how dilution changes the concentration of a solution. Imagine that we have 1 L of a solution with a concentration of 1 g/L. How will the concentration change if we add 3 L of water?

After the dilution, the quantity of the solute does not change: there is still 1 g of solute. However, the quantity of solution has changed: there is now 4 L of solution instead of 1 L. The concentration is now 1 g/4 L, or 0.25 g/L.

The particle model can help us visualize the dilution of a solution (Figure 1.18).

Mathematically, we can also use the following reasoning:

Since $C = \dfrac{m}{V}$, we can also write m = C V. Because the mass (m) of the solute stays the same before (m_1) and after (m_2) the dilution, therefore $m_1 = m_2$. Therefore:

$C_1V_1 = C_2V_2$,   where C_1 is the solution's initial concentration (in g/L)
V_1 is the solution's initial volume (in L)
C_2 is the solution's final concentration (in g/L)
V_2 is the solution's final volume (in L)

To find the concentration of the diluted solution find C_2:

$C_2 = \dfrac{C_1V_1}{V_2} = \dfrac{1 \text{ g/L} \times 1 \text{ L}}{4 \text{ L}} = 0.25 \text{ g/L}$

Therefore, the final concentration of the diluted solution is 0.25 g/L.

HOW TO PREPARE A SOLUTION

HOW TO SOLVE A MATHEMATICAL PROBLEM

SOLUBILITY

There is a limit to the amount of solute you can add to a solvent. The maximum amount of solute in a solvent corresponds to its solubility.

> ▶ SOLUBILITY is the maximum amount of solute that can be dissolved in a given amount of solvent.

Just like concentration, solubility can be expressed in a variety of ways, such as:

- g/L
- percent mass/volume (%m/V)
- percent volume/volume (%V/V)
- percent mass/mass (%m/m)

If a solution contains less than the maximum amount of solute, it is called *unsaturated*. If it contains exactly the maximum amount of solute, it is called a *saturated* solution. If it contains more than the maximum amount of solute, it is called *supersaturated*. In most cases, the surplus solute will appear as a **PRECIPITATE**.

> ▶ A SATURATED SOLUTION is one which contains exactly the maximum amount of solute that can be dissolved in it.

1.19 When there is too much solute, the excess falls to the bottom of the solution in the form of a precipitate. The result is a saturated solution with a solid precipitate.

Solubility depends on many factors, such as the nature of the solute and the solvent plus temperature and pressure. We will examine two of these factors: the nature of the solvent and temperature.

The nature of the solvent

The solubility of a given substance will vary depending on the solvent. For example, table salt is very soluble in water, but not in oil. Therefore, we say that salt is hydrophilic.

Hydrophilic comes from the Greek words *hudor*, meaning "water," and *philos*, meaning "friend."

On the other hand, a lipophilic substance is very soluble in oil. For example, many aromatic substances are soluble in oil. In cooking, we often add oil or another fatty substance to food to enhance its flavour.

Lipophilic comes from the Greek words *lipos*, meaning "fat," and *philos*, meaning "friend."

Soap has a special structure that allows it to be both hydrophilic and lipophilic. This is the reason that it can dissolve greasy stains that are otherwise not soluble in water.

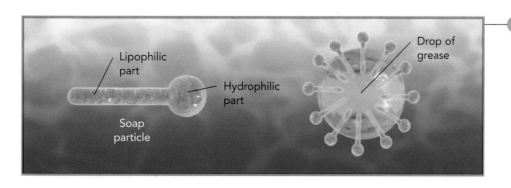

Lipophilic part

Hydrophilic part

Soap particle

Drop of grease

1.20 The lipophilic part of soap attaches itself to a drop of grease, while the hydrophilic part dissolves in the water. This is how soap "traps" the grease, which is then easily rinsed away with water.

It is often useful to know the solubility of a solute in a solvent; for example, when we want to remove stains from clothing. The best way to do this is to find out what caused the stain, and then choose the best solvent for its removal. Some substances (like mud) are easy to clean with water, others (like grease and oil) need soap. As for ink stains, they are best removed with an alcohol-based stain remover.

Temperature

Solubility also depends on temperature. The solubility of many solids increases with temperature (this is true, for example, with salt and sugar whose solubility in water increases with temperature) (Figure 1.21).

On the other hand, the solubility of many gases decreases with temperature (for example, the solubility of oxygen and carbon dioxide in water) (Figure 1.22). This is one of the reasons why, during summer heat waves, the level of oxygen in lakes decreases, leading to the death of some fish.

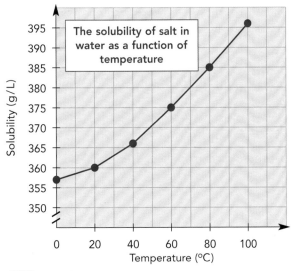

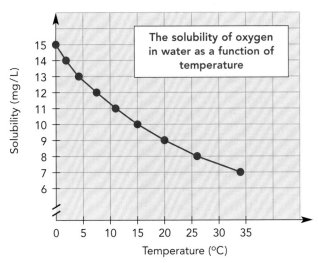

1.21 The rising slope on the graph shows that the solubility of solid salt in water increases with temperature.

1.22 The descending slope on the graph shows that the solubility of oxygen gas in water decreases with temperature.

In summary

Table 1.23 shows how the solubility of a solute—in this case, sugar—can vary depending on the temperature and solvent in which it has been dissolved.

1.23 SOLUBILITY OF SUGAR AT DIFFERENT TEMPERATURES AND IN DIFFERENT SOLVENTS (in g/L)

Temperature (°C)	Solvent		
	Water	Oil (soya oil)	Alcohol (methanol)
0	1783.7	Does not dissolve	Imperceptible
40	2345.0	Does not dissolve	0.55
60	2885.7	Does not dissolve	1.34
80	3690.1	Does not dissolve	Does not apply: methanol boils at 65°C.

CHAPTER 1

1.24 In order to get these jeans really clean, we need to choose a solvent in which the stains are the most soluble.

1.25 Sugar dissolves faster and in larger amounts in hot cocoa than in cold milk. The solubility of sugar increases as its temperature increases.

1.26 An open bottle of soda pop releases increasing amounts of carbon dioxide as its temperature increases.

2.4 SEPARATING MIXTURES

Mixtures exist everywhere in nature; in fact, there are practically no pure substances in nature. We have to apply purification techniques to obtain pure substances. Many techniques are physical separations, that is, they separate the constituents of a mixture without changing their nature (Figure 1.27, next page). When it is impossible to physically separate a substance any further, then we have a pure substance.

Here are a few examples of cases where we commonly separate the constituents of a mixture:

- to make water safe for drinking, we remove any impurities and **PATHOGENS** that may be present.
- to obtain gas, diesel fuel, tar, furnace oil and so on, we process oil, separating it into its various constituents.
- to obtain many of the metals that we use in manufacturing (such as gold, silver and copper), we purify their ore, that is, remove the rock that makes up part of the various minerals.

Sometimes, we need to use more than one separation technique in order to obtain the substance(s) we want. For example, in a water filtration plant, we use the processes of both decantation and filtration (next page) to make water safe for drinking. In spite of this, the water is still not 100 percent pure. If we wanted to purify the water completely, we would need to use a distillation process.

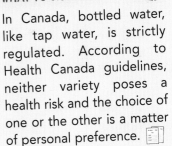

WHAT TO CHOOSE?

In Canada, bottled water, like tap water, is strictly regulated. According to Health Canada guidelines, neither variety poses a health risk and the choice of one or the other is a matter of personal preference.

HOW TO SEPARATE A MIXTURE

Decantation

A separation funnel

DESCRIPTION

When a mixture's constituents have different densities, they separate into different layers. Each layer can then be poured out individually.

Centrifugation

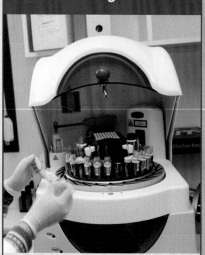

A centrifuge

DESCRIPTION

This technique accelerates and accentuates the decantation process using a centrifuge, which is an instrument that can spin a mixture at high speeds.

Filtration

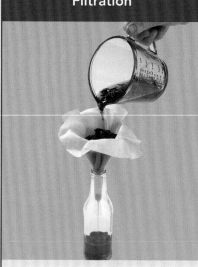

A filter

DESCRIPTION

This process involves passing a solid-liquid or a solid-gas (e.g. smoke) mixture through a filter. The solids stay on the surface of the filter.

Evaporation

A desiccator

DESCRIPTION

This technique makes it possible to collect a solid that has dissolved. The liquid in the solid-liquid mixture evaporates.

Distillation

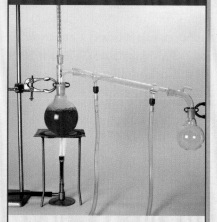

A laboratory setup for fractional distillation

DESCRIPTION

This technique is based on the different boiling points of a mixture's constituents. When heated, they boil off and condense at different temperatures.

Chromatography

A laboratory setup for paper chromatography

DESCRIPTION

This technique separates a mixture into its various constituents using porous paper and a solvent. The differences in the rates with which the constituents travel along the paper lead to their separation.

1.27 Different physical techniques for separating mixtures

3 PURE SUBSTANCES

A pure substance contains only one substance, one constituent. Distilled water, sugar, iron, copper and diamonds are examples of pure substances.

3.1 COMPOUNDS AND ELEMENTS

We have learned about the different physical separation techniques that can be used to separate the constituents of a mixture in order to obtain pure substances (preceding page). Some pure substances, however, are made up of at least two different elements, and are therefore called *compounds*. These pure substances can be separated by chemical techniques, such as electrolysis.

> ▶ An ELEMENT is a pure substance that contains only one type of atom; it is impossible to separate an element into other substances, using chemical separation techniques.

> ▶ A COMPOUND is a pure substance that contains at least two types of atoms that have chemically combined; it can be separated into its constituent elements, using chemical separation techniques.

It took a long time before scientists realized that some pure substances were, in fact, compounds. In 1781, the British physician and chemist, Henry Cavendish, demonstrated that water was composed of two different constituents. He applied electrolysis to water in its liquid state, and obtained gaseous oxygen and hydrogen. Until then, it was believed that water was indivisible, that is, it was an element in itself.

THE PERIODIC TABLE OF THE ELEMENTS

Elements are the building blocks of matter. There are more than 100 kinds of elements. All existing substances are formed by these elements.

Scientists classify the elements in a chart called the *periodic table of elements* (inside back cover of textbook). This table is very useful because it groups elements with similar properties together. For example, all of the elements in the last column are inert gases, often called *noble gases*. These gases do not normally react with other substances.

CYCLE ONE

- Elements
- Periodic table
- Characteristic properties
- Physical change
- Temperature
- Acidity and alkalinity
- Chemical change

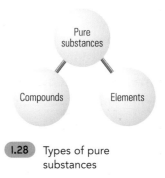

1.28 Types of pure substances

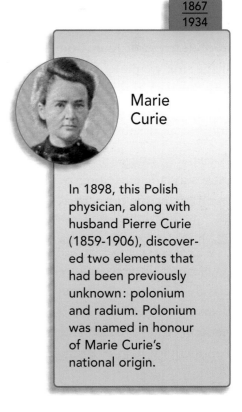

1867
1934

Marie Curie

In 1898, this Polish physician, along with husband Pierre Curie (1859-1906), discovered two elements that had been previously unknown: polonium and radium. Polonium was named in honour of Marie Curie's national origin.

The first version of the periodic table was developed by a Russian chemist named Dimitri Mendeleev in the late 1860s. The table has since evolved with the arrival of new scientific discoveries and technological procedures. Today, there are more than 100 elements in the table, and most are found naturally on Earth. The rest can be produced artificially in a laboratory.

Each element is represented by a symbol that is the same in every language and country. For example, the symbol for carbon is C, while silver is represented by Ag. The first letter is always a capital, and it is sometimes followed by one or two lower-case letters.

There are 25 elements that are essential to life, and four of them are particularly important: carbon, oxygen, hydrogen and nitrogen. These four alone make up 96 percent of the matter on Earth. They make up nearly all the molecules that form living organisms, from bacteria to humans, and include plants, mushrooms and all the animals in the world.

THE ELEMENTREE

The Québec chemist Fernando Dufour has developed a three-dimensional representation of the periodic table. His model looks like a tree. It has a central stem surrounded by a widening spiral. On this spiral, the elements are represented by discs, and placed in order of their atomic number.

3.2 PROPERTIES OF PURE SUBSTANCES

We can describe pure substances by describing their characteristic and non-characteristic properties.

A non-characteristic property cannot help us to tell one pure substance from another. While we can distinguish one clear plastic cup from another by its size and its shape, for example, these characteristics do not tell us what makes this clear plastic different from another transparent substance, such as glass, crystal, Pyrex, ice or another clear substance.

A characteristic property helps us to identify precisely a pure substance. Melting point and density are examples of characteristic properties. Certain plastics, glass and ice are all examples of transparent solids. Their melting points and their density, however, are very different.

There are some characteristic properties that help us classify substances by groups. For example, a litmus test helps us to determine if a substance is acidic, basic or neutral. Other characteristic properties, such as electrical conductivity, help us distinguish metals from nonmetals.

1.29 Size and shape help us to tell objects apart, but cannot help us distinguish one substance from another. Size and shape are non-characteristic properties.

► A CHARACTERISTIC PROPERTY is one that helps us identify a pure substance or the group to which the pure substance belongs.

Characteristic properties can be divided into two categories: characteristic physical properties and characteristic chemical properties.

CHARACTERISTIC PHYSICAL PROPERTIES

Characteristic physical properties help us to identify a pure substance without changing the nature of the substance in the process. For example, to find the boiling point of water, we need to change the phase of water. We need to heat it until it moves from a liquid to a gaseous phase (or cool it down so that it passes from a gaseous phase to a liquid). This change of phase, however, does not change the nature of water.

Table 1.30, below, contains some common physical properties of matter that are characteristic. There are many more, including electrical conductivity, heat conductivity, hardness, malleability and magnetism.

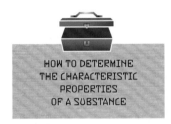

HOW TO DETERMINE THE CHARACTERISTIC PROPERTIES OF A SUBSTANCE

1.30 CHARACTERISTIC PHYSICAL PROPERTIES OF MATTER

Physical properties	Description	Examples
Melting point	• The temperature at which a solid becomes a liquid (or a liquid becomes a solid). • Can be expressed in °C.	• Water: 0°C • Ethanol: -117°C • Table salt: 801°C
Boiling point	• The temperature at which a liquid becomes a gas (or a gas becomes a liquid). • Can be expressed in °C.	• Water: 100°C • Ethanol: 79°C • Table salt: 1465°C
Density	• Mass per unit of volume • We often use the following formula: $\rho = \dfrac{m}{V}$ where p = density m = mass V = volume • Can be expressed in g/mL.	• Water: 1.0 g/mL • Ethanol: 0.79 g/mL • Gold: 19.3 g/mL
Solubility	• The maximum amount of solute that can be dissolved in a given volume of solvent. • Can be expressed in g/L or in % (% m/V, % m/m, % V/V).	• Table salt in water: 357 g/L • Carbon dioxide in water: 3.48 g/L • Sugar in water: 1792 g/L

Characteristic physical properties must be measured at a specific temperature and specific **PRESSURE**. A higher or lower temperature or pressure can change the physical properties of a substance. For example, water boils at 100°C at sea level, that is, when atmospheric pressure measures 101.3 kilopascals (kPa). If we go up to an altitude of 1600 m, atmospheric pressure decreases and the boiling point of water goes down to 94°C.

When we talk about data obtained under Normal Temperature and Pressure (NTP), we mean that the temperature was 0°C and the pressure was 101.3 kPa when the data were taken. When we say the data were obtained under Standard Ambient Temperature and Pressure (SATP), we mean that the temperature was between 20°C and 25°C and the pressure was 101.3 kPa.

CHARACTERISTIC CHEMICAL PROPERTIES

Chemical properties help us identify a substance, but in the course of making the identification, the nature of the substance may be changed. For example, to find the acidity of a substance, we need to use a pH indicator. This tool reacts with the substance being tested, giving rise to another substance whose colour indicates the pH of the original substance. Many characteristic chemical properties are reactions to **INDICATORS**.

Table 1.31 below lists some characteristic chemical properties often used in chemistry. In the fields of medicine and nutrition, we often use other indicators, such as Fehling's solution to detect the level of glucose, or an iodine solution to test for starch.

HOW TO DETERMINE THE CHARACTERISTIC PROPERTIES OF A SUBSTANCE

1.31 CHARACTERISTIC CHEMICAL PROPERTIES OF MATTER

Chemical properties	Description	Examples
Reaction of litmus paper	The colour of the litmus paper indicates whether the test substance is an acid, a base or neutral.	• If the paper turns red, the test substance is acidic (pH < 7). • If the paper turns blue, the test substance is basic (pH > 7). • If the paper turns purple, the test substance is neutral (pH = 7).
Reaction of cobalt chloride paper	The colour of the cobalt chloride paper indicates the presence or absence of water.	• If the paper turns pink or a different shade of blue, the test substance contains water.
Reaction of limewater	The reaction to the limewater indicates the presence or absence of gaseous carbon dioxide.	• If the limewater becomes milky (that is, if a precipitate forms), the test substance contains carbon dioxide gas.
Reaction of a glowing wood splint	The reaction of the test substance with the wood splint indicates the presence or absence of a substance that could cause combustion.	• If the splint reignites, the test substance contains a substance that can cause combustion, such as oxygen gas.
Reaction of a burning wood splint	The reaction indicates the probable presence or absence of an explosive gas.	• If an explosion occurs, the test substance probably contains an explosive gas, such as hydrogen gas.
Reaction to an open flame	The colour of the flame may indicate the presence of certain substances.	• If the flame turns purple, the test substance probably contains the element potassium. • If the flame turns green, the test substance probably contains the element barium. • If the flame turns red, the test substance probably contains the element strontium.

3.3 IDENTIFYING UNKNOWN SUBSTANCES

We can use the characteristic properties of matter to identify many pure substances. Imagine a liquid that is colourless and odourless. To find out if it is water or something else, we could perform a series of tests: if the unknown liquid boils at 100°C, freezes at 0°C, has a density of 1.0 g/mL and turns a strip of cobalt chloride paper pink, it's probably water.

We can identify a substance by comparing its characteristic properties with the data in a table that lists the properties of different substances. For an example of such a table, see Appendix 1, Properties of common substances on page 416. Table 1.32 on page 26 contains excerpts from this table. In it we can see, for example, that while water and glycerine are both colourless, odourless liquids, we can tell them apart by their characteristic properties.

The table of properties on page 26 can also help us to avoid using dangerous substances. For example, it indicates that placing hydrogen close to a flame is dangerous, because hydrogen explodes when exposed to fire.

We can also use a table of properties to choose the best material to build an object or a machine. Table 1.32 shows that tungsten is a good material to use for a light bulb's filament: its melting point is very high, it is a good electrical conductor and it does not oxidize easily.

1748
1822

Claude-Louis Berthollet

In 1789, this French chemist discovered the decolourizing properties of sodium hypochlorite. He named the substance *eau de Javel* [Javel water] in honour of a city renowned for its laundry industry. The name and the liquid are still in use today.

INDESTRUCTIBLE BLACK BOXES

At the scene of a plane crash, the black box is found among the plane debris and wreckage. This box contains precious information about the events of the flight. It is damaged, but still in one piece. What is its secret?

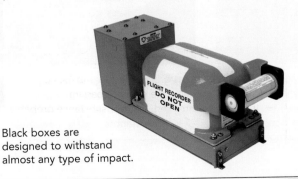

Black boxes are designed to withstand almost any type of impact.

Its secret is a stainless steel alloy, reinforced with titanium or aluminum and high-temperature silicone insulation, designed to withstand temperatures higher than 1500°C for more than one hour, immersion in salt water for 30 days, as well as immersion in a variety of other liquids from airplane fuel to oil. These black boxes— which are, in fact, orange—can also tolerate extremely high pressure.

Could we build a plane from the same metal as the black box? Yes, but the plane would certainly be too heavy to fly.

Adapted from Agence Science-Presse, "Indestructibles boîtes noires," September 18, 2001. *[Translation]*

I.32 EXCERPTS FROM THE TABLE OF PROPERTIES OF COMMON SUBSTANCES
(see Appendix 1 in this textbook)

Substances (chemical formulas)	Description	Dangers and precautions	Physical properties					Chemical properties
			FP (°C)	BP (°C)	ρ (g/mL)	EC	S	
Hydrogen (H_2)	• Colourless • Odourless	Explosive when exposed to an open flame	–259	–253	0.000 09	No	• 0.002 g/L of water	• Explodes when exposed to an open flame.
Water (H_2O)	• Colourless • Odourless	None	0	100	1.00	No	• N/A	• Cobalt chloride paper turns pink. • Neutral litmus paper turns violet.
Glycerine or glycerol ($C_3H_8O_3$)	• Colourless • Odourless • Viscous • Sweet taste	Explosive in certain conditions	18	290	1.26	No	• Soluble in water	• Explodes when exposed to certain substances.
Tungsten (W)	• Grey • Odourless • Shiny	Can irritate respiratory tract	3410	5900	19.35	Good conductor	• Not soluble in water	• Does not easily oxidize. • Reacts with nitric acid.

FP: freezing point   EC: electrical conductivity
BP: boiling point   S: solubility
ρ: density

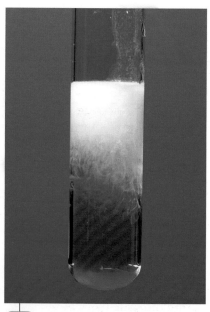

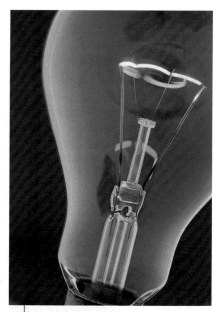

I.33 The gas in this test tube is probably carbon dioxide because it turns the limewater milky and has a density of 0.002 g/L.

I.34 Following the explosion of the Hindenburg in 1937, the use of hydrogen for hot-air balloons and dirigibles was banned because it is too dangerous.

I.35 We use tungsten to make the filaments for electric light bulbs because this metal is very resistant to high temperatures.

WHAT IS MATTER? (pp. 6–9)

1. How do we define matter?

2. What holds the particles of a solid together?

3. Using the particle model, describe two differences between a solid, a liquid and a gas.

4. The particles in a sample of matter are very close together.

   a) Using only this information, can you confirm that this sample is a solid? Explain your answer.

   b) What other information could you use to be certain that the sample is a solid?

5. What is the name of the smallest particle of matter that can be chemically divided?

 MIXTURES (pp. 10–20)

6. Look at the photo below. What type of mixture is each of the items in the photo?

7. What type of mixture is each of the following?

   a) a handful of earth
   b) air
   c) smog
   d) a stainless steel fork
   e) seawater
   f) whipping cream
   g) a raisin muffin

8. Give the term for each of the following definitions.

   a) a substance that can dissolve another substance
   b) a substance that can dissolve into another substance
   c) a homogeneous mixture made up of one substance dissolved in another substance

9. What determines the concentration of a solution?

10. A patient receives a prescription from the doctor for a medication that needs to be dissolved in water, at a concentration of 2 g/L. The dosage is the following: one teaspoon (5 mL) three times a day for 10 days.

    a) What is the minimum volume of the medication in solution that the patient will need?

    b) If you were the pharmacist, how would you prepare the medication from a powder? Describe what you would do and show all of the calculations you need to prepare the right quantity of medication for the patient.

11. A woman wants to dye her hair lighter than her natural colour. Her hairdresser uses a hydrogen peroxide solution at three percent V/V to lighten her hair. He needs to prepare 100 mL of this solution by diluting a concentrate to 30 percent. How should he do it? Describe how you reached your answer, showing all your calculations.

12. The label on a bottle of wine indicates that the wine contains 12 percent alcohol V/V. How much alcohol does a 750 mL bottle of wine contain? Show all the steps leading to your answer.

13. The Nutrition Facts label on a container of apple juice, indicates that 250 mL of juice contains 25 g of sugar. Calculate the concentration of sugar in the juice in g/L. Show all the steps leading to your answer.

Nutrition Facts
Per 250 ml (1 cup)

Amount	% Daily Value
CALORIES 120	
FAT 0 g	
SATURATED FAT 0 g	0%
+ TRANS FAT 0 g	
CHOLESTEROL 0 mg	0%
SODIUM 5 mg	0%
POTASSIUM 290 mg	0%
CARBOHYDRATE 29 mg	8%
FIBRE 0 g	10%
SUGARS 25 g	0%
PROTEIN 0.3 g	
VITAMIN A	
VITAMIN C	0%
CALCIUM	4%
IRON	0%
	4%

14. Name four factors that can affect the solubility of a substance.

15. How does the solubility of table salt in water change with temperature?

16. Look at the following graph. What is the solubility, in g/L, of this solid at a temperature of 60°C?

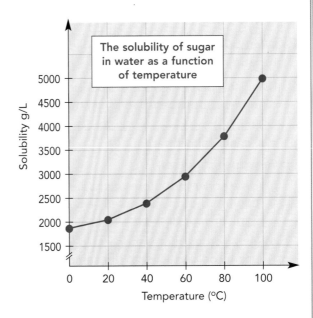

The solubility of sugar in water as a function of temperature

17. Some industries dump hot water into the environment. How is this practice harmful to fish?

18. How can we obtain pure substances from a mixture?

19. Indicate which separation technique you think would be the most appropriate for each of the following mixtures?
    a) a saltwater solution
    b) water mixed with sand
    c) a blood sample
    d) an oil-and-vinegar dressing
    e) water mixed with alcohol
    f) black ink
    g) toxic smoke
    h) oil

3 PURE SUBSTANCES (pp. 21–26)

20. Give two examples of non-characteristic properties.

21. We can identify a substance by observing its characteristic properties.

    a) What is the difference between a characteristic physical property and a characteristic chemical property?

    b) Give an example of a characteristic physical property.

    c) Give an example of a characteristic chemical property.

22. Why is density a characteristic physical property, but not mass or volume?

23. You are given three solid substances, all in the form of a white powder. How can solubility help you to identify each of the three substances?

24. A technician is given a gas sample to identify. She performs a series of tests and compiles her results as follows:

Properties	Results
Freezing point	–259°C
Density	0.000 09 g/mL
Colour	Colourless
Odour	Odourless
Reaction to limewater	No change
Reaction to open flame	An explosion

a) Study the results in the table. Which tests can be used to identify the gas?

b) What is the gas in the sample?

CONCEPT MAPS

HOW TO BUILD
A CONCEPT MAP

Prepare your own summary of Chapter 1 by building a concept map based on the following terms:

- Atoms
- Boiling point
- Characteristic chemical properties
- Characteristic physical properties
- Colloids
- Compounds
- Concentration
- Density
- Dilution
- Elements
- Heterogeneous mixtures
- Homogeneous mixtures
- Matter
- Melting point
- Mixtures
- Molecules
- Properties of pure substances
- Properties of solutions
- Pure substances
- Reactions to indicators
- Solubility
- Solutions

ELEMENTS ON OUR DINNER PLATE

Many elements, in their mineral form, are essential to the maintenance and the healthy functioning of the human organism. Our bodies are incapable of producing these elements, so we need to get them in our food. Nutritional deficiency, or a lack of certain elements in our diet, can lead to health problems. Table 1.36 contains several elements, as well as the roles they play in the human body.

1.36 ELEMENTS AND THEIR ROLES IN THE HUMAN BODY

Elements	Major roles	Signs of deficiencies
Calcium (Ca)	• Formation of teeth and bones • Coagulation of blood • Transmission in the nervous system	• Slow growth (rickets) • Fragile bones (osteoporosis)
Iron (Fe)	• Composition of hemoglobin • Function of the immune system	• Fatigue, weakness, pallor (anemia) • Immune deficiency (cold, influenza, infection)
Iodine (I)	• Composition of the hormones in the thyroid gland • Production of energy	• Enlargement of the thyroid gland (goitre)
Fluoride (F)	• Maintenance of healthy teeth	• Dental cavities
Sodium (Na)	• Maintenance of water balance • Regulation of blood pressure	• Muscle cramps • Loss of appetite • Low blood pressure

Many of these elements also act together. What is more, some elements are better assimilated when combined with others. For example, vitamin D boosts the body's absorption of calcium and phosphorous, while vitamin C boosts iron absorption.

1.37

The labels on bottles of water generally list the elements they contain, such as sodium, potassium, calcium, magnesium, chlorine, fluoride, copper, arsenic, lead and zinc.

1. Name at least one food that is a good source of each of the elements listed in Table 1.36.

2. Table 1.36 gives only a few examples of the elements that are indispensable to the body. Name at least two more.

CAROLE PÉCLET

Technological progress has helped us to develop instruments for analysis that are more and more sensitive and precise. Carole Péclet has devised a technique to detect certain substances, such as drugs and medicine, in the hair of crime suspects or victims. Hair keeps traces of such substances over long periods of time, well after they have already been eliminated from other parts of the body, rendering blood and urine tests useless. Péclet's technique can detect very small concentrations of the test substances in the hair of both dead and living bodies.

Human hair grows at a rate of about one centimetre every month. The position of the substance on the hair shaft help to approximate the date the substance was absorbed. The longer the hair, the farther in the past one can look, building a more complete history of the person in question. But watch it: you have to really know the physiology of hair and possible contaminants to be able to interpret the test results correctly.

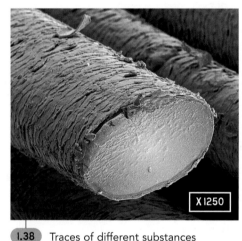

X 1250

I.38 Traces of different substances ingested by the body remain in hair for a long time.

NAME
Carole Péclet

JOB
Chemist in a forensic science and forensic pathology laboratory

AREA WHERE SHE WORKS
Montréal

EDUCATION
Bachelor's degree in biochemistry Master's degree in biochemistry

PROUDEST ACHIEVEMENTS
Developed a technique that helps to detect very small concentrations of certain substances in human hair

I.39 OCCUPATIONS CONNECTED TO PÉCLET'S WORK

Occupation	Education required	Length of study	Main tasks
Medical secretary	AVS* in medical secretarial work	450 hours	• Provide secretarial services in a doctor's office or clinic • Produce medical reports using basic medical terminology
Biochemistry laboratory technologist	DCS in laboratory techniques	3 years	• Use and maintain laboratory equipment
Biologist	Bachelor's degree in biology (with a concentration in medical biology)	3 years	• Develop new laboratory techniques • Conduct scientific research

* Attestation of Vocational Specialization

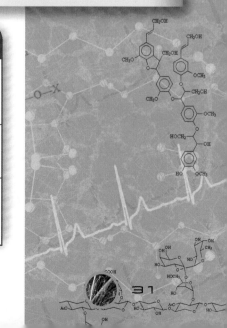

THE MATERIAL WORLD

1998	Inauguration of the windmill park in Cap-Chat on the Gaspé Peninsula
1976	Invention of the snow cannon
1944	Establishment of the Hydro-Québec corporation
1886	First electric streetlights on the streets of Montréal
1876	Development of the first four-stroke engine
1850	Invention of the first air conditioner
1831	Invention of the match
1800	Invention of the first electric battery
1789	Formulation of the law of conservation of mass
1742	Invention of the Celsius scale
1698	Patent for the first steam engine
CIRCA -250	Invention of the thermoscope, precursor to the thermometer
CIRCA -1500	Discovery of glass
CIRCA -3000	Discovery of oil
CIRCA -450 000	Taming of fire

THE HUMAN ORGANISM

AND THE POWER OF ENERGY

A ride on a roller coaster, the beat of a heart, the launch of a rocket, the leap of a frog: every one of these demands energy. Energy is everywhere, and everything depends on energy. In our daily lives, we often use expressions that refer to energy, such as "recharge," "energy drink" and "energy crisis." But what *is* energy? Where does it come from? How do our bodies produce it, and how do they use it? In this chapter, we will try to answer these questions, and more.

1 WHAT IS ENERGY?

We use the word energy quite a bit. Energy, however, is a difficult concept to define because it is abstract. It is also difficult to observe and to measure. It is often easier to study the effects of energy on matter and the countless forms it takes.

> *Energy* comes from the Greek word *energia*, meaning "activity, operation."

When a person lifts his or her arm, we can see the arm move. Scientifically speaking, this movement involves work. It's because of energy that the work gets done. Energy, then, is the capacity to do work.

In the spring, when the snow and ice melt, they change from a solid to a liquid phase. This change is made possible because of the energy from the sun. Energy, then, is also the capacity to produce change.

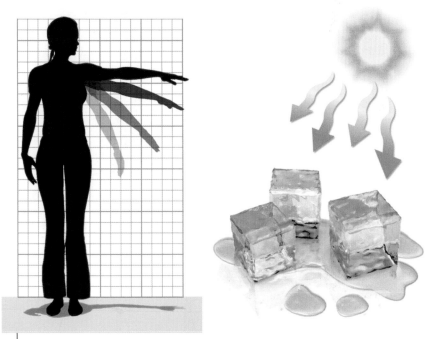

2.1 Lifting the arm is work that demands energy.

2.2 The melting of snow and ice is change that demands energy.

> ▶ **ENERGY** is the capacity to do work or to produce change.

In the International System of Units, energy is expressed in joules. One joule (J) represents the energy needed to lift an object weighing one newton (N) to a height of one metre. On Earth, an object that weighs 1 N has a mass of about 100 g.

Figure 2.3 on the next page shows what 1 J of energy looks like. Figures 2.4 and 2.5 show two ways of expending twice as much energy, or 2 J.

1818
1889

James Prescott Joule

This English physicist studied different aspects of energy, and his work led to the discovery of numerous scientific laws and theories. The unit measure of energy is called a *joule* in his honour.

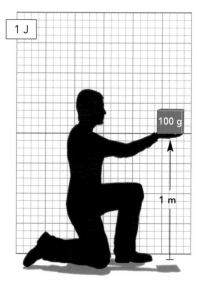

1 J

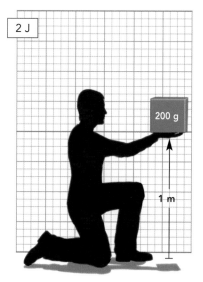

2 J

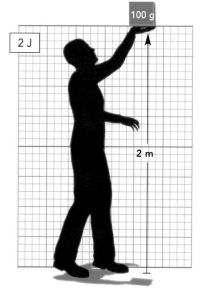

2 J

2.3 It takes 1 J of energy to lift a 100 g box to a height of 1 m.

2.4 If we double the mass of the box, we need to expend twice as much energy.

2.5 If we double the height, we need to expend twice as much energy.

2 FORMS OF ENERGY

Energy takes many different forms. For example, solar energy, which gives us light and heat, is a form of energy given off, or emitted, by the sun. Elastic energy is the form of energy that, among other things, allows a wire spring to return to its original shape after being stretched and released. Electrical energy makes a television work. As we can see, there are many forms of energy. Table 2.6 contains a list.

ENERGY CONSUMPTION

According to Statistics Canada, Canada and the United States are the two countries that consume the most energy per person. For example, in 2002, Canadians consumed (on average) twice as much energy as did the Russians.

2.6 FORMS OF ENERGY AND POSSIBLE SOURCES

Energy form	Energy source
Solar energy	Sun
Elastic energy	Wire spring
Electrical energy	Power station
Thermal energy	Fire
Radiant energy	Electric light bulb
Chemical energy	Living cell
Mechanical energy	Moving vehicle
Wind energy	Wind
Sound energy	Sound
Hydraulic energy	Waterfall
Nuclear energy	Nucleus of an atom

CYCLE ONE

– Natural energy sources
– Temperature
– Atom
– Molecule
– Volume
– Mass
– Light (properties)

In the following sections, we will take a closer look at four forms of energy: thermal, radiant, chemical and mechanical energy.

2.1 THERMAL ENERGY

When we take the **TEMPERATURE** of a substance, we are actually measuring the degree of agitation of its **ATOMS** and **MOLECULES.** Even if we don't see them, these particles of matter are constantly in motion. If the substance appears motionless, it is because the movement of the particles is happening in all directions at the same time.

Thermal energy is the energy associated with the movement of the particles that make up a substance. The higher the temperature of a substance with a given number of particles, the more thermal energy the substance contains, because there is greater movement of its particles (Figure 2.7).

Thermal comes from the Greek word *thermos*, meaning "hot."

As well, the more particles a substance has, at a given temperature, the more thermal energy it contains (Figure 2.8).

▶ **THERMAL ENERGY** is the energy that comes from the random motion of the particles that make up a substance.

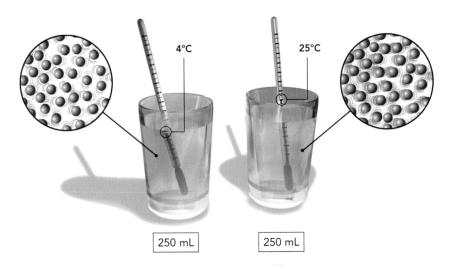

2.7 A glass of water at room temperature has more thermal energy than a glass of cold water. The greater the movement of the particles, the greater the thermal energy.

2.8 A jug of water has more thermal energy than a glass of water at the same temperature. Even if the movement of the particles is the same, the quantity of particles is different. The more particles, the greater the thermal energy.

Here are some examples of the work or change that can be accomplished by thermal energy:

- the melting of snow by the heat of the sun in springtime
- the production of water vapour in order to advance the train by the boiler of a steam engine
- the lifting of a hot-air balloon into the sky by the burner's heating of air inside the balloon

2.2 RADIANT ENERGY

The sun, a lit light bulb, fire, molten metal: all these produce light. Light is one particular wave-type belonging to a group of electromagnetic waves. There are other electromagnetic waves, such as the ultraviolet rays produced by a tanning bed, the X-rays produced by a diagnostic X-ray machine and microwaves produced by certain kinds of ovens.

The difference between the various electromagnetic waves is their wavelength, that is, the distance between two consecutive peaks or valleys (Figure 2.9). For example, the wavelengths of infrared and radio waves are longer than those of ultraviolet rays and X-rays.

> ▶ RADIANT ENERGY is the kind of energy that is contained in and transported by electromagnetic waves.

Electromagnetic waves can transport energy from one place to another. The quantity of the transported energy depends on the wavelength and on the quantity of the radiation. The shorter the wavelength of a given number of waves, the more energy the wave can transport. For example, X-rays contain and transport more energy than radio waves. The more radiation a source emits, the more energy it emits as well.

1900
1995

Maria Telkes

This American of Hungarian origin is considered to be one of the pioneers of solar energy. Among her most popular inventions are the solar oven and the solar-heated house.

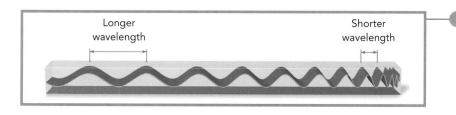

Longer wavelength

Shorter wavelength

2.9 The energy in an electromagnetic wave depends on its wavelength: the shorter it is, the greater its energy.

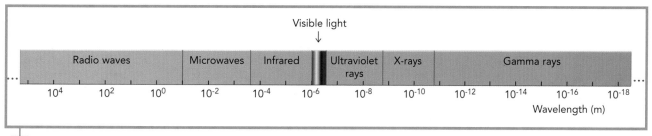

Visible light
↓

| Radio waves | | | Microwaves | Infrared | | Ultraviolet rays | X-rays | Gamma rays |

10^4 10^2 10^0 10^{-2} 10^{-4} 10^{-6} 10^{-8} 10^{-10} 10^{-12} 10^{-14} 10^{-16} 10^{-18}

Wavelength (m)

2.10 All of the different electromagnetic waves together form the electromagnetic spectrum.

Ancient works by Archimedes uncovered by X-rays

Using X-rays, scientists in California have been able to detect passages from two writings by Archimedes that had never been seen before. The two works are *On Floating Bodies* and *The Method of Mechanical Theorems*. They were produced in the 10th century by a scribe from papyrus and parchments left by this famous Greek philosopher when he died, 200 years before our era.

In the 12th century, a monk erased the ink from the manuscript to transcribe some prayers, and in the 20th century, the same manuscript was used for an imitation of a medieval painting. When experts discovered what was hidden under the painting, they made many attempts to recover the original text. Certain parts were visible using different lighting techniques, but other passages remained imperceptible. A team from Stanford University finally found the solution: using X-rays on the surface of the manuscript caused the iron in the ink used by the scribe to glow.

This 10th-century manuscript has many layers of text. Thanks to the use of X-rays, scientists have been able to uncover a text written by the Greek thinker, Archimedes.

Adapted from "Archimède aux rayons X," *Québec Science*, September 2006, p. 11. [*Translation*]

Here are some examples of the work or changes that can be accomplished by radiant energy:

- producing images of the inside of the body using X-rays
- getting suntanned and sunburned from ultraviolet rays
- treating certain cancers with gamma rays

2.3 CHEMICAL ENERGY

Atoms can be bonded together chemically to form molecules. The chemical bonds between the atoms in a substance are made up of a form of energy called *chemical energy*.

> ▶ CHEMICAL ENERGY is the energy stored in the bonds of a molecule.

Chemical energy is energy in reserve. On its own, it doesn't work or create change. To get the energy, the chemical bonds need to be reorganized. By reorganizing, we mean breaking the bonds to release the energy they contain, and remaking bonds differently. An example of liberating energy occurs when there is a power outage. People who keep candles handy, can simply light a candle, thus benefiting from the chemical energy stored in the candle's molecules.

The amount of energy in a chemical bond depends on the strength of that bond. In other words, the stronger the bond, the more energy it contains. Thus the amount of energy in a molecule depends on the number of its bonds.

Here are some examples of the work or changes that can be accomplished when chemical energy is released:

- the operation of a car motor by the combustion of gasoline
- the lighting of streetlights by the combustion of oil or gasoline
- photosynthesis, which occurs when the energy of the sun is transformed into chemical energy and is then stored in the bonds of a glucose molecule
- **CELLULAR RESPIRATION,** which helps living organisms use the chemical energy stored in the glucose molecule so they can grow, move, and think

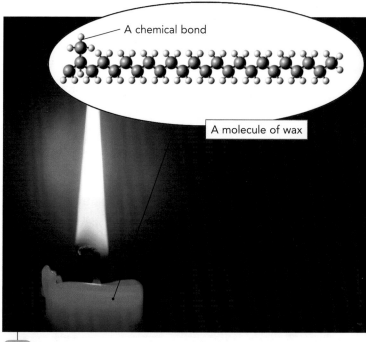

A chemical bond

A molecule of wax

2.11 Each bond linking atoms in a molecule of wax is a source of chemical energy. Since a molecule of wax contains many bonds, a candle is a good source of chemical energy.

2.4 MECHANICAL ENERGY

LAB 17

Mechanical energy depends on three factors: speed, mass and position in relation to surroundings.

Let's use the example of a car to understand how speed and mass can affect mechanical energy. If we compare the damage caused by an accident at 100 km/h and the damage from an accident at 30 km/h, we can see that the mechanical energy of a car increases with speed. The mass of the vehicle is also important. At the same speed, a large truck has more mechanical energy than a small car. The greater the mass, the greater the mechanical energy.

Now let's see how an object's relation to its surroundings can change its mechanical energy. Imagine a person standing and holding a rock. The rock is not moving, yet it contains mechanical energy. If the person lets go of the rock, the rock drops to the ground. The pain that the person feels if the rock hits his or her foot is proof of this energy. In this case, the mechanical energy of the rock depends on its distance from the ground: the higher the rock, the greater its energy.

> ▶ MECHANICAL ENERGY is the energy that results from the speed of an object, its mass and its relationship to its surroundings.

THE NEW WINDMILLS

In 2006, the vertical-axe wind turbine at Cap-Chat, on the Gaspé Peninsula, was the tallest in the world, standing at 110 metres tall. It is in one of the world's largest windmill parks, which holds 133 wind turbines.

Here is another example: A rock that falls off a cliff has velocity and mass, so it also has mechanical energy. We can see this energy in the damage it causes when it hits the ground. Its energy also depends on its starting point: the higher it is, the more mechanical energy it has. We can say that even before it falls, a rock at a certain height above the ground contains mechanical energy. Before it falls, though, the energy is in reserve.

Wind energy (the movement of air) and hydraulic ener–gy (the movement of water) are forms of mechanical energy.

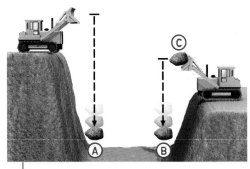

2.12 Rocks A, B and C all have the same mass. Rock A has more mechanical energy, because it begins its fall farther from the ground. Rocks B and C have the same mechanical energy, because they both begin their fall from the same height.

CONNECTIONS HISTORY

Lamplighters

In 1815, the city of Montréal installed its first oil lamps on rue Saint-Paul in response to pressure from local shop owners wanting pro-tection from robbery. The street was Montréal's first commercial artery. Little by little, streetlamps were installed on other streets too, and the profession of night watchman or security guard was born. As soon as the sun went down, the guards would walk along the streets, lighting the lamps and calling the time, "It's eight o'clock! All's well!"

The lamplighters had to fill the oil lamps by hand. They were difficult to clean and the light they gave off was dim. In 1837, they were replaced by gas lamps. This change didn't make the lamplighters' job any easier, however. They often had to make the rounds more than once, because a gust of wind could easily blow out a gas flame. Gas lamps were just as difficult to clean and the people living in the neighbourhoods complained about the dim light, the smell and the grime.

The streets of Montréal have been lit by electricity since 1886. On rue Sainte-Hélène, there are still 22 gas lamps. This type of light-ing matches the 19th-century architecture that characterizes the street.

From the 19th century until early last century, the lamplighters also acted as security guards.

Here are some examples of the work or changes that can be accomplished by mechanical energy:

- the creation of a crater by an asteroid
- the spinning of windmill blades by the wind
- the powering of a hydroelectric power station by a waterfall

3 ENERGY TRANSFORMATION AND TRANSFER

A burning log gives off energy. During combustion, some of the chemical energy stored in the wood molecules is transformed into radiant energy (light) and thermal energy (particle movement). Energy can change from one form to another. This is called the *transformation of energy*.

CYCLE ONE
└ Transformation of energy

▶ The TRANSFORMATION OF ENERGY is the changing of energy from one form to another.

2.13 During combustion, the chemical energy in wood is transformed into light and heat.

In the example of the burning log, the energy travels from the log to its surroundings, for example, to the people nearby. Energy can move from one place to another. This is called *energy transfer*.

▶ ENERGY TRANSFER is the movement of energy from one place to another.

Heat is a good example of energy transfer. From a scientific point of view, heat can be described as a transfer of thermal energy between two places whose temperatures are different. It is important to note that thermal energy always travels from the place with the highest temperature toward the place with the lowest temperature.

⚫ HEAT is the transfer of thermal energy from one place to another. Heat will always travel from the hotter place toward the colder place.

Figures 2.14 through 2.17 offer a few more examples of energy transfer and transformation.

Electrical energy → radiant energy and thermal energy

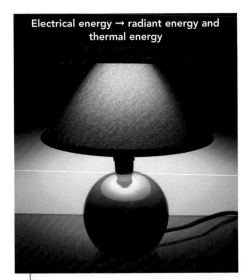

2.14 The lamp's electrical energy is transformed into radiant energy and thermal energy. The energy is also transferred to the lamp's surroundings.

Radiant energy → chemical energy

2.15 The sun's radiant energy is transferred to the plant. The plant transforms the radiant energy into chemical energy, storing it in its molecules during the process of photosynthesis.

Chemical energy → mechanical energy

2.16 The apple's chemical energy is transferred to the girl. It can then be transformed into mechanical energy, which will make it possible for her to move around.

Mechanical energy → mechanical energy

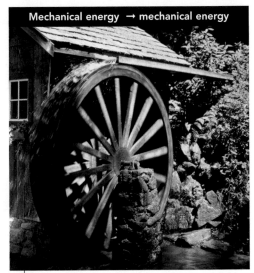

2.17 The mechanical energy in the falling water is transferred to the water wheel.

Energy transfer and transformation help us to carry out different kinds of change. This change may be chemical or physical. In the following sections, we will look at the role energy plays in these changes.

4 PHYSICAL CHANGES

Here are some examples of physical change: hanging clothes out to dry in the sun, adding salt to a bowl of soup, mixing soil to repot a plant, folding a piece of paper. In a physical change, only the shape and the appearance of the matter change.

> ▶ A PHYSICAL CHANGE does not affect the nature or the characteristic properties of matter.

The physical changes that we will discuss here are changes of phase, dissolution and deformation.

CYCLE ONE

– Physical change
– Characteristic properties
– Phases of matter
– Solutions

4.1 CHANGES OF STATE

The matter around us usually exists in three states (or phases): solid, liquid or gaseous. It can also go from one state to another.

> ▶ A PHASE CHANGE is the transformation from one state (or phase) to another.

When ice melts, it changes from a solid to a liquid. In science it is often called *fusion*. Each state change has its own name. Figure 2.18 lists the most commonly used names for changes of state.

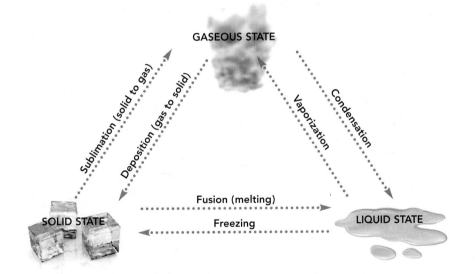

2.18 Changes of state

 Vaporization includes both evaporation and boiling. In evaporation, only the particles on the surface change into gas, like a puddle of water that evaporates. We talk about "boiling" when a liquid reaches its boiling point. When this happens, particles from under the surface can also change into gas. Since gas is lighter than liquid, it forms bubbles, which rise to the surface. When water starts to bubble it is boiling.

An examination of matter using the **PARTICLE MODEL** can help us to understand why a phase change does not affect the characteristic properties of a substance.

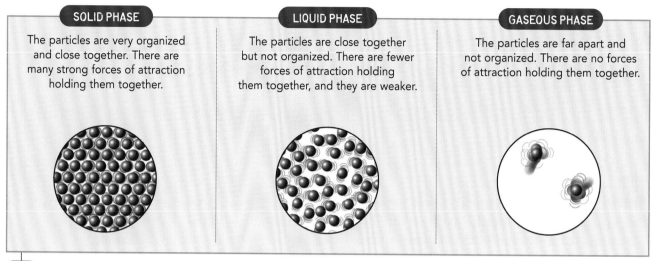

SOLID PHASE	LIQUID PHASE	GASEOUS PHASE
The particles are very organized and close together. There are many strong forces of attraction holding them together.	The particles are close together but not organized. There are fewer forces of attraction holding them together, and they are weaker.	The particles are far apart and not organized. There are no forces of attraction holding them together.

2.19 The particle model helps to explain the states of matter.

From one phase to another, only the forces of attraction change. The particles themselves don't change. The substance remains the same.

THE ROLE OF ENERGY IN PHASE CHANGES

Let's look at the vaporization of water as an example. When we heat a liquid, thermal energy is transferred from a heating element to a liquid. The water particles absorb the energy, which makes them move faster and faster until they have enough energy to change the forces of attraction between them. This is the beginning of the phase change: liquid water changing into water vapour.

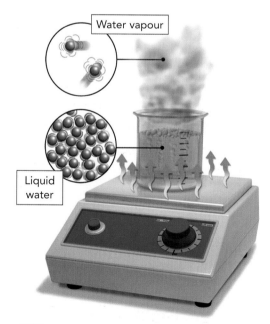

Water vapour

Liquid water

2.21 The transfer of thermal energy from a heating element to water makes the water vaporize.

Liquid water + energy ⟶ water vapour

2.20 The transformation of liquid water into water vapour absorbs energy.

Now let's look at how water freezes. The temperature of the air in a freezer is lower than the temperature of the water. The heat passes from the water to the cold air, which lowers the temperature of the water, slowing down its particles. As the water reaches its freezing point, its particles reorganize themselves. This is the beginning of the phase change: liquid water turning into ice.

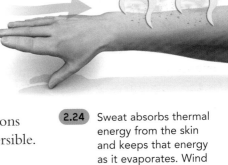

$$\text{Liquid water} \longrightarrow \text{ice} + \text{energy}$$

2.23 The transformation of liquid water into ice releases energy.

A phase or state change calls for an increase or a decrease in a substance's thermal energy, which in turn changes the forces of attraction among its particles.

Here is one last example. When we are hot, our body produces sweat. The sweat absorbs heat from our skin until it has enough energy to evaporate. This change of phase makes us feel cooler because the temperature of our skin decreases as the sweat evaporates. The greater the air circulation around our skin, the faster the evaporation. This is the reason that electric fans are so popular: they don't make the air any cooler, but they speed up the evaporation of sweat, which decreases body temperature.

It is fairly easy to make changes of state. The changes are transformations that require relatively little energy. What is more, the changes are reversible.

2.24 Sweat absorbs thermal energy from the skin and keeps that energy as it evaporates. Wind speeds up the process.

2.25 ENERGY ASSOCIATED WITH THE STATE CHANGES OF VARIOUS SUBSTANCES

Phase change	Energy (J/g)
Vaporization of liquid water	Absorbs 2260
Vaporization of ethanol (alcohol) (C_2H_6O)	Absorbs 920
Condensation of propane gas	Releases 336
Condensation of nitrogen	Releases 199
Fusion of ice (melted ice)	Absorbs 330
Fusion of iron (molten iron)	Absorbs 207
Sublimation of solid carbon dioxide (dry ice)	Absorbs 767

The Great Lakes are evaporating inch by inch

If current trends in climate change continue, the level of water in the Great Lakes could fall by at least one metre over the next 30 to 50 years, according to Canadian and American scientists. With projected increases in temperature, water evaporation will increase as well, especially in winter. Experts predict an important reduction (or even the disappearance) of the layer of ice that covers the Great Lakes in winter. This will speed up the transformation of liquid water into vapour.

Lower water levels in the Great Lakes will naturally have an impact on the level of the St. Lawrence (Fleuve Saint-Laurent) as well, as the lakes flow toward the river. Scientists believe that the rate of flow could fall by 20

The rate of flow in the St. Lawrence Seaway could fall by 20% to 40% over the next 30 to 50 years.

to 40 percent in the region of the St. Lawrence Seaway used by cargo carriers. If these projections are correct, we will have to reduce the number of carriers or even dig the seaway deeper—a solution that is unpopular with ecologists. We could also have problems getting clean drinking water. More than three million residents of Québec depend on the river every day for their water.

Adapted from Canadian Press "Le fleuve est menacé par la baisse de niveau des Grands Lacs," *Le Droit*, March 22, 2006, p. 27. *[Translation]*

 ## 4.2 DISSOLUTION

LAB 19

Many substances can be dissolved in other substances. For example, oxygen and carbon dioxide dissolve in nitrogen, creating the air we breathe. Carbon gas dissolves in water to make sparkling water. Salt dissolves in water to make salt water. And carbon dissolves in iron to make steel.

▸ **DISSOLUTION** is the creation of a solution by a solute dissolving in a solvent.

Once more, the particle model helps us understand how the characteristic properties of each substance are preserved during dissolution.

HOW TO PREPARE A SOLUTION

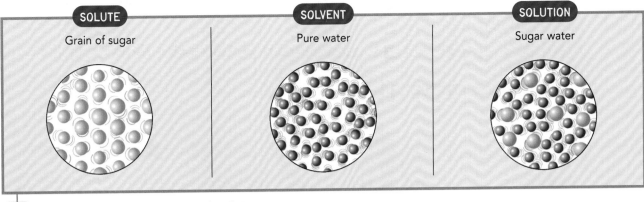

SOLUTE
Grain of sugar

SOLVENT
Pure water

SOLUTION
Sugar water

2.26 The particle model helps explain dissolution.

When sugar dissolves in water, sugar molecules break apart from each other until they are uniformly distributed throughout the water. The sugar molecules and the water molecules themselves don't change. Both substances remain the same.

THE ROLE OF ENERGY IN DISSOLUTION

Figures 2.27 and 2.28 help explain the role played by energy in dissolution.

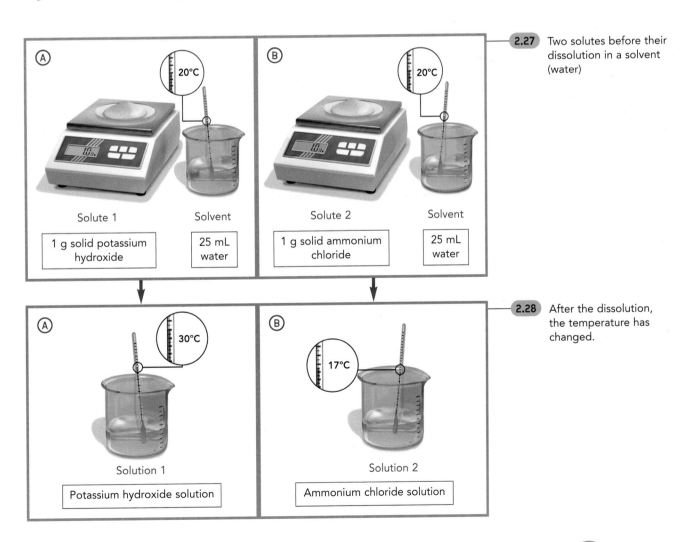

Ⓐ 20°C

Ⓑ 20°C

Solute 1

Solvent

Solute 2

Solvent

1 g solid potassium hydroxide

25 mL water

1 g solid ammonium chloride

25 mL water

2.27 Two solutes before their dissolution in a solvent (water)

Ⓐ 30°C

Ⓑ 17°C

Solution 1

Solution 2

Potassium hydroxide solution

Ammonium chloride solution

2.28 After the dissolution, the temperature has changed.

Figure 2.28 on the preceding page shows us that the temperature of example **A** increased, while the temperature of example **B** decreased. What happened?

Some substances, such as potassium hydroxide, release energy when they are dissolved in a solvent, which makes the temperature of the solution increase.

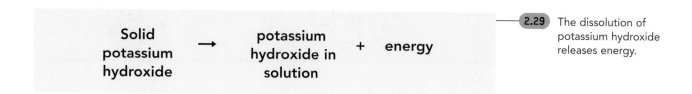

2.29 The dissolution of potassium hydroxide releases energy.

Other substances, like ammonium chloride, need to absorb energy in order to dissolve, thus lowering the temperature of the solution.

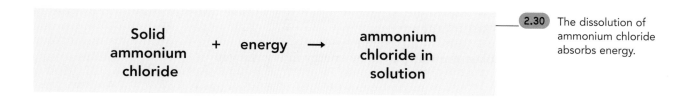

2.30 The dissolution of ammonium chloride absorbs energy.

Dissolution is a change that generally involves an absorption or release of energy.

Table 2.31 summarizes the role of energy during dissolution.

2.31 THE ROLE OF ENERGY IN DISSOLUTION

Direction of energy transfer	Result
When dissolution releases energy	Temperature increases
When dissolution absorbs energy	Temperature decreases

2.32 THE AMOUNT OF ENERGY ABSORBED OR RELEASED DURING THE DISSOLUTION OF ONE GRAM OF VARIOUS SUBSTANCES IN WATER

Substance	Chemical formula	Possible use	Energy (J/g)
Sodium chloride	$NaCl$	As table salt	Absorbs 66.7
Ammonium chloride	NH_4Cl	In fertilizer	Absorbs 276.7
Carbon dioxide	CO_2	In carbonated drinks	Releases 456.7
Potassium hydroxide	KOH	In soap	Releases 1021.3

There are many applications based on the transfer of energy that occurs during dissolution. Take for example the heating pouches used in first-aid kits or for use in winter boots and mittens. When we press on the pouch, we break an inner envelope that contains a substance that produces heat when it dissolves in the liquid or the solid surrounding it. This heat can then be transferred to the skin.

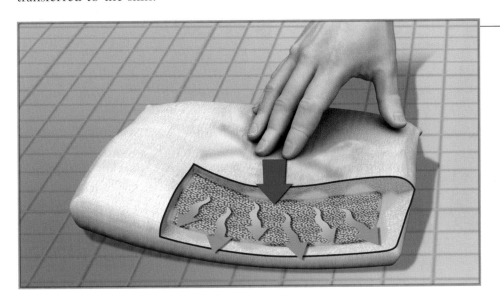

2.33 When we press down on the pouch, the pressure frees the solid from its wrapping and the solid releases heat as it dissolves.

Mint-flavoured candy and gum are also examples of energy transfer. They absorb the thermal energy in our mouth as the candy dissolves. This produces a "fresh" taste.

4.3 DEFORMATION

A lump of clay can be moulded and sculpted into an infinite array of different shapes. A wire spring can be stretched, and then released, allowing it to regain its original shape. A metal sheet can be folded, bent, cut or torn. All of these objects can undergo deformation.

> ▶ DEFORMATION means changing the shape of a material.

Some deformations are reversible (as in the case of stretching a coil, for example) and some are permanent (like tearing a sheet of metal).

THE ROLE OF ENERGY IN DEFORMATION

Figure 2.34 illustrates how the mechanical energy of people jumping on a trampoline is transferred to the surface of the trampoline, where it is transformed into elastic energy. A deformation always involves an energy transfer, and often more than one transformation of energy.

2.34 The mechanical energy of the jumpers causes the reversible deformation of the trampoline surface.

There are many forms of energy that can produce deformation. Figures 2.35 and 2.36 offer two examples.

2.35 The thermal energy of a fire caused the permanent deformation of this calculator.

2.36 The mechanical energy of the wind caused the permanent deformation of these trees.

5 CHEMICAL CHANGES

The baking of bread, the exploding of fireworks, the exposing of a photographic plate to light, the making of soap and the combustion of petroleum products are all examples of chemical changes. A chemical change involves the production of one or more new substances.

CYCLE ONE

– Chemical change
– Conservation of matter
– Photosynthesis
– Cellular respiration

▶ A CHEMICAL CHANGE changes the nature and characteristic properties of matter.

Scientists often use the expression *chemical reaction* to describe a chemical change. During a chemical change, one or more substances [the reagent(s)] react to make new substances [the product(s)]. This is why the term *reaction* is used. The expressions chemical change and chemical reaction are synonymous.

Figure 2.37 illustrates the chemical reaction involved in the formation of hydrogen chloride. It shows a hydrogen molecule (H_2) reacting with a chlorine molecule (Cl_2) to form two molecules of hydrogen chloride (HCl).

DO-IT-YOURSELF DISINFECTANT ⓘ

Instead of buying chlorine to disinfect your pool water, you can make it yourself: Use electrolysis to change table salt (sodium chloride) into chlorine (sodium hypochlorite).

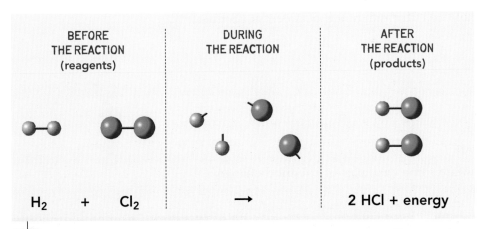

BEFORE THE REACTION (reagents)	DURING THE REACTION	AFTER THE REACTION (products)
H_2 + Cl_2	$\longrightarrow$	2 HCl + energy

2.37 During the reaction, the bonds between the two hydrogen atoms and between the two chlorine atoms are broken and new bonds are formed to make molecules of hydrogen chloride.

During a chemical change, the bonds between the atoms of the reagents are changed. The products are new substances therefore, with characteristic properties that differ from those of the reagents.

Even if new substances are formed, however, the law of conservation of mass continues to apply. This law, formulated by Antoine Laurent de Lavoisier in the 18th century, states that "Nothing is lost, nothing is created, all is transformed." During a chemical change, the number of atoms is always constant. It is the bonds between the atoms that break up and re-form to make new substances.

Table 2.38 shows us how the number of atoms for each element remains constant in a chemical reaction.

2.38 NUMBER OF ATOMS IN THE REACTION LEADING TO THE FORMATION OF HYDROGEN CHLORIDE

Before the chemical reaction		After the chemical reaction	
Reagents	Number of atoms	Product	Number of atoms
$H_2 + Cl_2$	2 atoms of H 2 atoms of Cl	2 HCl	2 atoms of H 2 atoms of Cl

The chemical formula for the reagents ($H_2 + Cl_2$) is not the same as the product (2 HCl). However, there are exactly the same number of hydrogen atoms (2) and the same number of chlorine atoms (2) before and after the reaction. The law of conservation of mass is respected.

1743
1794

Antoine Laurent de Lavoisier

This French philosopher and chemist is considered to be the father of modern chemistry. Because of the precision of his measurements, he was able to discover that during a chemical reaction, the total mass of the reagents is always equal to the total mass of the products. His observations led him to formulate the law of conservation of mass in 1789.

There are many clues that help tell the difference between a chemical change and a physical change:

- the release of a gas
- greater changes of heat
- the generation of light
- a change of colour
- the formation of a **PRECIPITATE**

Figures 2.39 through 2.42 illustrate some examples of chemical change.

2.39 When sodium bicarbonate (baking soda) and vinegar are mixed, we can see gas being released.

Very oxidized copper

Slightly oxidized copper

2.40 The oxidation of the copper roof on the Château Frontenac, in Québec City, produces a change of colour.

2.41 When paper burns, it produces light and heat.

Precipitate

2.42 A precipitate forms when lead nitrate is mixed with potassium iodide.

In the following sections, let's take a look at the following chemical reactions: synthesis, decomposition, oxidation and precipitation.

 5.1 SYNTHESIS

Atoms form chemical bonds to make molecules. Molecules bond together to make new molecules. The chemical reaction that results in the formation of a new molecule is called *synthesis*.

> ▶ **SYNTHESIS** is the formation of a complex molecule from atoms or simpler molecules.

For example, two hydrogen atoms (H_2) can react with an oxygen molecule (O_2) to form two water molecules (H_2O). We call this the *synthesis of water*.

In this reaction, the hydrogen and the oxygen are considered to be simple molecules because together they produce the more complex molecule, water.

THE ROLE OF ENERGY IN SYNTHESIS

The synthesis of water is an explosive reaction that releases a great deal of energy. So much energy is released that it can be used to power a rocket engine.

$$2\,H_2 + O_2 \longrightarrow 2\,H_2O + energy$$

2.43 The synthesis of water releases lots of energy.

On the other hand, the formation of two molecules of nitrous dioxide (NO_2) by combining a nitrogen molecule (N_2) with two molecules of oxygen (O_2) is a process that absorbs energy. Here is the equation for the synthesis of NO_2:

$$N_2 + 2\,O_2 + energy \longrightarrow 2\,NO_2$$

2.44 The synthesis of nitrous dioxide absorbs energy.

Synthesis is a chemical reaction that either absorbs or releases energy.

Many syntheses take place in living organisms. We can compare a living organism to a factory for the production of complex molecules such as proteins, carbohydrates, fats and DNA.

1874
1940

Carl Bosch

Carl Bosch was a German chemist and engineer. He won many awards for his work in industrial chemistry, and received the Nobel prize for chemistry in 1931. He developed various procedures that made numerous synthetic reactions more efficient, such as the synthesis of ammonia, a cleaning product still in use today.

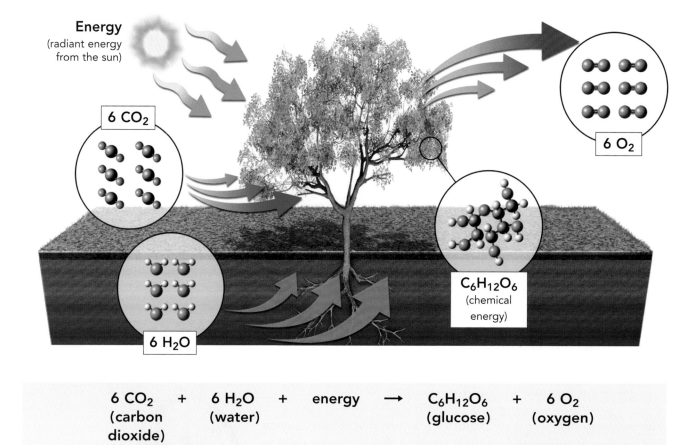

Energy
(radiant energy
from the sun)

6 CO₂

6 H₂O

6 O₂

$C_6H_{12}O_6$
(chemical
energy)

$$6\ CO_2 \quad + \quad 6\ H_2O \quad + \quad energy \quad \longrightarrow \quad C_6H_{12}O_6 \quad + \quad 6\ O_2$$

6 CO₂   +   6 H₂O   +   energy   →   C₆H₁₂O₆   +   6 O₂
(carbon   (water)   (glucose)   (oxygen)
dioxide)

2.45 The chemical reaction photosynthesis

Figure 2.45 illustrates how plants transform energy from the sun in a chemical reaction called *photosynthesis*. During this process, plants transform radiant energy from the sun into chemical energy, which is then stored in the bonds of glucose molecules. Living organisms incapable of **PHOTOSYNTHESIS,** like animals, benefit from this energy by consuming the plants or other animals.

Photosynthesis comes from the Greek words *photos,* meaning "light," and *synthesis,* meaning "putting together."

Human beings are also incapable of producing glucose like plants. Our bodies, however, can store energy in the form of glycogen, a molecule that is actually a collection of many glucose molecules. This synthesis absorbs energy, which it gets from the chemical energy stored in our liver and muscles.

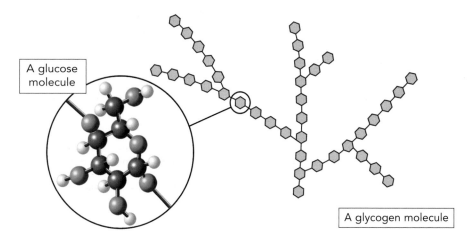

A glucose
molecule

A glycogen molecule

2.46 During the synthesis of glycogen, chemical energy is stored in the bonds between the atoms of this molecule.

Synthesis in living organisms always absorbs energy. The energy is transformed into chemical energy and stored in the bonds of the molecules that are produced.

2.47 ENERGY INVOLVED IN THE SYNTHESIS OF VARIOUS SUBSTANCES

Substance	Energy (J/g)
Nitrogen dioxide (NO_2)	Absorbs 737
Glucose ($C_6H_{12}O_6$)	Absorbs 7 072
Ammonia (NH_3)	Releases 2 718
Methane (CH_4)	Releases 4 688
Carbon dioxide (CO_2)	Releases 8 957
Water (H_2O)	Releases 13 444

5.2 DECOMPOSITION

The process of decomposition is the opposite of synthesis. During decomposition, the bonds in a molecule are broken and two or more smaller molecules are formed.

> **DECOMPOSITION** is the transformation of complex molecules into simpler molecules or into atoms.

THE ROLE OF ENERGY IN DECOMPOSITION

During decomposition, the chemical energy in a molecule is usually released and transformed into other forms of energy.

In living organisms, decomposition always involves a release of energy. For example, when an organism needs energy, it can change the bonds within molecules of glycogen. In scientific terms, it is said that glycogen decomposes into glucose. This decomposition releases energy, principally in the form of thermal energy.

Certain decompositions, however, require energy. This means that more energy is required to reorganize the bonds within a molecule than the bonds contain. Water electrolysis is an example. (We use the term _electrolysis_ when electrical energy is required for a reaction.) The decomposition of two water molecules produces two hydrogen molecules (H_2) and one oxygen molecule (O_2).

$$2 \ H_2O \ + \ \text{electrical energy} \longrightarrow 2 \ H_2 \ + \ O_2$$

2.49 The electrolysis of water absorbs energy.

2.48 The electrolysis of water requires more energy than it releases. Therefore, this is a reaction that absorbs energy.

Electrolysis is made up of the prefix _electro-_, meaning "electricity," and the suffix _-lyse_, meaning "dissolution, releasing."

Decomposition is therefore a chemical reaction that absorbs or releases energy.

The quantity of energy associated with decomposition is the same as that required for its synthesis. The energy transfer, however, goes in the opposite direction. In other words, if the synthesis of a molecule absorbs energy, its decomposition releases energy, and vice versa.

5.3 OXIDATION

LAB
22

The best-known oxidation process is surely the formation of rust.

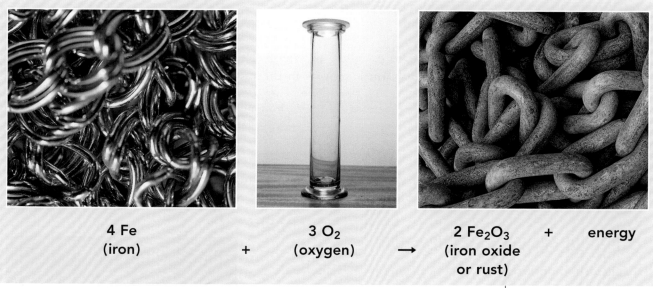

4 Fe   +   3 O₂   ⟶   2 Fe₂O₃   +   energy
(iron)   (oxygen)   (iron oxide
                                             or rust)

2.50   The oxidation of iron (that is, the formation of rust) releases energy.

Iron isn't the only metal that oxidizes. Actually, most metals do. Oxidation is characterized by the deterioration of metal, a phenomenon also known as *corrosion*.

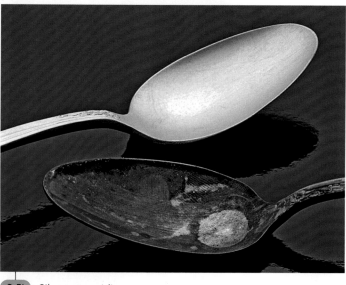

FILL 'ER UP...
WITH IRON!

In the future, drivers may be stopping at the service station to fill their tanks with powdered metal. Trials using iron particles have been promising. When exposed to oxygen, the metal oxidizes and releases a large quantity of energy: twice as much as the same volume of gas.

2.51   Silver can oxidize.

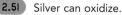 

What is oxidation? In general terms, oxidation is defined as the combining of a substance with oxygen. For chemists, oxidation can involve any substance that has properties similar to oxygen, such as sulphur, chlorine and fluoride. For example, the blackish deposit resulting from the oxidation of silver is principally silver sulphide (Ag_2S). In this case, the substance that caused the oxidation is sulphur, not oxygen.

> ▶ OXIDATION is a chemical reaction involving oxygen or a substance that has similar properties to oxygen.

Food can also be oxidized. This reaction often changes their taste and their appearance, including their colour. When bananas and apples are oxidized, they turn brownish.

2.52 Oxidized bananas are less appetizing.

THE ROLE OF ENERGY IN OXIDATION

Oxidation generally involves a release of energy. This energy, however, is sometimes difficult to see when the reaction is slow, as in the case of rust formation.

2.53 ENERGY INVOLVED IN THE OXIDATION OF VARIOUS METALS

Substance	Energy (J/g)
Copper	Releases 1 175
Iron	Releases 5 150
Magnesium	Releases 15 000

In other oxidation processes, such as combustion, the release of energy is much more evident because the reaction is rapid.

Fire is the most spectacular form of combustion. The heat produced by its thermal energy can be used to cook food or heat air, while its radiant energy produces light.

Various oxidation processes inside the human body are also forms of combustion. Like fire, they release large amounts of energy. But unlike fire, they are controlled. For example, glucose (from our food) reacts with oxygen (from the air we breathe). This oxidation process involves the reorganization of the bonds in the glucose molecules, releasing the stored chemical energy. The energy helps us stay warm, move around, and keep the organs in our bodies in working order. The reaction also releases carbon dioxide and water.

2.54 Fire needs oxygen. It is an oxidation process, which releases a great deal of energy; in other words, it is combustion.

Figure 2.55 outlines the oxidation process for glucose, which is also called *cellular respiration*.

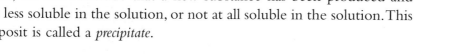

$$C_6H_{12}O_6 \quad + \quad 6\,O_2 \quad \rightarrow \quad 6\,CO_2 \quad + \quad 6\,H_2O \quad + \quad \text{energy}$$
$$\text{(glucose)} \qquad \text{(oxygen)} \qquad\qquad \text{(carbon dioxide)} \qquad \text{(water)}$$

2.55 The oxidation of glucose is a slow combustion process that releases energy.

Cellular respiration is the opposite of photosynthesis (page 54). Respiration releases energy, photosynthesis absorbs energy.

2.56 AMOUNTS OF ENERGY INVOLVED IN THE COMBUSTION OF VARIOUS SUBSTANCES

Substance	Energy (J/g)
Wood	Releases 18 830
Gas	Releases 48 000
Natural gas	Releases 18 830
Glucose (digestion)	Releases 15 630
Proteins (digestion)	Releases 14 650

5.4 PRECIPITATION

LABS 23–24

When we mix two solutions, the dissolved substances sometimes react to form a new substance. When we see a solid substance fall to the bottom of a solution, we can conclude that a new substance has been produced and that it is less soluble in the solution, or not at all soluble in the solution. This solid deposit is called a *precipitate*.

> ● PRECIPITATION is the formation of a solid that is less soluble, or not soluble, following the mixing of two solutions.

This is what happens when we mix vinegar and milk. The vinegar reacts with a protein in the milk, called *casein*, to produce a precipitate.

Precipitation is used in certain purification procedures. It is easier to separate the elements of some mixtures when part of the mixture can be changed into a solid and collected, using filtration or decantation.

Precipitation is a process that requires very little energy.

2.57 The addition of enzymes or other acidic substances to milk or cream produces precipitation, in this case called *curdling*. This is how cheese is made.

CHECKUP

1 WHAT IS ENERGY? (pp. 34–35)

1. Energy has the ability to do two things: what are they?

2. What unit of measurement is used to measure energy?

3. Read the passage below.

> In the past, water wheels were used to carry out hard work. The wheels were generally built close to fast-running rivers. The water's movement turned the wheel for the mill. This movement was connected to other functions, for example, a saw for cutting wood, millstones for grinding grain into flour or devices for spinning wool. In this way, small industry was born. Water wheels were later replaced by steam engines. The steam from boiling water kept the engines running.

Name each type of work and each change (mentioned in the text above) that is produced by energy. List your answers in a table similar to the one below.

Work	Change

2 FORMS OF ENERGY (pp. 35–41)

4. What forms of energy are involved in each of the examples below?

   a) causes particles of a substance to move

   b) produces a beam of light

   c) is stored in the bonds between atoms in a molecule

   d) results from the speed of an object, its mass or its relationship to its surroundings

5. Look at the following photos.

① ② ③ ④

Make a table similar to the one below. In the first column, list the actions shown in the photos on the preceding page. In the second column, list at least one form of energy involved in each action.

Action	Form of energy

6. Imagine that you are watching a diving competition. There are three platforms: the first is 1 m high, the second is 3 m high, and the third is 10 m high. Three divers with relatively the same mass are preparing for their dives. Which one will hit the water with the most mechanical energy? Explain your answer.

3 ENERGY TRANSFORMATION AND TRANSFER (pp. 41–42)

7. Look at the following photo.

The chemical energy of the substances contained in the rocket boosters is launching the space shuttle. Is there energy transformation or energy transfer happening, or both? Explain your answer.

8. Heat is a transfer of what form of energy?

4 PHYSICAL CHANGES (pp. 43–50)

9. Name two examples of physical change.

10. Carbon dioxide freezes at -80°C. It can then be used for a variety of purposes. For example, it can be used to keep certain substances frozen during transportation. It is a good choice because it is very cold and doesn't make a mess. When it undergoes a change of state or phase, it is as if carbon dioxide just disappears: it changes from a solid to a gas, hence its nickname "dry ice."

a) What is this change of state called?

b) During this change of state, what form of energy is transferred?

c) How is the energy transferred during this change of state? Indicate the direction of the transfer and where it takes place.

11. Let's say you dissolve a certain quantity of a substance in water. You observe that the temperature of the resulting solution is higher than the temperature of the water was. Did this dissolution absorb or release energy? Explain your answer.

5 CHEMICAL CHANGES (pp. 50–58)

12. Give two examples of chemical change.

13. Your body needs energy. Does it need to synthesize or decompose molecules in order to fill its need? Explain your answer.

14. In a natural gas fireplace, the flame is produced by the combustion of methane. During this reaction, a methane molecule (CH_4) and two oxygen molecules (O_2) react to form one carbon dioxide molecule (CO_2) and two water molecules (H_2O).

    a) Is this an oxidation process? Explain your answer.

    b) Does this process absorb or release energy? In what form(s)?

    c) Write the chemical equation for this reaction.

15. For each of the following examples, indicate whether a physical change or a chemical change is involved, and indicate the name of the change.

    a) a person making clouds with their breath

    b) a cut apple turning brown

    c) a person digesting a meal

    d) a crumpled piece of paper

    e) a person cleaning a grease spot with soap

    f) a factory producing ammonia (NH_3) from nitrogen (N_2) and hydrogen (H_2)

    g) limewater that becomes milky when exposed to carbon dioxide

CONCEPT MAPS

HOW TO BUILD A CONCEPT MAP

Prepare your own summary of Chapter 2 by building a concept map based on the following terms:

- Change
- Change of state (or phase)
- Chemical change
- Chemical energy
- Decomposition
- Deformation
- Dissolution
- Energy
- Energy transfer
- Energy transformation
- Forms of energy
- Mechanical energy
- Oxidation
- Physical change
- Precipitation
- Radiant energy
- Synthesis
- Thermal energy
- Work

DIFFERENCES IN BODY TEMPERATURE

There are many exchanges of thermal energy that occur within our bodies and between our bodies and our environment. This helps us to maintain a body temperature of about 37°C. Our bodies are, however, sometimes exposed to such extremes in temperature that they can lead either to hypothermia or to hyperthermia.

2.58 HYPOTHERMIA

Definition	Symptoms	Treatment
Hypothermia is the result of prolonged exposure to cold air or cold water.	• Internal temperature below 35°C • Pale skin • Shivering (which stops when the body's temperature reaches between 30°C and 32°C) • Loss of consciousness • Coma or death (in a serious case)	• Make sure the person is dry (dry body and clothing). • Have the person increase muscular activity (for example, jumping on the spot). • Dress the person in layers of warm clothes. • Have the person drink warm non-alcoholic liquids. • Cross the person's arms over his/her chest.

2.59 HYPERTHERMIA

Definition	Symptoms	Treatment
With hyperthermia, the body cannot decrease its temperature on its own. It is caused either by prolonged exposure to heat or by intense physical effort.	• Internal temperature over 38°C • Dry, red, hot skin • Panting • Intense headaches • Dizziness • Fatigue • Coma or death (in a serious case)	• Give the person cool liquids to drink. • Dress the person in cool, light-coloured clothing. • Guide the person to a cool, shaded spot. • Immerse or splash the person with tepid water.

Fever is a form of hyperthermia. It is not the environment, however, that produces the fever, but the person's own body in its fight against infection.

1. You're on a winter hike and it's really cold outside.
    a) What precautions should you take against hypothermia?
    b) If the person with you says that he or she is cold, or if the person is shivering uncontrollably, how could you increase his or her body temperature?

2. During a sports marathon, there are usually volunteers handing out cool drinks along the course. What are the benefits in this for the runners?

YVES SERGERIE

In the beginning of the 1990s, an engineer working on the construction of the Montréal Biodôme asked Yves Sergerie to develop an air-conditioning system for the penguin habitat. In response, Sergerie came up with two gigantic machines that produce crushed ice, capable of producing about 6000 kg per day. The thermal energy transfers between the ice and the penguin habitat help cool down the air and maintain the air and water temperature at an ideal level for these arctic-dwelling creatures. Sergerie spent nearly 400 hours designing the system and another four months building it. Three refrigeration technicians worked with him, along with employees of the city of Montréal.

NAME
Yves Sergerie

JOB
President of a family-owned air-conditioning, heating, ventilation and refrigeration systems business

AREA WHERE HE WORKS
Montréal

EDUCATION
DCS in mining technology, with a specialization in ventilation and use of underground mines

PROUDEST ACHIEVEMENT
Designed the cooling system for the penguin habitat at the Montréal Biodôme

2.60 The penguin habitat at the Montréal Biodôme

2.61 OCCUPATIONS CONNECTED TO SERGERIE'S WORK

Occupation	Education required	Length of study	Main tasks
Cooling systems mechanic	DEP in refrigeration	1800 hours	• Install and maintain different cooling and air-conditioning systems
Architectural technologist	DCS in architectural technology	3 years	• Draw and design building details • Coordinate building projects
Construction engineer	Bachelor's degree in civil engineering	3 1/2 years	• Draw and design buildings • Oversee building projects

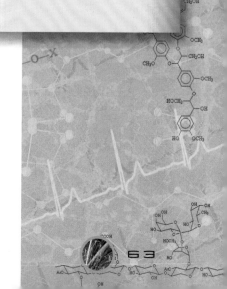

2005 — Kyōto Protocol comes into force, for the reduction of CO_2 emissions

1955 — Invention of the hovercraft

1931 — First use of freon gas for refrigeration

1881 — Invention of the sphygmomanometer for the measurement of arterial blood pressure

1850 — Invention of the hypodermic syringe

1797 — First recorded parachute jump

1783 — Invention of the hot air balloon

1738 — Demonstration of Bernoulli's principle, which explains air currents

1690 — Design of a vapour-driven piston pump

1643 — Invention of the barometer

CIRCA 600 — Beginning of the use of windmills

CIRCA 50 — Invention of a water pump to feed a water fountain

CIRCA -100 — Construction of the first water mill

CIRCA -5000 — Invention of skis

THE HUMAN ORGANISM

AND THE BEHAVIOUR OF FLUIDS

Water is certainly the best-known fluid: we use it for washing, for playing, for putting out fires and for carrying all kinds of stuff. Water is essential for life. From 60 percent to 70 percent of our total body weight is made up of water. The air we breathe and that surrounds us is a fluid; we couldn't live without it. What do fluids, such as air and water, have in common? What mechanisms enable these fluids to circulate and carry substances throughout the human organism? This is what we will explore in this chapter.

1 WHAT IS A FLUID?

A |fluid| is any substance that can flow or spread. If poured into a container, it assumes the shape of the container. Fluids are said to be 100 percent adaptable.

Fluid comes from the Latin word *fluidus*, meaning "that flows."

▶ **A FLUID** is a substance that has the capacity to flow and assume the form of the container into which it has been poured.

Let's use the examples of water and air, as they correspond quite well to this definition. Water poured into a glass takes on the shape of the container. The air we breathe assumes the shape first of our nasal passages, then our trachea and our lungs.

3.1 A liquid can be a fluid.

Air

3.2 A gas can be a fluid.

All liquids, such as water, milk and juice, are fluids. In the human body, blood and saliva are fluids. Gases, such as air, helium and ozone, are also fluids.

How do we explain the capacity that fluids have to flow and to deform? We can use the **PARTICLE MODEL** to look at the arrangement of particles in a fluid. Let's look again at the examples of water and air. In Figures 3.3. and 3.4, we can see that:

- the particles in a liquid, such as water, are close together and are held together by forces of attraction that are relatively weak. In this way, the particles can slide over each other to take on the form of any container.

- the particles of a gas, such as air, are much farther apart and are not bound together by forces of attraction. They move in every direction and occupy all available space.

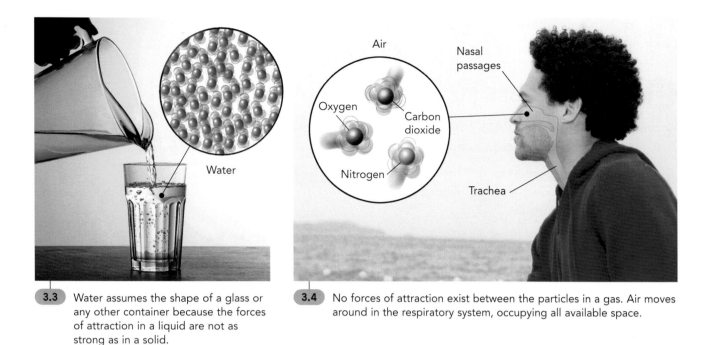

3.3 Water assumes the shape of a glass or any other container because the forces of attraction in a liquid are not as strong as in a solid.

3.4 No forces of attraction exist between the particles in a gas. Air moves around in the respiratory system, occupying all available space.

It is sometimes difficult to determine if a substance is a fluid. Here are a few cases in particular.

Some substances are mixtures in a liquid or gaseous phase that contains solid particles. Since these substances are still capable of flowing, they are considered to be fluids. For example, smoke—a mixture of air and solid particles in suspension—is a fluid, as well as a colloid (page 11).

Other substances, such as gels and pastes, are more difficult to identify as liquids or solids. If they can flow and take on the form of their containers, they are fluids.

If a solid exists in tiny pieces, like sand, and can flow, is it considered to be a fluid? No. Sand doesn't flow continually like a liquid. Neither does it naturally assume the shape of its container. It forms a pile instead of a flat surface.

3.5 A fluid can be a gas or a liquid containing solid particles in suspension.

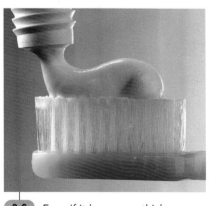

3.6 Even if it has a very thick consistency, toothpaste is a fluid.

3.7 Sand is not a fluid because it doesn't naturally assume the shape of its container.

There are two types of fluids: compressible fluids (gases) and incompressible fluids (liquids).

1.1 COMPRESSIBLE FLUIDS

A compressible fluid is one that can be compressed, that is, its volume can change in response to a change in pressure.

> *Compressed* comes from the Latin word *comprimere*, "to press together."

To illustrate this phenomenon, let's look at the example of a closed syringe, which is two-thirds filled with gas. Figure 3.8 **A** shows that, in this case, the particles are quite far apart.

What happens when we push the plunger of the syringe? As Figure 3.8 **B** shows, the gas particles move closer together and redistribute themselves evenly in what's left of the available space. This gas is a compressible fluid because its volume can be reduced.

What happens if we pull the plunger back? As Figure 3.8 **C** shows, the particles move farther apart to occupy the newly available space. The volume of a compressible fluid can also be increased.

> ➲ A COMPRESSIBLE FLUID is a fluid whose volume can change. Gases are compressible fluids.

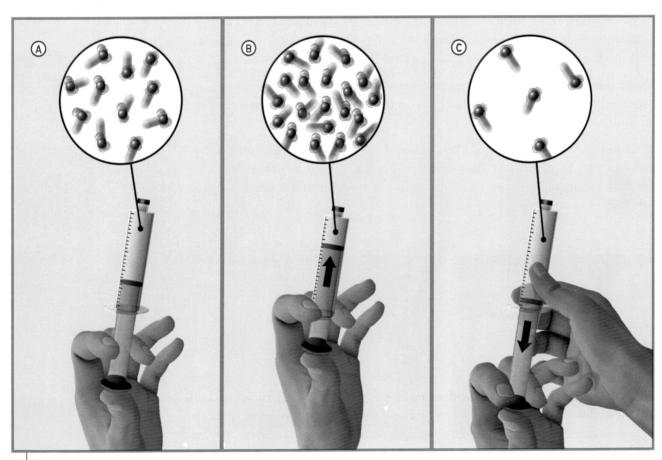

3.8 The volume of a compressible fluid can change because the space between the particles in the fluid can vary.

1.2 INCOMPRESSIBLE FLUIDS

Let's return to the preceding example of a closed syringe, filled to two thirds, but instead use a liquid instead of a gas (Figure 3.9 **A**). Would we get the same result? Would the volume of the liquid decrease when we push in the plunger? As we can see in Figure 3.9 **B**, there is no noticeable change in volume. The particles in a liquid are already very close together. We cannot condense them any more. This is why we use the term *incompressible*.

In Figure 3.9 **C**, the syringe plunger is pulled back and the volume of the liquid doesn't change.

> ⊙ An INCOMPRESSIBLE FLUID is a fluid whose volume cannot be varied. Liquids are incompressible fluids.

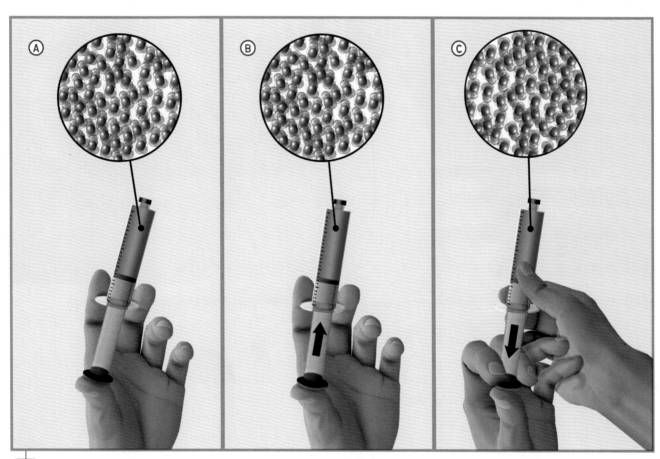

3.9 The volume of an incompressible fluid is practically invariable because its particles are very close together.

Understanding the difference between compressible and incompressible fluids is essential for a thorough understanding of pressure. The particles in each of these fluids are organized differently and they exert pressure in different ways. In the following section, we will examine pressure. But first, we must define what it means.

2 WHAT IS PRESSURE?

We use the term *pressure* all the time. The water in the tap flows with a certain pressure. Blowing up a balloon requires gas under pressure. In the weather report, we hear about atmospheric pressure. When we put our elbows on a table, we are putting pressure on the table.

In science, the concept of pressure involves both force and the surface area on which that force is exerted.

CYCLE ONE

├ Effects of a force
├ Universal gravity
└ Mass

▶ PRESSURE is the result of a force applied in a perpendicular fashion to a surface.

3.10 The finger is applying pressure to the piano key.

3.11 The finger is applying pressure to the pastry.

Let's take a look at two of the variables involved in pressure: force and surface area.

● What is a *force?* Force is an action that modifies the movement of an object (by causing it to accelerate, slow down, change course or stop), or that causes the shape of an object to change. In the examples shown above, one finger exerts force on a piano key (causing the key to change its movement) and another finger exerts force on pastry (causing the shape of pastry to change).

● Force can be produced by an action, but it can also be produced by the attraction between an object and the Earth. For example, a person standing on the ground is subject to a force of attraction that depends on his or her mass. The greater the mass, the stronger the force.

What is *surface area?* Surface area is the surface dimension of an object. Only part of the surface of a finger is in contact with the piano key or the pastry. In order to measure the pressure that is being exerted, we need to take the area of that surface into account.

2.1 FORCE AND PRESSURE

In order to understand the role played by force in pressure, let's take the example of the force of attraction between an object and the Earth. Figure 3.12 shows two people with different masses who are wearing the same size boots (same surface area). In this case, it is the person with the greatest mass (and thus subject to the greatest force) who exerts the greatest pressure on the snow and who sinks deeper.

The stronger the force, the greater the pressure. Below is a table that sums up the role that force plays in measuring pressure:

3.12 A person with more mass sinks deeper in the snow than a person with less mass because that person exerts a greater pressure.

3.13 THE EFFECT OF A VARIATION IN FORCE ON PRESSURE
(if surface area remains constant)

Variation in force	Result
If the force increases	Pressure increases
If the force decreases	Pressure decreases

2.2 SURFACE AREA AND PRESSURE

In order to understand the role played by surface area in pressure, let's take a look at Figure 3.14. If a person is wearing snowshoes to walk in the snow, there is less pressure on the snow and the person sinks much less than if he or she were just wearing boots. Thanks to the snowshoes, the force is distributed over a greater area (a larger surface area). Each unit of surface therefore experiences less force, which decreases pressure.

The greater the surface area that experiences or is exposed to the force, the less the pressure. Here is a table that sums up the role that surface area plays in measuring pressure:

3.14 A person who is not wearing snowshoes sinks deeper in the snow because the surface area in contact with the snow is smaller.

3.15 THE EFFECT OF A VARIATION IN EXPOSED SURFACE AREA ON PRESSURE
(if force remains constant)

Variation in surface area	Result
If the surface area exposed to a force increases	Pressure decreases
If the surface area exposed to a force decreases	Pressure increases

2.3 CALCULATING PRESSURE

In the International System of Units, pressure is measured in pascals.

Since pressure corresponds to the force applied per unit of surface area, the mathematical equation for calculating pressure is as follows:

$$P = \frac{F}{A}$$, where P is pressure, measured in pascals (Pa)

F is force, measured in newtons (N)

A is the exposed surface area, measured in square metres (m²)

Let's use, as an example, a 1 kg (10 N) box placed on a table.

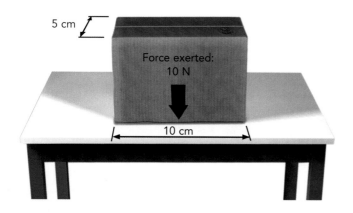

5 cm

Force exerted: 10 N

10 cm

How much pressure is this box exerting on the table?

$$P = \frac{F}{A} = \frac{10 \text{ N}}{0.005 \text{ m}^2} = 2000 \text{ Pa or 2 kPa}$$

Thus, the box is exerting 2 kPa of pressure on the table.

 The Newton (N) is the unit of measure for force. 1 N is the force necessary to impart an acceleration of 1 m/s² to a 1 kg object, which is the same as bringing an immobile object to a speed of 1 m/s in 1 second.

Because the Earth exerts a force of attraction that is about 10 N/kg, we can say that the Earth exerts a force of 1 N on all objects having a mass of 0.1 kg. Thus, to estimate the force exerted by the Earth on an object, simply multiply its mass by 10.

1623
1662

Blaise Pascal

The unit of measure for pressure, the pascal, was named in honour of the French philosopher, mathematician and physician, Blaise Pascal. Part of his extensive scientific research explored phenomena related to pressure.

THE CLOWN AND THE ELEPHANT

Pressure exerted on a floor by one of a clown's stilts is nearly 10 times greater than the pressure of an elephant's foot. In fact, the pressure involved is 1000 kPa per stilt (an 80 kg clown, with the end part of each stilt exposed to the ground measuring 2 cm by 2 cm) and 100 kPa per foot (a 3000 kg elephant, with each foot measuring 30 cm in diameter).

3 THE PRESSURE EXERTED BY FLUIDS

How is pressure exerted by a fluid? Is there a difference, for example, in the ways that compressible and incompressible fluids exert pressure? Yes, there is. We'll explore this difference in the following sections.

First, however, there is an important rule to keep in mind for all fluids: since the particles in a fluid are in constant motion, the pressure is exerted equally in all directions.

3.1 THE PRESSURE EXERTED BY AN INCOMPRESSIBLE FLUID

 LAB 26

When we dive deep in a pool, we can feel the pressure blocking our ears. This is an effect of the pressure exerted on us by the water.

In the case of an incompressible fluid, such as water, the force exerted comes from the mass of the fluid that is situated above the object. The total quantity of fluid is not important. For example, at a depth of 1 m, we feel the same pressure in a pool as in a lake.

The more fluid above an object, the greater the force exerted by the fluid and the greater the pressure.

3.17 In diving, it is the mass of water above the diver that determines the pressure he or she feels.

3.18 The liquid coming out of the bottom of the container is under more pressure than the liquid coming out the top. This is why it spurts out farther.

There is another factor to consider when calculating pressure: the **DENSITY** of the fluid.

For example, if a person dove into a liquid that has a greater density than water, such as mercury, or one that is less dense than water, like alcohol, what would the difference be in the pressure exerted on the diver? The denser the fluid, the greater the pressure, and conversely, the less the density, the smaller the pressure.

To sum up: the pressure exerted on an object by an incompressible fluid depends on:

- the depth of the object in the fluid
- the density of the fluid

3.19 THE DENSITY OF VARIOUS LIQUIDS

Liquid	Density (in g/ml)
Gas	0.75
Ethyl alcohol	0.79
Olive oil	0.92
Water	1.00
Seawater	1.03
Glycerine	1.26
Mercury	13.55

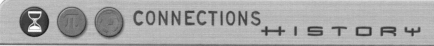

CONNECTIONS HISTORY

Underwater station in freezing waters

Joseph MacInnis, a Canadian doctor born in 1937, was the first man to swim in the waters under the North Pole. MacInnis wanted to study the reactions of the human body in deep water and improve the security of divers who participate in scientific research in Arctic waters. In 1972, he invented a submarine shelter, the *Sub-igloo*. Located at the bottom of Resolute Bay in Nunavut, the shelter became the first official station under ice and the first to be used in the Arctic.

The *Sub-igloo* consisted of a clear plastic shell on a structure made up of thousands of aluminum bars. The whole thing weighed nine tonnes, and was built to resist the pressure of the water above. Water was pumped out of the *Sub-igloo* through a tube and replaced by air. The air pressure inside the structure was kept equal to the water pressure outside, which prevented water from entering the shelter.

Thanks to this underwater station, divers could stay underwater longer. When they needed it, they could take a break by breathing the air inside the *Sub-igloo* instead of going back up to the surface. They could even communicate with people on the surface through a telephone system inside the shelter.

The *Sub-igloo* was used by 10 submarine research expeditions in Arctic waters.

The *Sub-igloo* allowed divers to take breaks in deep freezing water.

There are different instruments for measuring pressure in an incompressible fluid. Examples include depth gauges, U-shaped manometers and tonometers. The choice of the instrument depends on what is being measured.

3.20 A depth gauge measures water pressure and indicates diving depth in metres.

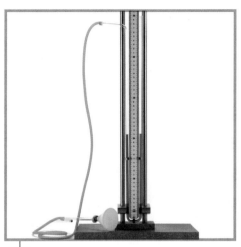

3.21 In a laboratory, we measure the pressure of an incompressible fluid with a U-shaped manometer. The pressure of the fluid is measured by the difference in the levels of the two columns of liquid.

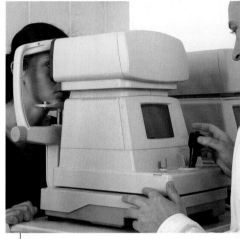

3.22 A tonometer can measure the fluid pressure in the eye.

3.2 THE PRESSURE EXERTED BY A COMPRESSIBLE FLUID

LAB 27

The particles of a compressible fluid (a gas) move randomly in all directions. When they meet an obstacle, they change direction. The obstacle may be an object, the wall of a container or another particle. During each collision, the fluid particles exert a force on the obstacle. It is the sum of these forces that is at the origin of the pressure of a compressible fluid.

In a compressible fluid, then, the pressure depends on:

- the number of collisions involving fluid particles, whether with other fluid particles or objects.

The more collisions there are, the greater the pressure. There is thus a direct relationship between pressure and the number of collisions.

Factors that affect the number of collisions:

- Number of particles: The more particles, the more they collide.

- Temperature: According to the particle model, the speed of the particles is directly related to temperature. The faster the particles move, the more they collide.

- Volume of fluid: We will explore in detail the relationship between pressure and the volume of a compressible fluid in the following section.

3.23 The more particles there are, the more frequently they collide, and the greater the pressure.

There are numerous types of instruments for measuring the pressure of a compressible fluid. In a laboratory, we use a U-shaped manometer. We can also use a pressure gauge or a dial-faced gauge, depending on what we want to measure.

3.24 In a laboratory, we use a U-shaped manometer to measure the pressure of a compressible fluid. This pressure is measured by the difference in height between the two columns of liquid.

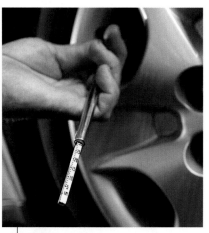

3.25 We can measure the air pressure in our automobile tires with a pressure gauge.

3.26 This dial-faced gauge helps us measure the pressure of a gas in a canister.

THE RELATIONSHIP BETWEEN THE PRESSURE AND THE VOLUME OF A COMPRESSIBLE FLUID

As we saw in Section 1.1, the volume of a compressible fluid is variable. If the volume is decreased, what happens to the pressure? At the same temperature, when the volume of a compressible fluid is decreased, the particles move closer together. They have less space to move around, and the frequency of collisions increases. This brings about an increase in pressure, since pressure is directly related to the number of collisions. What happens when the volume of the fluid increases? We see the opposite effect: the pressure decreases.

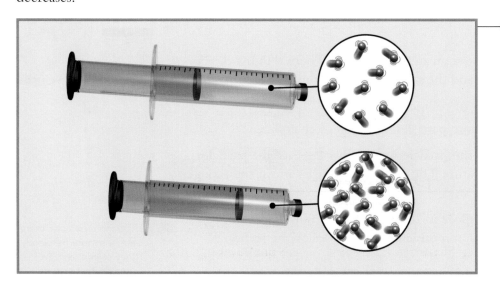

3.27 When the volume of a gas decreases, the number of collisions goes up, which increases the pressure.

Put air in your tires and save money!

Either through ignorance or negligence, more than half of all Canadian drivers consume too much gas simply because they don't check the air pressure in their tires.

Check tire pressure once a month as well as before taking a long trip. Unfortunately, not many people check often enough. By maintaining optimal pressure in your tires, you extend their lifespan and ensure efficient fuel consumption.

Tire pressure is measured with a gauge (many models are available on the market for a cost of about $10) and measuring only takes a few minutes. Check your air pressure when the tires are not heated up, since air pressure also changes with temperature.

The Rubber Association of Canada estimates that, with proper tire maintenance, the average driver could save around two weeks' worth of gas in a single year.

Adapted from Sylvie Rainville, "*Faites des économies en vérifiant la pression des pneus*," *La Presse*, May 1, 2006. [*Translation*]

Here is a table that summarizes the role played by volume in the pressure of a compressible fluid:

3.28 THE EFFECTS OF VARIATIONS IN VOLUME ON THE PRESSURE OF A COMPRESSIBLE FLUID (when temperature and the number of particles remain constant)

Variation in volume	Result
If volume increases	Pressure decreases
If volume decreases	Pressure increases

When temperature and number of particles are constant, the pressure of a compressible fluid is inversely proportional to its volume.

This relationship remains the same when we observe the effects of a variation in pressure on the volume of a compressible fluid. For example, in Figure 3.27 (page 76), when we push the plunger the pressure in the tube increases and the volume of the fluid decreases.

3.29 THE EFFECT OF A CHANGE IN PRESSURE ON THE VOLUME OF A COMPRESSIBLE FLUID (when temperature and the number of particles are constant)

Change in pressure	Result
If pressure increases	Volume decreases
If pressure decreases	Volume increases

The relationship between the volume and the pressure of a compressible fluid, the Boyle-Mariotte law, can be summarized as follows:

● At a constant temperature, the volume of a compressible fluid is inversely proportional to pressure. If the pressure increases, volume decreases, and vice versa.

The following example illustrates this law. When a weather balloon is released, its volume increases as it gains altitude, because pressure decreases as altitude increases. The volume of the balloon increases until it pops. The instruments for measurement that were attached to the balloon float downward with the help of a parachute.

1627
1691

Robert Boyle

In 1661, this Irish physicist and chemist formulated the relationship between the volume and the pressure for a gas. Shortly after, in 1676, the French physicist Edme Mariotte demonstrated the same law, now called the *Boyle-Mariotte law.*

3.30 A weather balloon used for meteorology, the study of the weather

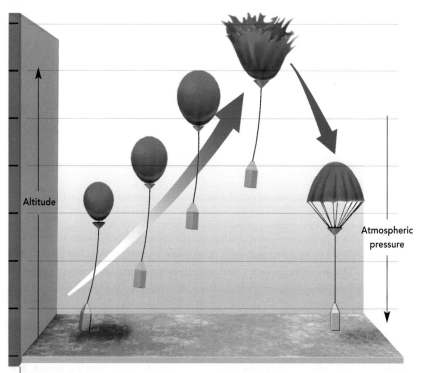

3.31 The volume of the weather balloon increases as the balloon ascends because atmospheric pressure decreases.

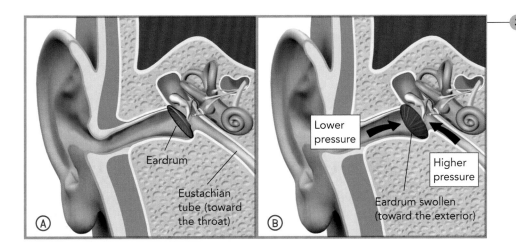

Eardrum

Eustachian tube (toward the throat)

Lower pressure

Higher pressure

Eardrum swollen (toward the exterior)

A similar phenomenon happens inside the ear. When the external pressure decreases, for example when we fly high in an airplane, the eardrum swells (Figure 3.32 **B**). The discomfort disappears when the pressure returns to normal on both sides of the eardrum as air enters through the eustachian tubes.

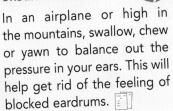

UNDER PRESSURE

In an airplane or high in the mountains, swallow, chew or yawn to balance out the pressure in your ears. This will help get rid of the feeling of blocked eardrums.

ATMOSPHERIC PRESSURE

The atmosphere is the layer of air that surrounds the earth. This air is a mixture of different gases, and it exerts pressure on us. We call this **ATMOSPHERIC PRESSURE.** Even if we don't notice it, the pressure is actually considerable. Figure 3.33 shows an experiment (first performed by Otto von Guericke in 1650), which demonstrates the amount of pressure exerted by the atmosphere.

Atmosphere comes from the Greek words *atmos*, meaning "humid vapour," and *sphaira*, meaning "celestial sphere."

CYCLE ONE
Atmosphere

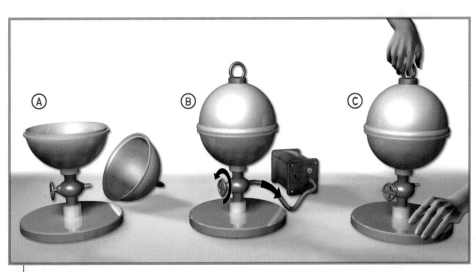

3.33 The two halves of a sphere in A can be put together to form the sphere. In B, the air inside the sphere is pumped out, creating a vacuum inside. In C, the atmosphere exerts so much pressure on the empty sphere that the two halves cannot be pulled apart.

If atmospheric pressure is so strong, why are we not crushed by its force? The reason is because the particles in the atmosphere (the air) hit us equally from all sides, which cancels out their effect.

Atmospheric pressure varies with altitude. At sea level, which is used as a reference point, atmospheric pressure averages 101.3 kPa. As altitude increases, pressure decreases, because there are less particles in the air and thus fewer collisions between particles.

An instrument called a barometer measures atmospheric pressure.

The illustration below shows how the mercury barometer invented by Evangelista Torricelli works. Air exerts pressure on the mercury (a liquid), keeping the column of mercury stable in the upside-down tube. The level of the column of liquid varies with changes in pressure. A measurement of 760 mm of mercury (Hg) corresponds to 101.3 kPa of pressure. It is this instrument that provides the measurement *millimetres of mercury* that we still use today when talking about pressure.

Barometer comes from the Greek words *baros*, meaning "weight" and *metron*, meaning "measurement."

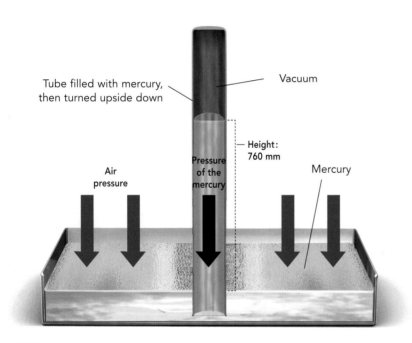

Tube filled with mercury, then turned upside down

Vacuum

Air pressure

Pressure of the mercury

Height: 760 mm

Mercury

3.34 The mercury barometer and how it works

 Quite often, the pressure of a gas, as measured by a gauge or a manometer, is relative: it depends on atmospheric pressure. In this case, a positive result indicates pressure greater than atmospheric pressure, and a negative result indicates pressure that is less than atmospheric pressure. There are instruments, however, that can measure absolute pressure, that is, the real pressure.

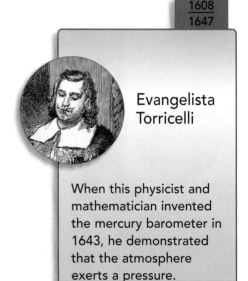

1608
1647

Evangelista Torricelli

When this physicist and mathematician invented the mercury barometer in 1643, he demonstrated that the atmosphere exerts a pressure.

MECHANISMS RELATED TO VARIATIONS IN THE PRESSURE OF FLUIDS

In the preceding section, we saw how pressure behaves inside fluids. Now let's take a look at various ways that pressure can be put to work, because of the properties of fluids.

4.1 GENERAL PRINCIPLES AND THEIR TECHNICAL APPLICATIONS

To begin with, let's examine the principles behind the variations in the pressure of fluids.

First principle: A fluid naturally moves from a zone of high pressure toward a zone of low pressure.

Pressure transfers produced by mechanisms, such as pistons, valves or pumps, can change the pressure within a fluid. Such changes bring about the circulation of the fluid.

Here's an example: When the valve of a gas canister is opened under pressure, the gas is propelled out of the canister, since the outside pressure is lower. When the pressure inside the canister becomes equal to the pressure outside, the gas, therefore, no longer flows outside. (A canister of gas, therefore, is never empty unless the remaining gas is pumped out.)

There is a similar phenomenon for fluids in a liquid state. For example, when a pump in a well produces an increase in pressure in the well, it causes water to travel through the pipes to places within the house, where the pressure is lower.

Lower pressure

Higher pressure

3.35 The gas moves from inside the canister, where pressure is high, to the outside, where pressure is lower.

Second principle: Pressure applied to the surface of a fluid inside a closed container gets uniformly distributed to every part of the fluid.

This simple principle, called *Pascal's principle*, has many applications. For example, when we push the plunger of a closed syringe, the pressure of the liquid inside the syringe increases. If we remove the plug from the syringe, the liquid is forced out of the syringe, according to the first principle. The harder we push down, the more forcefully the liquid is ejected. This example demonstrates that the pressure exerted on the plunger is transferred to the liquid.

It is this same principle at work that makes the disc brakes of a car function. When we press down on the brake, the pressure travels to the discs on the wheels.

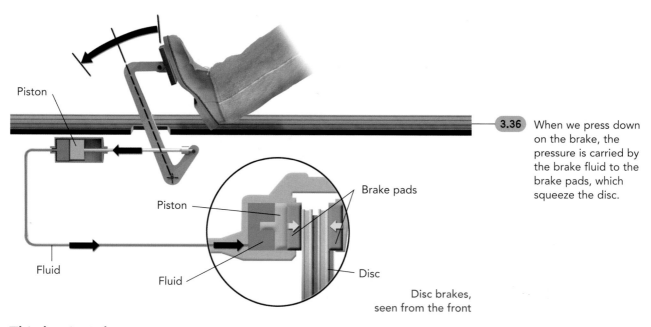

Piston

Piston

Brake pads

Fluid

Fluid

Disc

3.36 When we press down on the brake, the pressure is carried by the brake fluid to the brake pads, which squeeze the disc.

Disc brakes, seen from the front

Third principle: A transfer of pressure in a fluid can increase the force involved.

This is the principle behind hydraulic mechanisms, that is, those mechanisms that use energy transmitted through water or other fluids in order to work. The hydraulic apparatus in Figure 3.37 is one example.

Hydraulic comes from the Latin word *hydraulicus*, meaning "moved by water."

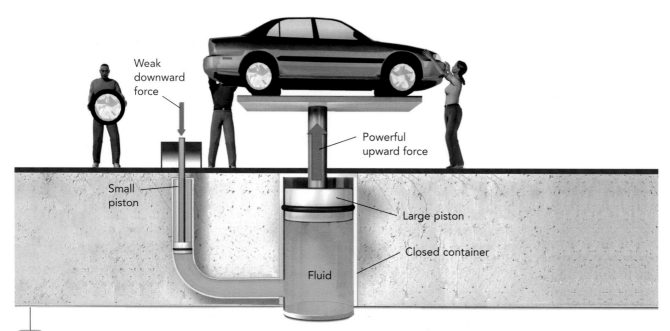

Weak downward force

Powerful upward force

Small piston

Large piston

Closed container

Fluid

3.37 When pressure is applied to the surface of a fluid in a closed system, it spreads equally throughout the system. Since the pressure is the same at each end of the mechanism above, the force exerted by the large piston on the right (with its greater surface area for contact) is greater than the force exerted by the small piston on the left (with its smaller surface area). This mechanical advantage makes it possible to increase the force through the fluid, and thus lift heavy objects, such as a car.

4.2 NATURAL MECHANISMS

The principles that we have just seen can also be used to explain the way many natural mechanisms work.

For example, the heart works like a pump. It provides the necessary changes in pressure so that blood keeps circulating through the rest of the body. In the arteries, blood pressure normally varies between 16 kPa (120 mm Hg), the maximum pressure when the heart is beating, and 10 kPa (75 mm Hg), the minimum pressure when the heart is resting. Inside the veins, pressure is almost zero. The blood circulates in the arteries toward the veins, and is then pumped by the heart. We measure the blood pressure in the arteries using a sphygmomanometer (or a blood pressure cuff).

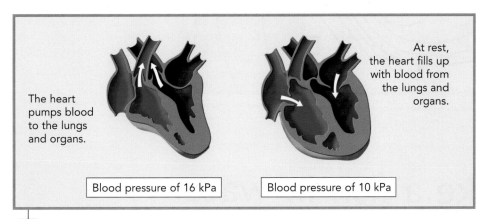

The heart pumps blood to the lungs and organs.

At rest, the heart fills up with blood from the lungs and organs.

Blood pressure of 16 kPa

Blood pressure of 10 kPa

3.38 The heart provides the necessary changes in pressure to help the blood circulate through the body.

Something similar happens when we breathe. When we breathe in, our thorax swells and the volume of the lungs increases. This increase in volume lowers the pressure in the lungs relative to that of the air, so that air flows into the lungs. When we breathe out, the volume of the lungs decreases, which increases the pressure in the lungs, so the air flows out of the lungs to the outside where the air pressure is lower.

THE BENEFITS OF GARLIC

Research has shown that eating garlic helps to lower blood pressure and prevent such diseases as atherosclerosis, which is caused by the accumulation of fatty deposits inside the blood vessels.

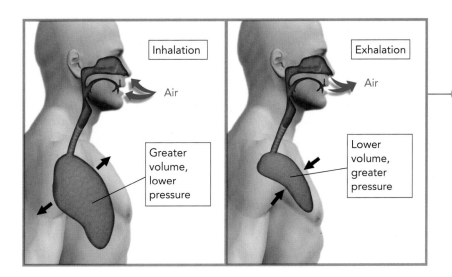

Inhalation

Air

Greater volume, lower pressure

Exhalation

Air

Lower volume, greater pressure

3.39 When breathing in and out, the volume of the lungs changes, letting air in and out of our body.

Wind is a natural phenomenon that depends on changes in atmospheric pressure. This pressure changes with altitude and with weather conditions. Masses of air move from zones of high pressure to zones of low pressure, generating wind.

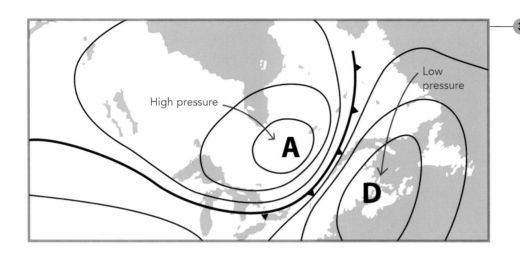

3.40 Wind is the movement of air from a high-pressure zone (or anticyclone, A) toward a low pressure zone (or depression, D).

High pressure

Low pressure

Like a fish in water

Divers could stay longer in deep water if they were able to use the air dissolved in the water to breathe, like fish do.

Right now, deep-sea divers need to use tanks to breathe under water. But these tanks can only hold so much air. An Israeli inventor, Alon Bodner, has developed a system that will help divers to breathe without their tanks. This system uses the air that is dissolved in water, the way fish do with their gills.

When he developed his system, Alon Bodner used Henry's law, a law that all physicists are familiar with. This law states that the amount of a given gas that can be dissolved in a liquid is directly proportional to the pressure of the gas on that liquid. Bodner's invention lowers the pressure around the divers. The dissolved air is set free in the form of large bubbles, which can then be used for breathing.

After building and testing a model of his system in a laboratory, the inventor believes that he will be able to build the first life-sized model within just a few years.

Adapted from "Comme un poisson dans l'eau,"
Science et Vie Junior, March 2006.
[Translation]

1 WHAT IS A FLUID? (pp. 66–69)

1. What are the characteristics of a fluid?

2. a) In what states do the substances that we consider to be fluids exist?

   b) For each of the states, list the characteristics of the particles that give them the properties of fluids. Present your answers in a table like the one below.

State	Particle characteristics

3. Look at the following photos.

Find the compressible and the incompressible fluids in these photos. Present your answers in a table like the one below.

Compressible fluids	Incompressible fluids

4. What is the difference between a compressible and an incompressible fluid? In other words, how is it that one can have a variable volume and not the other?

2 WHAT IS PRESSURE? (pp. 70–72)

5. In the International System of Units, what is the unit measure for pressure?

6. There are many types of vehicles on the roads: cars, motorcycles, trucks, etc. Because trucks can damage the road surface, they are sometimes not allowed on certain roads.

   a) Using the concept of pressure, explain how trucks damage the roads.

   b) Large trucks generally have numerous wide tires. What is the advantage of having these tires for the roadways?

7. A man's foot has a surface area of 0.03 m^2 and a snowshoe has a surface area of 0.3 m^2. How does the pressure exerted on the snow change for this man, with and without snowshoes? Explain your answer.

8. Let's say you place two rocks on the sand. The first rock has a mass of 5 kg and the second has a mass of 15 kg. If the two have the same contact surface, which of the two rocks exerts more pressure? Explain your answer.

9. A cylinder with a radius of 10 cm (and a surface area of 0.03 m^2) and a force of 10 N is placed upright on a table. What is the pressure exerted by the cylinder on the table?

3 THE PRESSURE EXERTED BY FLUIDS (pp. 73–80)

10. What changes the pressure in a liquid?

11. In a laboratory, it is useful to measure the pressure of a gas with a U-shaped manometer (such as the one illustrated below). How is pressure measured with this instrument?

The gas whose pressure is to be measured

Liquid

12. Even if a gas is very light, it can still exert a lot of pressure. What is the principal element that determines the pressure of a gas?

13. Look at the following illustration of a hydroelectric dam.

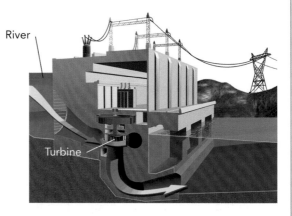

River

Turbine

Why do you think that it is preferable to install an inflow pipe to the turbine as low as possible with respect to the dam?

14. Decompression sickness, also known as "the bends," is a well-known condition among deep-sea divers. It is caused by gas bubbles developing in the blood when a diver ascends to the surface too quickly. The bubbles are formed by changes in pressure. Explain the relationship between the pressure and the volume of gas bubbles.

15. Certain animals, like tree frogs, have suction cups on their feet. These suction cups reduce the amount of air beneath their feet and stick to surfaces easily.

a) Explain how these tiny suction cups help tree frogs "stick" to surfaces.

b) Would this system work in space, where pressure is practically nonexistent? Explain your answer.

16. When we increase the temperature of a gas, what happens to its pressure? Explain your answer.

4. MECHANISMS RELATED TO VARIATIONS IN THE PRESSURE OF FLUIDS
(pp. 81–84)

17. In the summer, some people find fun playing with water guns. When the trigger of a water gun is pulled, water shoots out. The farther away the target is, the harder the trigger has to be pulled. Explain what happens to the pressure of the liquid in the water gun when the trigger is pulled.

18. How do fluids circulate through a (closed) system?

19. When pulling away the tab on a can of soda pop, why does some of the gas escape?

20. We know that on Earth a canister of gas can never fully empty on its own. Would the same be true in space, where pressure is practically nonexistent? Explain your answer.

21. A hydraulic system, like the one illustrated below, allows us to increase a force. Using the concept and principles of pressure, explain how this is possible.

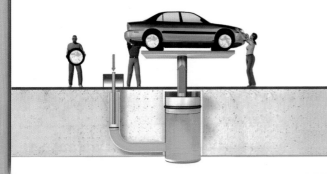

CONCEPT MAPS

HOW TO BUILD A CONCEPT MAP

Prepare your own summary of Chapter 3 by building a concept map based on the following terms and phrases:

- Compressible fluid
- Depth of a submerged object
- Fluid
- Fluid density
- Fluid volume
- Gaseous state
- Incompressible fluid
- Liquid state
- Number of particle collisions
- Pressure exerted

COUGHING: SYMPTOM OR REMEDY?

Coughing is an involuntary reflex that helps clear our breathing passages. It eliminates a surplus of fluid, such as mucus, or foreign particles, such as dust. Coughing is a result of a sudden, violent expulsion of air from the lungs with the contraction of the thorax. The projected air can reach a speed of about 500 km/h.

Coughing has many causes. If it is infrequent, there is no need to worry. A frequent or chronic cough, however, can be a symptom of a cold or a more serious infection, such as bronchitis. Coughing is helpful in such cases because it removes the contaminated mucus. If the breathing passages are not cleared, more serious infections can develop.

Coughing can also be triggered by allergens, physical effort or stress in a person suffering from asthma. Asthma attacks are brought on by a constriction of the breathing passages. Unfortunately, in such a case, coughing is an irritant that can worsen the attack. To control an asthma attack, bronchial dilators are necessary. These are a form of medication that helps to bring breathing back to normal.

3.41 A cough can be a symptom of a serious infection.

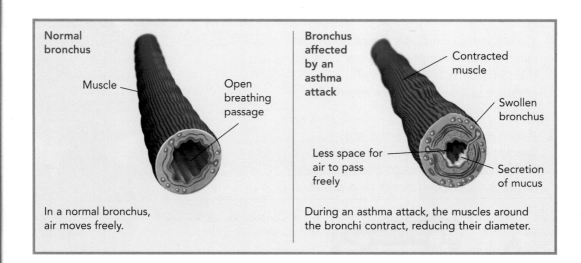

Normal bronchus

Muscle

Open breathing passage

In a normal bronchus, air moves freely.

Bronchus affected by an asthma attack

Contracted muscle

Swollen bronchus

Less space for air to pass freely

Secretion of mucus

During an asthma attack, the muscles around the bronchi contract, reducing their diameter.

1. A cold (of which coughing is a symptom) is spread by the fluids of the person who has it. What can we do to prevent colds from spreading?

2. What factors can trigger or worsen certain respiratory illnesses?

SCIENCE AT WORK

BENOÎT DE MONTIGNY

The design of a project such as the tunnel in the Parc Aquarium du Québec requires the collaboration of many people. It was Benoît de Montigny who, in the early 2000s, was in charge of the technical and architectural aspects of this project. He was responsible for the coordination of all of the different activities involved. He had a mandate to build a tunnel where visitors could walk underwater. In order to decide on the best way to proceed, de Montigny first consulted with experts from around the world. Then he decided on a final design for the tunnel and chose the best materials for resisting the water pressure. The tank that contains the tunnel is very deep, and contains nearly 350 000 L of water!

NAME	
Benoît de Montigny	
JOB TITLE	
Architect (retired)	
AREA WHERE HE WORKED	
Québec City	
EDUCATION	
Bachelor's degree in architecture	
PROUDEST ACHIEVEMENT	
Coordinated the building of the tunnel for the Parc Aquarium du Québec	

3.42 The tunnel in the Parc Aquarium in Québec City.

3.43 OCCUPATIONS CONNECTED TO DE MONTIGNY'S WORK

Occupation	Education required	Length of study	Main tasks
Water and liquid waste treatment plant and system operator	DEP in water treatment procedures	1800 hours	• Operate machines for the treatment of water • Conduct tests to analyze water
Aquaculture technician	DCS in aquaculture	3 years	• Design and help build habitats • Determine the needs of different species
Civil engineer	Bachelor's degree in civil engineering	4 years	• Develop building plans • Solve design problems • Supervise building installations

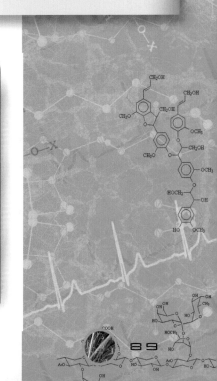

1997 — Invention of the DVD

1979 — Activation of the first portable
telephones

1943 — Invention of the colour television

1925 — Invention of the black and
white television

1906 — First broadcast of speech and
music on AM radio

1876 — Invention of the telephone

1874 — Invention of the electric light bulb

1849 — First precise measurement
of the speed of light

1801 — Discovery of ultraviolet rays

1636 — First measurement of
the speed of sound

1589 — Discovery of how prisms
can split light

1285 — First use of corrective
lenses for the eyes

CIRCA 50 — Demonstration of the law
of reflection

CIRCA -2500 — Use of a darkroom to
produce an inverted
image

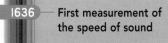

THE HUMAN ORGANISM

AND THE PERCEPTION OF LIGHT AND SOUND

We are surrounded by waves at all times. Our eyes see shapes and colours by capturing light waves. Our ears perceive sound waves in the form of music, voices, and other noises. A microwave oven, because of the waves it emits, can heat up a meal in a matter of minutes. X-rays reveal bone fractures. And these are just a few of the waves that exist. What are the characteristics of waves? How do waves behave? This is what we will explore in this chapter.

1 WHAT IS A WAVE?

When we throw a stone in a lake, waves ripple across the surface of the water. When we pluck the string of a guitar, vibrations travel through the air to our eardrums. When an earthquake occurs, the Earth's crust transmits the resulting vibrations. In each of these scenarios, there is a wave involved, that is, a **DISTURBANCE** that spreads or propagates. A disturbance is a localized and temporary change in the properties of a particular environment or medium (such as water, air or ground).

> ▶ A WAVE is a disturbance that travels through a medium. A wave transports energy; it does not transport matter.

A wave transports energy, and energy alone, from one place to another. When we look at the duck, in Figure 4.2, as it sits on the surface of a calm lake, we can see that the ripples (small waves of water), produced by the duck as it swims, travel from one side of the lake to the other. Meanwhile, however, the matter (the water and the duck), though it rises and falls, remains basically in the same spot as the ripples move away.

1.1 WAVE CHARACTERISTICS

Waves come in a variety of shapes and sizes. We can distinguish them by the way they propagate, by their amplitude, by their wavelength and their frequency.

HOW WAVES PROPAGATE

Waves are distinguished by the two ways they propagate through a medium. There are transverse waves and longitudinal waves.

Transverse waves

When a transverse wave propagates, its medium moves perpendicular to its motion. In Figure 4.3, for example, the wave moves from left to right and the medium moves up and down.

4.1 Ripples are the result of a disturbance that propagates across the surface of the water.

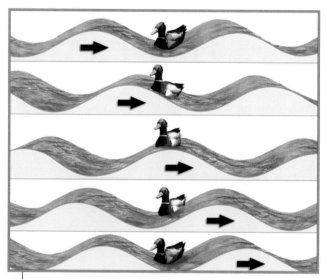

4.2 The waves cause the duck to rise and fall with the water, but the duck always returns to its original position after the waves move away. (The arrow indicates the direction of the waves.)

LABS
29 and 30

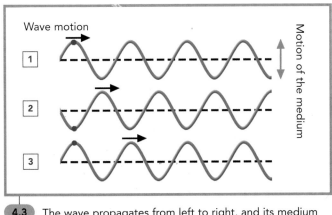

4.3 The wave propagates from left to right, and its medium (represented by the red dot) moves up and down. This is a transverse wave.

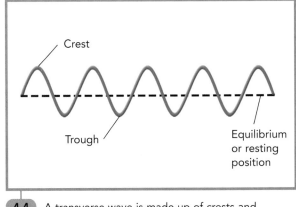

4.4 A transverse wave is made up of crests and troughs.

▶ **A TRANSVERSE WAVE** is a wave that propagates perpendicular to the motion of its medium.

The highest part of the wave in relation to its equilibrium position is called the crest, and the lowest part is called the trough.

Longitudinal waves

A wave's medium can move parallel to the direction of the wave's motion. When this happens, the wave is called a *longitudinal wave*. Figure 4.5 shows an example of a longitudinal wave in the vibration of a spring. When the spring is stretched, a vibration can be created in the coils by pushing or pulling on the ends.

▶ **A LONGITUDINAL WAVE** is a wave that propagates parallel to the motion of its medium.

When a longitudinal wave propagates through a medium, its particles move closer together, then farther apart, but always parallel to the direction of the wave's motion. The region where the particles are closer than normal is called *compression,* and the region where the particles are farther apart is called *rarefaction*.

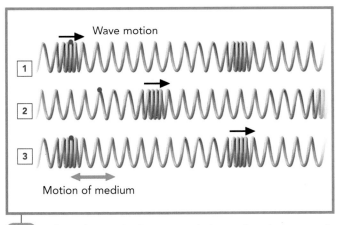

4.5 When a longitudinal wave travels, its medium (represented by the red dot) moves parallel to the motion of the wave.

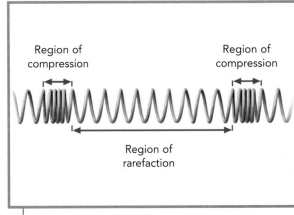

4.6 A longitudinal wave is made up of regions of compression and rarefaction.

AMPLITUDE

Amplitude is one of the properties of waves. It is symbolized by the letter A. Amplitude depends on the energy transmitted by a wave. The more energy transmitted by a wave, the greater the wave's amplitude. When we cause a rope to undulate, we transmit energy to the rope. The energy makes the rope vibrate and form a wave. If we want to increase the height or the amplitude of the wave, we need to put more energy into moving the rope.

> 🔊 The AMPLITUDE of a wave corresponds to the maximum distance travelled by a particle in the medium compared to its position at equilibrium.

For transverse waves, amplitude is the maximum height of the crest or maximum depth of the trough, from the wave's position at equilibrium.

4.7 It is possible to create a wave by "turning" a jump rope. The more energy transmitted to the rope, the greater its amplitude.

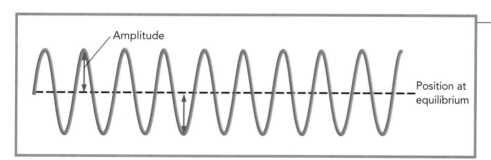

4.8 The amplitude of a transverse wave corresponds to the distance between its equilibrium position and the highest point of its crest, or the distance between its equilibrium position and the lowest point of its trough.

The amplitude of a longitudinal wave is more difficult to measure. It depends on the density of compression. The denser the region of compression, the greater the amplitude.

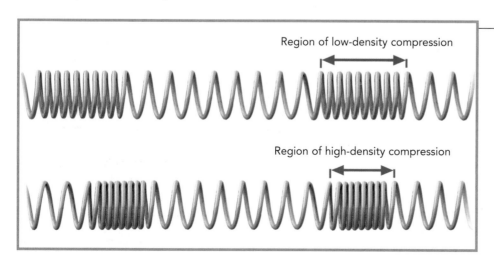

4.9 The amplitude of the longitudinal wave on top is less than the amplitude of the second longitudinal wave on the bottom.

WAVELENGTH

Wavelength is symbolized by the Greek letter λ, which is pronounced "lambda." A wave's length is the measurement of one complete cycle of a wave. In the case of a transverse wave, the length of one complete cycle is the distance that separates two crests or two troughs. In the case of a longitudinal wave, one complete cycle includes one compression and one rarefaction.

▶ **A WAVELENGTH is the length of a wave's complete cycle.**

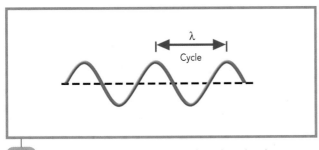

4.10 In a transverse wave, the wavelength is the distance that separates two consecutive crests or two consecutive troughs.

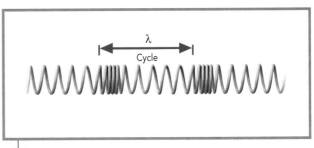

4.11 In a longitudinal wave, the wavelength is the length of one compression and one rarefaction.

FREQUENCY

Frequency, another property of waves, can be compared to the number of cars that pass by a given point on a road in one day. If a counter on the road registers 100 cars in one day, the traffic frequency would be 100 cars per day. To measure the frequency of a wave, we count the number of complete waves (or cycles) that are formed at a given point over a certain amount of time.

▶ **FREQUENCY corresponds to the number of cycles per unit of time.**

The frequency of a wave is measured in hertz (Hz), which corresponds to the number of cycles per second. If a wave has a frequency of 1 Hz, it completes one full cycle in one second.

 Generally speaking, speed is the measurement of a distance travelled per unit of time. A wave with a frequency of 1 Hz and a wavelength of 10 cm thus has a speed of 10 cm/s, since the wave travels a distance of 10 cm in 1 second. To determine the speed at which a wave travels, we multiply its frequency by its wavelength.

Speed = frequency × wavelength

1857
1894

Heinrich Hertz

This German physicist was the first to produce radio waves with one of his inventions. The unit of measurement for frequency bears Hertz's name in honour of his many contributions to the study of the properties of sound and radio waves.

1.2 TYPES OF WAVES

There are two types of waves: mechanical waves and electromagnetic waves.

MECHANICAL WAVES

Mechanical waves need a medium, or an environment (such as a liquid, solid or gas), through which to move; they cannot propagate in a vacuum. For example, water is the medium for water waves, air is the medium for sound waves and the ground is the medium for seismic waves that propagate during an earthquake. All the examples of waves that we have looked at so far have been mechanical waves.

> ▶ A MECHANICAL WAVE is a wave that requires a medium in order to propagate.

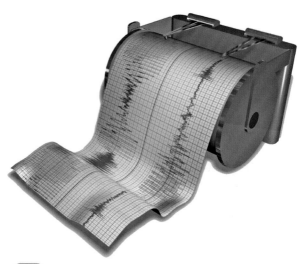

4.12 A seismograph measures and records seismic waves, an example of mechanical waves.

Generally speaking, a mechanical wave arises from a localized disturbance, such as occurs when a rock is thrown into a lake or a musical instrument is played. The disturbance changes the physical state of the medium. It causes the water to move vertically or the air pressure to vary. The changes are transmitted to neighbouring particles, and so on. This is how a mechanical wave forms and propagates. We will look at one example of mechanical waves, sound waves, in greater detail later on in this chapter.

ELECTROMAGNETIC WAVES

Electromagnetic waves, such as light waves referred to in Chapter 9, are transverse waves that move just as easily in a vacuum as in a medium. The rays of the Sun reach us in this manner through the vacuum of interstellar space and the atmosphere. Like all waves, electromagnetic waves carry energy from one point to another. The form of energy associated with electromagnetic waves is radiant energy.

> ▶ An ELECTROMAGNETIC WAVE is a wave that can travel in both a vacuum and a medium.

The speed of electromagnetic waves depends on the medium in which they are travelling. In a vacuum, electromagnetic waves travel at 300 000 km/s. This speed is so great that electromagnetic waves in the form of light seem to travel instantaneously.

MOVIES AND SOUND

There is no sound in space because sound waves cannot travel in a vacuum. Since a movie without any sound, however, wouldn't be very interesting, most science-fiction movies do not respect this scientific fact.

There are many categories of electromagnetic waves. They are classified according to their frequency and wavelength. The greater the frequency of an electromagnetic wave, the more energy the wave is transporting. All electromagnetic waves together form the *electromagnetic spectrum*, shown in Figure 4.14 on pages 98 and 99. Visible light makes up only a very small part of this spectrum.

▶ The ELECTROMAGNETIC SPECTRUM organizes all electromagnetic waves according to their wavelength and their frequency.

The following table illustrates the differences between mechanical waves and electromagnetic waves.

4.13 TYPES OF WAVES

Types of waves	Medium	Examples
Mechanical waves	Can only move in a medium.	Seismic waves, sound waves, water waves
Electromagnetic waves	Can propagate in a medium and in a vacuum.	Radio waves, light waves, ultraviolet rays, X-rays, infrared rays, gamma rays

Addicted to tanning salons

The ultraviolet rays used in tanning salons can create a physical addiction in their users, similar to that of compulsive gambling. According to dermatologist Mandeep Kaur, at Wake Forest University in North Carolina, when ultraviolet rays contact skin, they set off a chain reaction that releases endorphins, which are molecules that provide a sense of well-being. Kaur made this discovery in the course of a research project, in which she demonstrated that individuals who had received naltrexone (an endorphin blocker) were less attracted to ultraviolet tanning beds than those who had not taken the naltrexone.

"We wanted to know why certain people continue to visit tanning salons, despite the risk of skin cancer," Kaur explained. "Some people keep on going, even after they themselves have been diagnosed with cancer."

Adapted from Mathieu Perreault, "Accros aux salons de bronzage," *La Presse*, August 27, 2006, *Plus*, p. 4. [Translation]

Some people become addicted to the effects of the ultraviolet rays used in tanning salons.

THE ELECTROMAGNETIC SPECTRUM

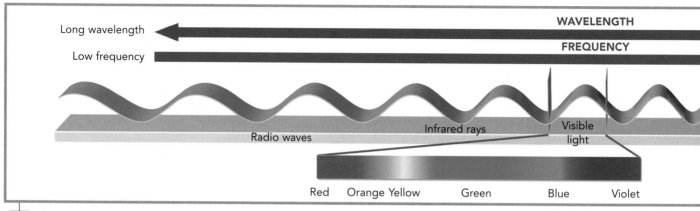

Long wavelength ← **WAVELENGTH**

Low frequency **FREQUENCY**

Radio waves   Infrared rays   Visible light

Red   Orange Yellow   Green   Blue   Violet

4.14 The electromagnetic spectrum classifies the various categories of electromagnetic waves according to their wavelength and their frequency.

RADIO WAVES

DESCRIPTION

Radio waves have the smallest frequency on the spectrum. They are invisible and transport little energy. Microwaves are radio waves with a high frequency, which makes certain particles vibrate and raises the temperature of matter.

TECHNOLOGICAL APPLICATIONS

- Radio, television
- Magnetic resonance imaging
- Microwave ovens
- Cellular telephones (microwaves)
- Radar (microwaves)

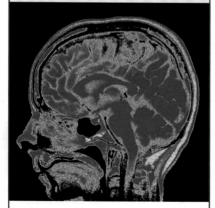

Magnetic resonance can produce very clear images of the brain using radio waves.

INFRARED

DESCRIPTION

Infrared rays have a wavelength and a frequency that are between radio waves and the waves of the colour red. They are invisible, but we can feel the warmth that they emit.

TECHNOLOGICAL APPLICATIONS

- Infrared thermography
- Night vision goggles
- Space observation satellites
- Short-distance communication (remote controls, optical scanners, optical computer mouse, and wireless keyboards)

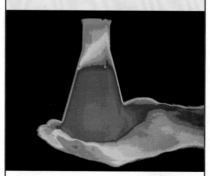

A thermograph can produce an image of an object by taking advantage of the infrared rays emitted by the object. Colour variations represent variations in temperature.

VISIBLE LIGHT

DESCRIPTION

As its name suggests, visible light is based on the only type of electromagnetic wave that can be seen by humans. It can be divided into six colours: red, orange, yellow, green, blue and violet. Each colour has its own wavelength. All of these colours together make up white light.

TECHNOLOGICAL APPLICATIONS

- Lighting
- Laser technology
- Photography
- Cinema
- Computer screens
- Microscopes
- Telescopes

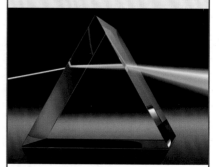

With a prism, we can split white light into different colours.

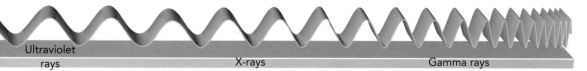

Short wavelength

High frequency

Ultraviolet rays

X-rays

Gamma rays

ULTRAVIOLET RAYS

DESCRIPTION

Ultraviolet (UV) rays are invisible to humans, but some animals can perceive them. Since UV rays have a greater frequency than visible light, they transport more energy. It is this energy that is responsible for suntans and that causes cancer. However, our bodies need a certain quantity of UV rays to process vitamin D.

TECHNOLOGICAL APPLICATIONS

- Treatment of certain ailments (such as rickets or jaundice in newborns)
- Sterilization of surgical instruments

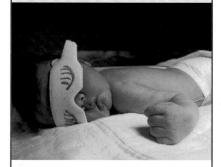

UV rays are used to treat jaundice in newborns.

X-RAYS

DESCRIPTION

Because of their high frequency, X-rays transmit a large quantity of energy. They can travel (with different degrees of ease) through a variety of media that are normally opaque in visible light. We can see bones in an X-ray because the bones are denser than the surrounding tissue. Prolonged exposure to X-rays causes burns and cancer.

TECHNOLOGICAL APPLICATIONS

- Radiography
- Baggage inspection in airports
- The study of crystalline substances

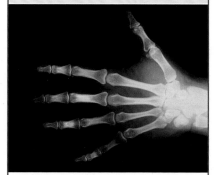

X-rays allow us to "photograph" the bones inside our bodies.

GAMMA RAYS

DESCRIPTION

Gamma rays are the form of radiation that has the highest frequency and they transport the most energy. Gamma rays travel very easily through matter. One centimetre of lead, six centimetres of concrete or nine centimetres of earth will only block 50 percent of them. Depending on the degree of exposure, gamma rays can cause burns, cancer and genetic mutation. We use them in controlled situations for medical purposes and to preserve food, because they can destroy harmful cells and bacteria.

TECHNOLOGICAL APPLICATIONS

- Cancer treatment
- Food preservation

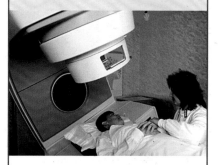

Gamma rays are used in the treatment of cancer.

2 SOUND WAVES

LAB 32

Sounds are longitudinal mechanical waves. They are produced when a localized disturbance causes a change in the environment. For example, if a chair falls to the floor, its impact causes the particles in the floor to vibrate. The disturbance is then passed on to the surrounding medium, such as the air. The wave that is then produced transmits sound energy.

> ◗ **SOUND is a longitudinal mechanical wave produced by the vibration of an object and transmitted to the object's environment.**

Let's examine in more detail the way a sound wave is produced and how it propagates. Take the example of a drum. When we hit the drumhead, the membrane vibrates. As the membrane rises, it pushes the air next to it. Therefore the air particles move closer together, creating an increase in pressure and a region of compression. As the membrane returns to its original position, the air particles move farther apart, lowering the air pressure and creating a region of rarefaction. In this way, the variations in air pressure cause the sound wave to propagate through the air. Only the sound wave propagates, however. The air particles move back and forth slightly. Sound waves don't create wind.

Anything that creates sound produces a longitudinal mechanical wave. Loudspeakers, musical instruments and thunder cause the air particles around them to vibrate.

1629
1695

Christiaan Huygens

Around 1670, this Dutch scholar demonstrated that sound is a longitudinal mechanical wave. He also made many more discoveries about sound and light waves.

4.15 Variations in air pressure created by the vibrations of a drumhead produce regions of compression and rarefaction, or a longitudinal wave.

Regions of compression   Regions of rarefaction

When we speak or sing, a similar phenomenon occurs. The vocal cords, located in the larynx, are folds of tissue that act like guitar strings. Guitar strings vibrate when they are plucked. Vocal cords vibrate with the passage of air in the throat, creating a sound wave.

CHAPTER 4

100

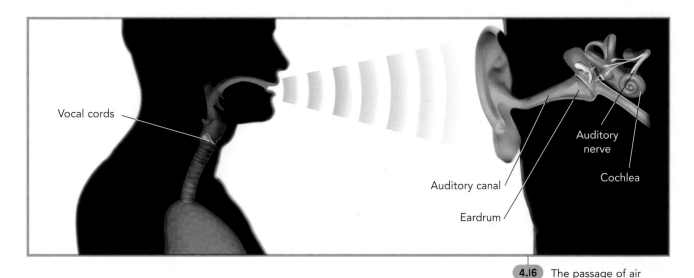

Vocal cords

Auditory nerve

Cochlea

Auditory canal

Eardrum

We hear sound when a sound wave propagates to our ear. The first part of the sound wave contacts the eardrum, causing it to vibrate in rhythm with the sound wave, similar to the vibration of the drumhead in the example above. The vibration of the eardrum, however, occurs next to the fluid inside the cochlea, which is covered with receptor cells that capture information. The auditory nerve transmits this information from the receptor cells to the brain to be analyzed.

Sound also propagates through solids and liquids. For example, deaf people can "hear" music by touching the speaker box and feeling it vibrate, and by feeling the vibrations of the dance floor. In a similar way certain marine animals, such as whales, communicate very well underwater.

4.16 The passage of air causes the vocal cords to vibrate. The vibration leads to the production of sound. The ear is a sensory organ that makes it possible for us to perceive sound waves.

2.1 THE SPEED OF SOUND

There are great variations in the speed of sound from one medium to another. In the air, the speed of sound is about 340 m/s or 1224 km/h. We often use this value as a reference point. In aeronautics, for example, the speed of sound (1224 km/h) is equal to Mach 1, a standard aeronautical reference point. A supersonic plane that flies at twice the speed of sound is flying at Mach 2.

4.17 Supersonic planes can fly faster than the speed of sound.

Table 4.18 demonstrates the speed of sound as it passes through various media at a temperature of 25°C. It shows that the speed of sound is greater in liquid or solid substances than in air. Contrary to what some people believe, gas is not an efficient sound transmitter. We can "hear" a car approaching by putting our ear to the road before we hear the noise it makes in the air.

 THE SPEED OF SOUND IN VARIOUS MEDIA (AT A TEMPERATURE OF 25 °C)

Medium	Speed (m/s)	Speed (km/h)
Air	346	1 246
Water	1 490	5 364
Plastic	1 800	6 480
Wood	4 000	14 400
Steel	5 200	18 720

1588
1648

Marin Mersenne

This French scholar and priest made a great contribution to the world of science. In particular, in 1636 he measured the speed of sound. In addition, he calculated the mathematical relationship between the frequencies of the notes in a musical scale.

2.2 THE DECIBEL SCALE

Sound can be soft like a whisper or loud like a yell. The volume of a sound depends on its intensity, that is, the energy it is transmitting. The greater the energy, the louder the sound. A whisper, therefore, transmits less energy than a yell.

How does the energy of sound vary? Since the energy of a sound wave depends on its amplitude, when the amplitude increases, the intensity of the sound also increases. A loudspeaker is an example of a tool that can help increase sound volume by increasing its amplitude.

The intensity of sound is measured in decibels (dB). A decibel is not a precise measurement of the intensity or the amplitude of a sound wave. It is a relative scale that represents the perception of sound by the human ear. A sound measuring 0 dB is barely perceptible, a sound measuring 10 dB is 10 times more intense.

> The DECIBEL SCALE is a relative scale that represents the perception of the intensity of sound by the human ear.

Variations on the decibel scale are measured by a factor of 10, which means that for each increase of 10 dB, a sound becomes 10 times louder. A sound measuring 20 dB is 100 times louder than a 0 dB sound. A sound measuring 40 dB is 100 times louder than a 20 dB sound.

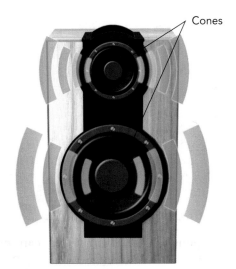

Cones

4.19 A loudspeaker transmits sound by making its cones vibrate. It amplifies sound by changing the vibration of the cones.

It should be noted that decibels are not cumulative: two 50-dB sounds, one coming from a trumpet and one from a guitar, do not add up to make one 100-dB sound. Instead the two sounds together produce a sound that is twice as loud, for an intensity of about 53 dB.

Prolonged exposure to sounds louder than 100 dB can cause long-term hearing damage. Starting at 120 dB, sound can cause pain and immediate loss of hearing. People who are exposed to such levels must wear ear protection.

The following table lists various sounds and their relative intensity in decibels.

4.20 THE RELATIVE INTENSITY OF SOUND IN DECIBELS

Sound source	Intensity (dB)
Human breathing (at a distance of 3 m away)	10
Murmur (at a distance of 2 m away)	20
Calm classroom	35-40
Soft music	50
Busy department store	60
Intense road traffic (at a distance of 3 m away)	70
Motorcycle without a muffler (at a distance of 2 m away)	100
Rock music concert	110-120
Jet engine (at a distance of 14 m away)	120
Spacecraft engine (at a distance of 50 m away)	200

2.3 FREQUENCY AND THE PERCEPTION OF SOUND

It is not just the intensity of sound that can change. Sound can also have different tones, that is, higher or lower pitches. Low-frequency sounds, like those made by the keys on the left of a piano keyboard, are lower; high-frequency sounds, like those made by the keys on the right of the keyboard, are higher. Thus the tone of a sound depends on its frequency.

In general, the human ear can hear sounds with frequencies ranging from 20 to 20 000 Hz. The range of sound perception is different for each animal species.

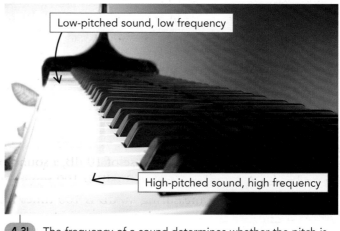

Low-pitched sound, low frequency

High-pitched sound, high frequency

4.21 The frequency of a sound determines whether the pitch is low or high.

The following table illustrates the range of perceptible sound for humans and a few other animals.

4.22 RANGE OF PERCEPTIBLE SOUND (IN Hz)

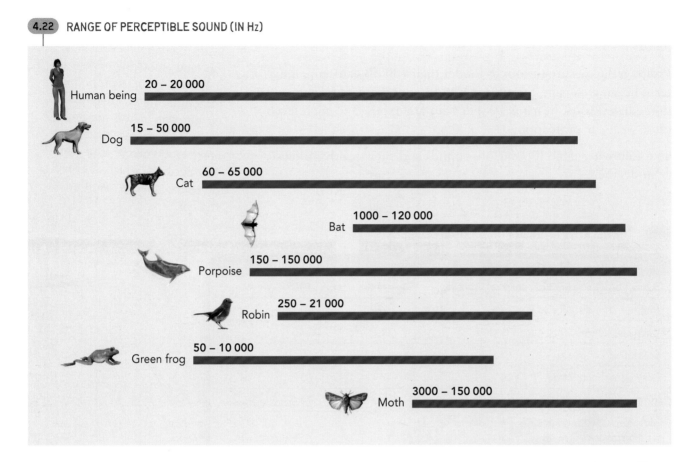

Human being 20 – 20 000

Dog 15 – 50 000

Cat 60 – 65 000

Bat 1000 – 120 000

Porpoise 150 – 150 000

Robin 250 – 21 000

Green frog 50 – 10 000

Moth 3000 – 150 000

A sound that only teens can hear

A sound with an extremely high frequency that is imperceptible to older people is circulating in cyberspace. And many teens are downloading it to use as a ring tone on their cellular telephones.

Commonly known as *teen buzz*, this particular sound is generally only heard by people under 30 because most older adults suffer from presbycusis, a natural age-related hearing loss. With time, their ears becomes less sensitive to high-pitched frequencies over 8 000 Hz. The frequency of teen buzz is between 14 400 Hz and 17 000 Hz.

Not surprisingly, some teens take advantage of teen buzz to trick their parents, who can't hear their kids' cellphones ringing during dinner time, homework time or any other time!

Adapted from Fabien Deglise, "Un son que seuls les ados peuvent entendre," *Le Devoir*, June 17, 2006, p. A1. *[Translation]*

The highly attuned ear of young people lets them hear a sound that older people can't detect.

INFRASOUNDS AND ULTRASOUNDS

Sounds under 20 Hz are considered infrasounds and sounds higher than 20 000 Hz are ultrasounds. Although such sounds are not captured by the human ear, many other animals can sense them and use them as a way to communicate. Elephants, for example, emit infrasounds to warn their fellow elephants of imminent danger. Dolphins, on the other hand, use ultrasound to communicate. Dogs are quite sensitive to high frequencies, which is why we can train them with ultrasound whistles.

4.23 Elephants use infrasound to alert other elephants of imminent danger.

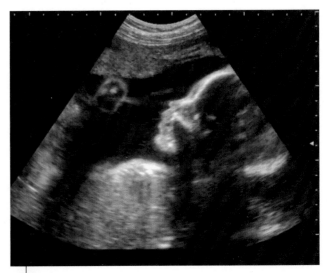

4.24 An ultrasound is a medical imaging technique that relies on ultrasonic waves.

Many phenomena combine ultrasound with an echo effect, since a sound wave bounces back when it meets an obstacle. The echo of ultrasounds is used for certain medical imaging techniques, such as pregnancy sonograms. Some animals use **ECHOLOCATION.** For example, bats emit ultrasonic waves and estimate the location of objects in their environment by their perception of the resulting echoes. Sonar used by boats and submarines relies on the same principle.

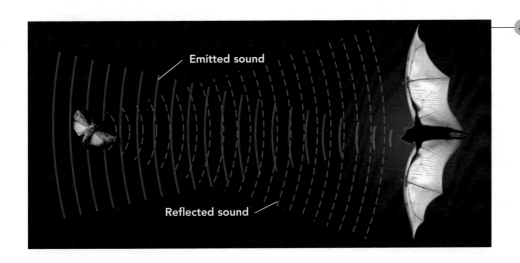

Emitted sound

Reflected sound

4.25 Bats emit ultrasounds that enable them to localize surrounding objects.

3 LIGHT WAVES

As we have seen, light waves (which make up what we call *light*) are electromagnetic waves. These waves come from different sources, such as light bulbs, the sun or fire.

> ◗ **LIGHT is an electromagnetic wave that is visible to the human eye.**

CYCLE ONE
Light (properties)

Light waves travel in straight lines (this is why light is usually represented as straight lines in simplified diagrams; this is also why they are called *light rays*). When light waves strike an object, they are reflected, refracted or absorbed, depending on the capacity of the object to allow light to travel through it. In this section, we will take a look at two of these phenomena: reflection and refraction.

3.1 REFLECTION

When we throw a rubber ball, it rebounds on contact with a wall. In the same manner, when light waves hit the surface of an object, they can be reflected. Reflection occurs when a light ray propagates through one medium (such as air) and rebounds (when it strikes) a different kind of medium (such as a mirror or a balloon).

> ◗ **REFLECTION is the rebounding of light that occurs when a light ray hits a different medium and "bounces back" to the medium from which it came.**

All objects in our surroundings reflect light to some degree, depending on their colour and their light source. If we can see an object, it is because reflection brings light to our eyes.

Figure 4.26 illustrates what happens when light is reflected. To interpret the illustration, let's learn some definitions related to reflection:

- The *incident ray* is the ray that contacts the surface of an object.
- The *reflected ray* is the ray that rebounds.
- The *normal* is a line perpendicular to the surface at the point of reflection.
- The *angle of incidence* is the angle formed by the incident ray and the normal.
- The *angle of reflection* is the angle formed by the reflected ray and the normal.

LAB 33

965
1039

Ibn Al-Haytham Alhazen

This Iraqi mathematician and physicist defined various rules concerning the science of optics, and made the important distinction between vision and light. He stated that the eye captures light rays coming from an object. Until that point, it was believed that the eye produced the light rays that allowed us to see.

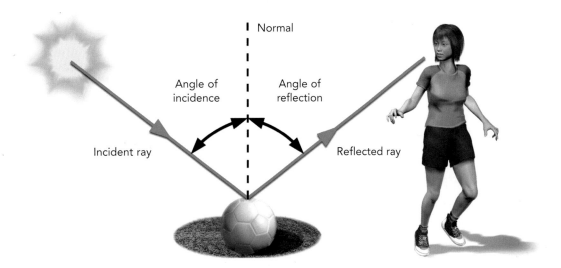

The reflection of light rays is governed by two laws:

- The angle of incidence is always equal to the angle of reflection.
- The incident ray and the reflected ray are always on the same plane.

4.26 We can see objects that don't themselves emit light because of the phenomenon of reflected light.

Geometric reflection

In mathematics, reflection is a geometric transformation, an operation that changes a two-dimensional figure into a new figure. The

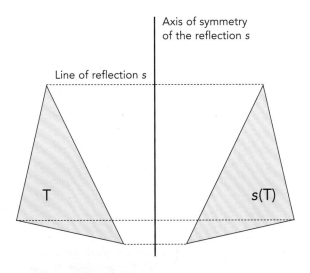

The reflection s produces an image s(T) of the object T.

straight line that characterizes reflection is called the *axis of symmetry*. The newly formed image assumes a position in which each point of the original figure is the same distance from the axis of symmetry as its image. Any line drawn between an object and its image by reflection is called a *line of reflection*. A line of reflection is always perpendicular to the axis of symmetry.

A reflection is an *orthogonal symmetry*, because its lines are perpendicular to the axis of symmetry.

Reflection is a mathematical model that allows us to describe not only the phenomenon of mirror reflection (the mirror assuming the position of the axis of symmetry), but also symmetry on an axis, the folding of an object on an axis, and, on a Cartesian plane, the value of certain trigonometric relationships.

There are two types of reflection: diffuse reflection and specular reflection.

DIFFUSE REFLECTION

Some surfaces, such as a piece of paper or the surface of a balloon, can appear to be perfectly smooth to the naked eye. They are often, however, uneven and rough. We can see this by taking a look at the surface of a piece of paper through a microscope (Figure 4.28).

Most objects have a rough surface. When parallel light rays hit such a surface, they are reflected in all directions. This is what we call **DIFFUSE REFLECTION.** In this case, the direction of the light rays does not respect the laws of reflection.

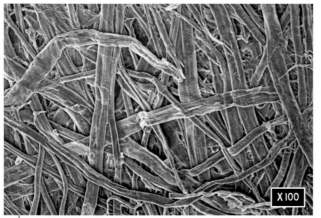

4.27 With the help of a microscope, we can see that the surface of a piece of paper is irregular.

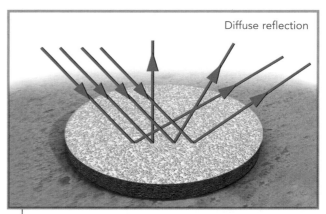

Diffuse reflection

4.28 When parallel light rays strike an uneven surface, they are reflected back in all directions. This is diffuse reflection.

SPECULAR REFLECTION

When light contacts a surface that is perfectly smooth, such as a mirror or the surface of a lake, the rays follow the laws of reflection. When parallel light rays contact a smooth surface, their reflections are parallel, producing a true mirror image. This type of reflection is called SPECULAR REFLECTION.

Specular comes from the Latin word *specularis*, meaning "mirror, transparent."

4.30 Specular reflection produces a true mirror image of the object.

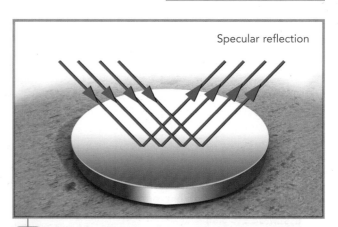

Specular reflection

4.29 When parallel light rays strike a smooth surface, the reflected rays are also parallel. This is specular reflection.

As shown in Figure 4.30, the reflected image in a plane mirror (that is, a mirror without any curvature) demonstrates the following characteristics:

- The image appears to be behind the mirror, at a distance equal to the distance between the mirror and the reflected object.
- The image is virtual. A **VIRTUAL IMAGE** is one that can't be captured on a reflecting surface (like a mirror), because it is made by the prolongation of reflected rays. On the other hand, a **REAL IMAGE** is produced at the real crossing of light rays.
- The image is the same size as the object.
- The image is horizontally inverted, that is, the left side of the object corresponds to the right side of the image.

It is possible to localize a virtual image beyond the plane of the mirror by drawing incident rays from the object and the resulting reflected rays. The image is produced at the meeting point of the prolongation of the reflected rays. Figure 4.31 illustrates these lines.

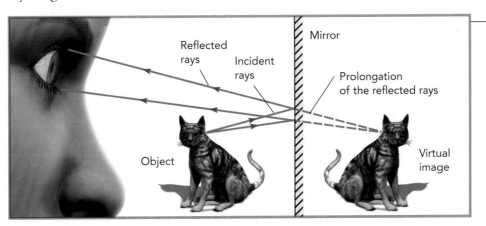

4.31 By prolonging the reflected rays, it is possible to localize the virtual image behind the mirror. (The mirror is represented here by its symbol, a straight line with hatching on the back side).

A liquid mirror on the Moon

Even Hergé didn't go this far in his futuristic *Destination Moon!*

Ermano Borra, a researcher at Université Laval, has found a way to transport a 20-m diameter mirror to the Moon: he liquified the mirror. How did he do this?

He put liquid mercury in a rotating parabolic dish. Because of the spinning effect, the mercury formed a thin film that perfectly assumed the shape of the dish and became a reflecting surface. The surface was clearer even than the traditional polished glass, and above all, it was unbreakable.

NASA recently gave the researcher a grant of nearly $100 000 to explore the feasibility of installing a liquid mirror telescope on our satellite. Now that the American space agency is investing in space exploration once more, NASA wants to make the Moon a base camp for launching an exploration of Mars.

Adapted from Violaine Ballivy, "Une glace sur la Lune," *Le Soleil*, January 8, 2005, p. D7. *[Translation]*

Liquid mercury creates a reflecting surface that is much clearer than polished glass.

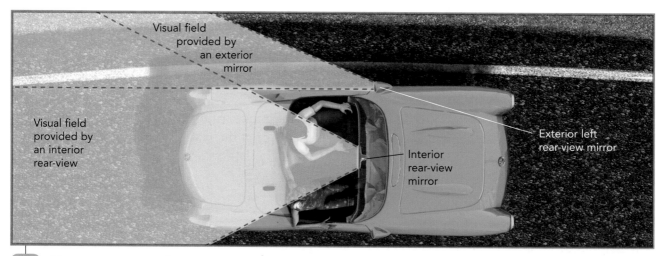

4.32 The rear-view mirrors of a car increase a driver's field of vision, as the driver can see objects behind the car.

Plane mirrors have a number of applications based on two simple principles:

- They change the trajectory of light rays by reflection.
- They increase the observer's field of vision.

The rear-view mirrors of a car, the mirrors used by dentists, as well as the mirrors inside cameras, microscopes, telescopes and periscopes are applications of these principles. In all of these examples, the mirrors change the trajectory of light rays so that the rays can reach the eye of the observer.

3.2 REFRACTION

When we look at the stem of a flower in water (Figure 4.33), we get the impression that the stem is broken. This is due to refraction.

Refraction occurs when a ray of light is altered as it passes from one transparent medium (such as air) to another transparent medium (such as water). The alteration takes place because the speed of light depends on the medium through which it passes. In this case, the speed of light changes as it passes from air to water, and so the light ray deviates. This is what we call refraction.

▶ **REFRACTION** is the deviation of a light ray as it passes from one transparent medium to another.

Refraction changes our perception of objects when we look at them through a transparent medium. The most common application of the principle of refraction is in lenses.

Refraction comes from the Latin word *refringere*, which means "to break."

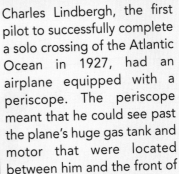

4.33 The stem of this flower appears to be broken due to refraction.

A PERISCOPE IN A PLANE

Charles Lindbergh, the first pilot to successfully complete a solo crossing of the Atlantic Ocean in 1927, had an airplane equipped with a periscope. The periscope meant that he could see past the plane's huge gas tank and motor that were located between him and the front of the plane!

3.3 LENSES

Lenses are objects made of transparent materials that have at least one curved surface, and the ability to refract light as it passes through them.

Lenses have many applications, from corrective eyeglass lenses to magnifying glasses and camera lenses. They are also used in microscopes and telescopes. Lenses can help us see objects that are far away and magnify the image of smaller objects.

There are two types of lenses:

● converging lenses
● diverging lenses

Converging lenses bring together light rays that pass through them. Diverging lenses disperse them. Table 4.35 shows some of the common forms of these two types of lenses, and the symbols used to represent them.

4.34 A small magnifying glass enlarges the images of little objects for better viewing of details.

Converging comes from the Latin word *convergere*, meaning "inclining together."

Diverging comes from the Latin word *divergere*, meaning "bending away."

4.35 CONVERGING AND DIVERGING LENSES

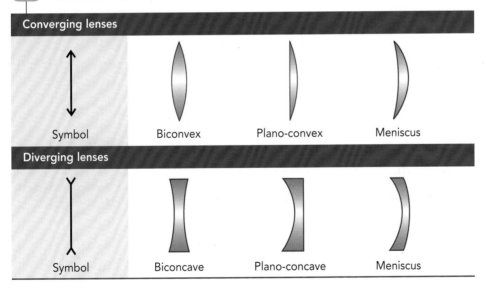

The centre of a lens is called the optical centre (OC). The principal axis of a lens is the straight line that is perpendicular to its surface, through its optical centre.

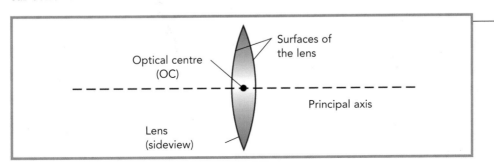

4.36 A lens, its principal axis and its optical centre (OC)

THE FOCAL POINT OF A LENS

The term *focal point* has several meanings. In optics, the focal point of a lens is defined differently depending on whether the lens in question is a converging lens or a diverging lens.

Converging lens

When parallel light rays travel through a converging lens, they are refracted and pass through a single point, that is, the focal point. In this case, the focal point is real.

> ▶ The **FOCAL POINT OF A CONVERGING LENS** is the real point where the refracted rays actually meet when the incident rays run parallel.

If the rays that contact a lens travel parallel to the principal axis, the point where they meet on the far side of the lens is called the **FOCAL POINT** (F). Since light can travel through a lens from both sides, the lens has a second principal focal point (F') located at the same distance on the side of the lens nearest to the rays' point of origin. Even if the curvatures of the lens surfaces are different, the two focal points are located at the same distance on either side of the lens.

In the case of a converging lens, the principal focal point is on the far side of the light source where the rays are refracted.

1535
1615

Giambattista Della Porta

This Italian physicist and humanist was the author of many works on the subject of lenses. In 1589, he carried out a variety of experiments that involved splitting light into numerous colours with the use of prisms.

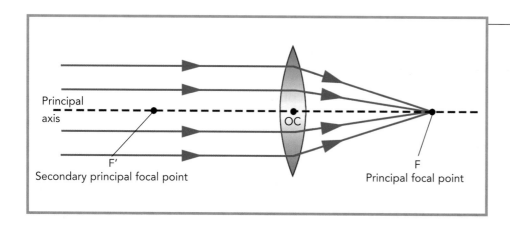

Principal axis

F'
Secondary principal focal point

OC

F
Principal focal point

4.37 When rays travelling parallel to the principal axis pass through a converging lens, they are refracted to meet at the principal focal point of the lens.

Diverging lens

When rays travel parallel to the principal axis and pass through a diverging lens, they are refracted and diverted from each other, as if they all originated at the same point. This point is the focal point of the diverging lens. Since the refracted rays don't actually originate at this point, the focal point of a diverging lens is virtual.

A diverging lens, just like a converging lens, has a secondary principal focal point, which is on the other side of its principal focal point.

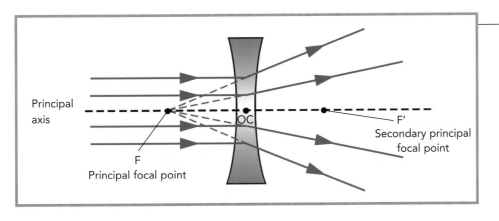

4.38 When rays running parallel to the principal axis pass through a diverging lens, they are refracted as if they all originated at a virtual focal point.

With a diverging lens, the principal focal point is located on the near side of the lens, that is, the same side as the light source. The secondary focal point is located on the far side of the lens, where the rays are refracted. These two focal points are at the same distance from the lens.

> ▸ The **FOCAL POINT OF A DIVERGING LENS** is the virtual point from which the refracted light rays appear to emanate when the incident rays run parallel.

THE IMAGE PRODUCED BY A LENS

To determine the location of the image formed by a lens and the type of image that is produced, it is necessary to draw the rays from a specific point on the object being observed.

Converging lens

The rules for drawing rays to locate the image formed by a converging lens are as follows:

1 A ray that travels parallel to the principal axis is refracted through the principal focus point of a converging lens.

2 A ray that travels straight through the optical centre of a converging lens is not refracted.

3 A ray that travels straight through the secondary focal point of the converging lens is refracted parallel to the principal axis.

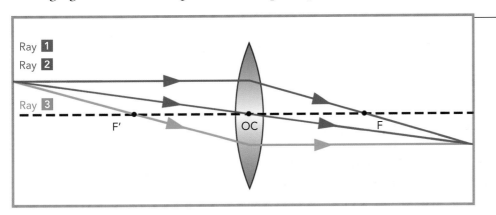

4.39 Here are the three rays drawn to locate the image formed by a converging lens.

Only two of these rays (any two) are needed to determine the location of an image.

Depending on the location of the object in relation to the lens, the final image has different characteristics. These characteristics relate to the type of image (real or virtual), its position, its size and its orientation. The images formed by a converging lens depend on the location of the object being observed, as shown in Table 4.40. In situations 1, 2 and 3, the observer sees an image on the screen when the rays from that image are reflected back to his or her eyes.

HOW TO LOCATE
THE FOCAL POINT
OF A CONVERGING LENS

4.40 THE VARIOUS IMAGES FORMED BY A CONVERGING LENS

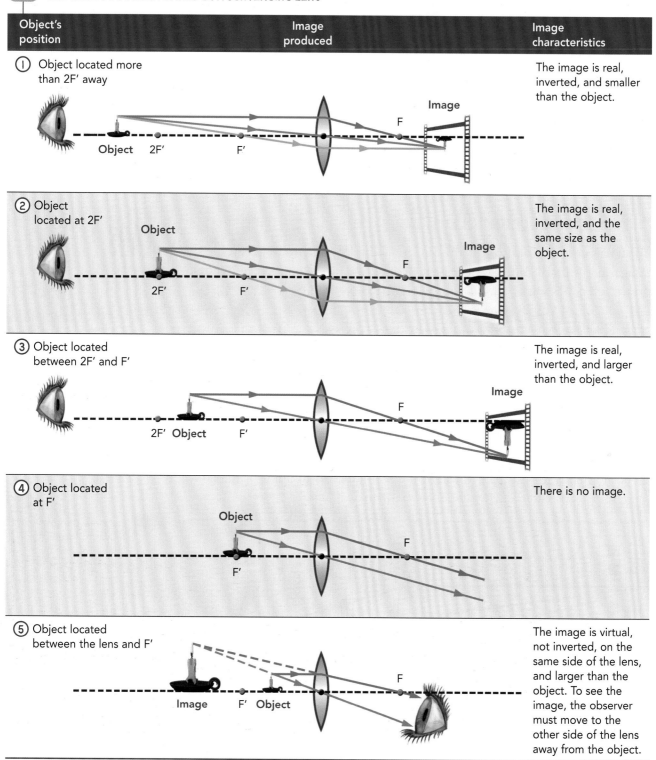

Object's position	Image produced	Image characteristics
① Object located more than 2F' away		The image is real, inverted, and smaller than the object.
② Object located at 2F'		The image is real, inverted, and the same size as the object.
③ Object located between 2F' and F'		The image is real, inverted, and larger than the object.
④ Object located at F'		There is no image.
⑤ Object located between the lens and F'		The image is virtual, not inverted, on the same side of the lens, and larger than the object. To see the image, the observer must move to the other side of the lens away from the object.

Diverging lens

The same rules apply to localizing the image formed by a diverging lens as that by a converging lens. Only two of the three rays need be drawn. The rules for drawing rays to locate the image formed by a diverging lens are as follows:

1 A ray running parallel to the principal axis is refracted, appearing to originate from the focal point.

2 A ray passing through the diverging lens' optical centre does not deviate.

3 A ray travelling toward the secondary focal point is refracted parallel to the principal axis.

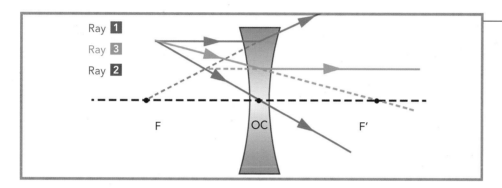

4.41 Here are the three rays drawn in order to locate an image formed by a diverging lens.

The images obtained by a diverging lens are always the same, irrespective of the position of the object. The image is thus always virtual, not inverted and smaller than the object. Moreover, the image is always located between the principal focal point and the lens. Figure 4.42 shows an example of an image formed by a diverging lens.

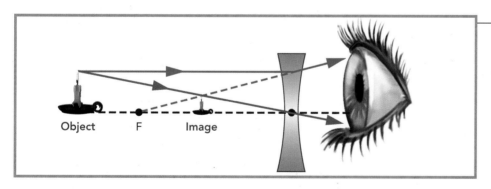

4.42 The image formed by a diverging lens is always virtual and smaller than the object.

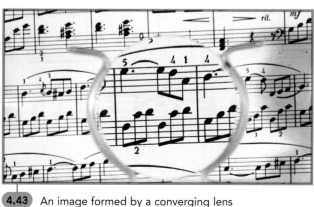

4.43 An image formed by a converging lens

4.44 An image formed by a diverging lens

VISION: DISORDERS AND CORRECTIONS

The following table shows the formation of an image for a person with normal eyesight. It also shows how, due to certain disorders, the formation of an image can be faulty, and how these disorders can be corrected using either converging or diverging lenses.

NORMAL VISION

The cornea of the eye is a converging lens. It uses its supporting muscles to adjust its shape, changing the position of its focal point according to the distance of the objects being observed. The cornea focuses automatically, rather like a camera. In a normal eye, the image—which is smaller than the object and inverted— is formed on the retina. The brain analyzes the information and then reconstructs the image.

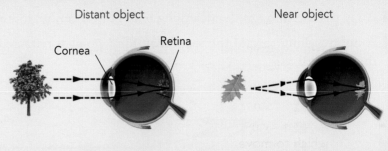

MYOPIA

For someone suffering from myopia (or nearsightedness), the image of an object far away forms in front of the retina. Therefore, a myopic person cannot clearly see objects at a distance; they appear fuzzy.

<u>CORRECTION</u>

A diverging lens corrects myopia. The lens helps the image to form properly on the retina.

HYPEROPIA

For someone suffering from hyperopia (or farsightedness), the image of a near object is formed behind the retina. Therefore, the person cannot clearly see objects that are close up, for example, the words in a book. Hyperopia comes from a malformation of the eye that can be detected at an early age.

<u>CORRECTION</u>

A converging lens corrects hyperopia. The lens helps the image to form properly on the retina.

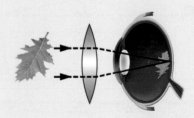

Presbyopia is another vision anomaly. It is caused by the ageing of a lens' support muscles.

With age, and especially after age 45, the lens can no longer adjust its shape to clearly see objects close up. The image is formed behind the retina, as with hyperopia. A converging lens corrects presbyopia as well.

NO MORE GLASSES?
Laser surgery helps reshape the cornea and correct such problems as myopia and hyperopia.

CHECKUP

1 WHAT IS A WAVE? (pp. 92–99)

1. True or false?

   a) When a wave propagates it transports the medium in which it moves.

   b) When a wave propagates it transports energy from one point to another.

   c) A wave always needs a medium in which to move.

2. Indicate whether the waves in each of the following examples are transverse or longitudinal.

   a) sound waves produced by a musical instrument

   b) water waves formed on an ocean

   c) undulations of a rope

   d) compressions and rarefactions of a spring

3. Name the numbered elements in the following diagrams.

   a)
   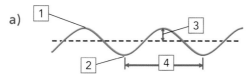

   b)
   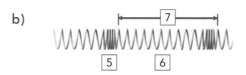

4. Look at the following diagrams of waves.

   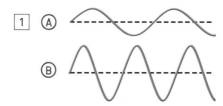

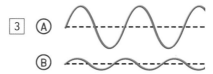

For each pair of diagrams, select the wave with:

   a) the greatest amplitude

   b) the highest wavelength

5. Imagine that you are on vacation by the sea, watching the waves crashing on the beach. In 10 minutes, you count 60 waves. What is the frequency of the waves in hertz (Hz)?

6. What is the difference between a mechanical wave and an electromagnetic wave?

7. For each of the following examples, describe the type of wave.

   a) Bread is browned in a toaster with heat emitted by its filaments.

   b) Televisions capture waves transmitted by various stations.

   c) Some people believe that cellular telephones are harmful to our health.

   d) It is possible to see a rainbow as it forms.

   e) Some people believe that tanning salons should be off-limits to anyone under 18.

   f) Doctors order X-rays when they think a bone may be broken.

2 SOUND WAVES (pp. 100–105)

8. What type of wave is a sound wave? Explain your answer.

9. How does a sound wave travel? Explain your answer.

10. You are listening to music in a car with its windows down.

   a) If you increase the volume by 20 dB, how many times is the intensity of the sound amplified?

   b) A truck drives by the car. If the overall sound is twice as loud, would the number of decibels be doubled? Explain your answer.

11. If you were next to a loudspeaker listening to very loud music, would you feel the air moving? Explain your answer.

12. What are the units of measurement:

   a) for the intensity of sound?

   b) for the frequency of sound?

   c) for the speed of sound?

13. Some whistles produce sounds that can be heard by dogs, but not by humans. Explain.

14. What is the principle that makes a boat's sonar work?

3 LIGHT WAVES (pp. 106–116)

15. What is the difference between specular reflection and diffuse reflection?

16. Imagine that a tomcat looks in a mirror and sees the image of a mouse behind him to the right. Sketch the scene on a piece of paper and include the incident rays and reflected rays to show how the tomcat can see the mouse.

17. For each of the following illustrations, indicate whether the principles of reflection in a plane mirror are being respected. Explain your answer.

   a) Object   Image

   b) Object   Image

   c) Object  Image

   d) Object  Image

   e) Object   Image

18. For each of the following situations:

   a) Draw on a piece of paper two of the three rays involved.

   b) Describe the image that is formed.

   1) An object located between the focal point of a converging lens and the lens.

   2) An object located twice the distance from the focal point to the converging lens.

   3) An object located twice the distance from the focal point to the diverging lens.

   4) An object located at the focal point of a converging lens.

19. Look at the following photo.

a) Name the phenomenon that allows the penguin to see its reflection in the water?

b) Name the phenomenon that makes the stones in the water seem closer than they really are?

20. Indicate whether each of the following is a converging or a diverging lens.

a) a magnifying glass

b) a corrective lens for a person with presbyopia

c) the following symbol, as it appears on a diagram:

d) a lens that always forms an image smaller than the object

e) a lens that brings the rays that travel through it closer together

f) a biconvex lens

21. What is the difference between presbyopia and hyperopia?

CONCEPT MAPS

HOW TO BUILD
A CONCEPT MAP

Prepare your own summary of Chapter 4 by building a concept map using the following terms:

- Amplitude
- Converging lens
- Diffuse reflection
- Diverging lens
- Electromagnetic waves
- Frequency
- Gamma rays
- Infrared rays
- Lens
- Mechanical waves
- Mirror
- Radio waves
- Reflection
- Refraction
- Sound waves
- Specular reflection
- Ultraviolet rays
- Visible light
- Wavelength
- Waves
- X-rays

WHEN SOUND WAVES ARE NOT "HEARD"

Anybody suffering a hearing loss, no matter how minimal, is considered to be deaf from a medical point of view. In some cases, hearing specialists use audiometric tests to determine the degree of deafness. They also help distinguish between two types of deafness. The following tables briefly outline the two types.

4.45

A cochlear implant is an electronic device that can bring back the hearing of a person who has suffered a partial or complete loss of hearing.

CONDUCTIVE HEARING LOSS

DESCRIPTION	TEMPORARY CAUSE	PERMANENT CAUSE	CORRECTION
Sound vibrations are unable to reach the liquid in the cochlea.	Accumulation of cerumen (wax) in the ear	• Perforation of the eardrum • Fusion of the ossicles	• Hearing aid • Cochlear implant

SENSORY HEARING LOSS

DESCRIPTION	TEMPORARY CAUSE	PERMANENT CAUSE	CORRECTION
Deterioration of the cells in the inner ear that causes a decrease in the messages transmitted by the nerves to the brain	Exposure to sounds of intense volumes	• Prolonged exposure or extreme proximity to sounds measuring 100 to 120 dB • Exposure to sounds over 120 dB	• Hearing aid

1. Indicate the degree of risk of hearing loss, for each of the following actions:
   a) cleaning the ear with a cotton swab
   b) listening to loud music on earbud headphones
   c) regular use of very loud tools
2. Why are hearing specialists also called ear, nose and throat (ENT) doctors?

KENT NAGANO

Kent Nagano is a renowned orchestra conductor. As such, he coordinates the performances of the musicians and guides them to respect the rhythm of the music. He needs to study the music very carefully in order to find the best gestures and facial expressions to communicate all of the emotion he wants to convey. The possession of a sensitive ear for music is essential because a conductor must be able to hear the sounds of each individual instrument at the same time as the sound made by the entire orchestra. The musical coherence and the consistency of a symphony orchestra depend on the balance of the sounds produced by each instrument. The conductor of a symphony not only requires solid musical training, but also sensitive communication skills. Happily, Kent Nagano has both.

NAME

Kent Nagano

JOB

Symphony conductor

AREA WHERE HE WORKS

Montréal and around the world

EDUCATION

Bachelor's degree in sociology
Master's degree in music

PROUDEST ACHIEVEMENT

Conducted several symphony orchestras, including the Orchestre symphonique de Montréal

4.46 Kent Nagano directing the Orchestre symphonique de Montréal

4.47 OCCUPATIONS CONNECTED TO NAGANO'S WORK

Occupation	Education	Length of study	Main tasks
Assistant technician in a recording studio	AVS* in studio recording	450 hours	● Operate recording equipment or sound console
Sound or lighting technician	DCS in theatre lighting and stage techniques	3 years	● Design and produce sound elements for theatre productions ● Design and produce lighting elements for theatre productions
Music composer-arranger	Bachelor's degree in music	3 years	● Create or adapt a composition for a soloist or an ensemble

* Attestation of vocational specialization

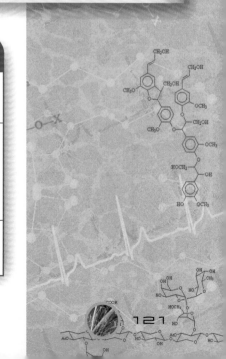

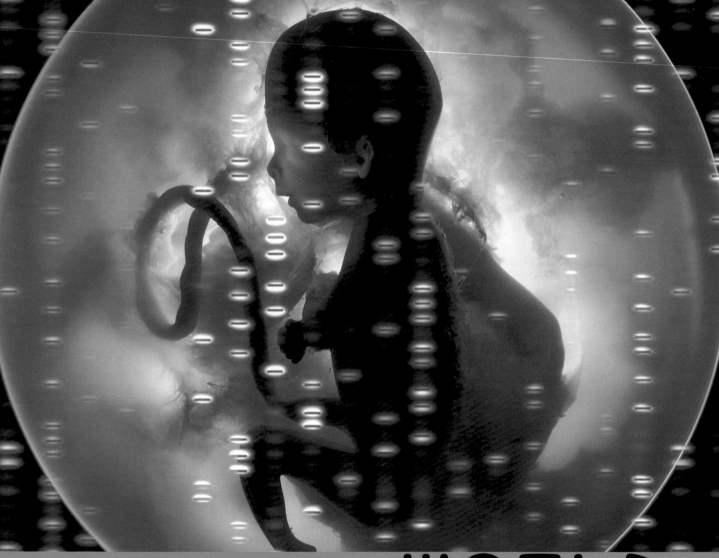

THE LIVING

WORLD

THE HUMAN ORGANISM ARISES FROM A SINGLE CELL.

A myriad cell divisions are needed to create all the systems that make up our bodies. These systems interact in complex ways and are responsible for all the functions that keep us alive. They enable us to nourish ourselves, interact with the environment and reproduce. To understand how our bodies work, we must start at the beginning, with cell division and specialization. Then we must proceed up the structural ladder to the main systems of the human body.

CONTENTS

2003 — Decoding of human genome completed

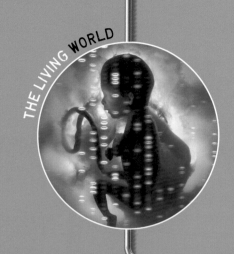

THE LIVING WORLD

1972 — First mouse born from a frozen embryo

1953 — Discovery of the double-helix structure of DNA

1944 — Discovery that DNA carries genetic information

1933 — Invention of the electron microscope

1904 — Discovery of sex chromosomes

1902 — Discovery of hormones

CIRCA 1901 — Discovery of the role played by the cell membrane

1831 — First observations of the cell nucleus

1824 — Discovery of the function of sperm

CIRCA 1680 — First observations of microscopic organisms

CIRCA 1590 — Invention of the multiple lens microscope

1420 — First artificial fertilization of fish eggs

THE HUMAN ORGANISM

AND THE

PERPETUATION OF LIFE

Humans are complex beings made up of billions of cells. How does a single microscopic cell develop into a fully formed adult? Are the cells that make up our muscles, blood and brain identical? What are the functions of our cells and how do they perform these functions? Why do we resemble both our mother and our father? What makes each one of us unique? These are some of the questions we will try to answer in this chapter.

1 THE CELL

Cells are the basic structure of all living beings, from single-cell bacteria to giant sequoias, flies to elephants, fungi to human organisms.

> Cell comes from the Latin word *cellula*, meaning "small room."

▶ **The CELL is the basic unit of life.**

All living beings must be able to nourish themselves, breathe, eliminate waste, grow, and reproduce. How are our bodies able to do this? The study of human cell structure and function will allow us to answer questions about the cell's role in these activities.

1.1 THE STRUCTURE AND FUNCTION OF THE HUMAN CELL

Most cells are so small they can only be observed under a microscope. An optical microscope, for example, allows us to distinguish three cell components: the cell membrane, the cytoplasm and the nucleus.

- The cell membrane is a flexible barrier that surrounds the cell content, allowing the cell to interact with its environment.
- The cytoplasm is the gelatinous fluid inside the cell membrane and outside the nucleus.
- The nucleus, easily distinguishable by its darker colour, is the cell's control centre.

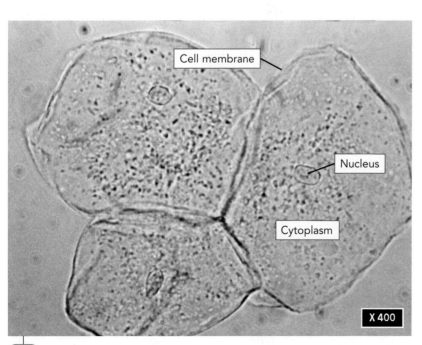

Cell membrane

Nucleus

Cytoplasm

X 400

5.1 Cells drawn from the inside of the human cheek, viewed with an optical microscope

1635
1703

Robert Hooke

This English scientist perfected the microscope, which he used to describe numerous animal and plant structures. He was the first to observe cells and he coined the term *cells* to describe the little cavities he observed in a cork sample.

An electron microscope provides a more detailed viewing and better under-standing of cell structure. Thanks to this type of microscope, we now know that the cytoplasm is made up of cytosol, a clear gelatinous substance, and that it envelops small structures called *organelles*, which include mitochon-dria, ribosomes, endoplasmic reticulum, lysosomes and the Golgi apparatus (Figure 5.2). We can also see that the nucleus is surrounded by a membrane, called the *nuclear membrane*, and that it contains a molecule that controls all cell activity: DNA.

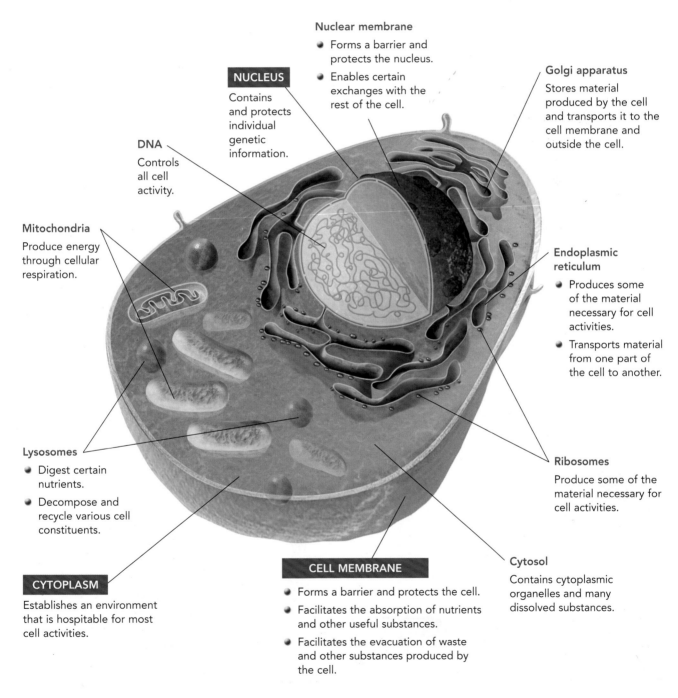

Nuclear membrane
- Forms a barrier and protects the nucleus.
- Enables certain exchanges with the rest of the cell.

NUCLEUS
Contains and protects individual genetic information.

DNA
Controls all cell activity.

Golgi apparatus
Stores material produced by the cell and transports it to the cell membrane and outside the cell.

Mitochondria
Produce energy through cellular respiration.

Endoplasmic reticulum
- Produces some of the material necessary for cell activities.
- Transports material from one part of the cell to another.

Lysosomes
- Digest certain nutrients.
- Decompose and recycle various cell constituents.

Ribosomes
Produce some of the material necessary for cell activities.

CYTOPLASM
Establishes an environment that is hospitable for most cell activities.

CELL MEMBRANE
- Forms a barrier and protects the cell.
- Facilitates the absorption of nutrients and other useful substances.
- Facilitates the evacuation of waste and other substances produced by the cell.

Cytosol
Contains cytoplasmic organelles and many dissolved substances.

5.2 Illustration of a typical human cell. The function of each cell structure is indicated below its name.

THE STRUCTURE
AND FUNCTION OF DNA

DNA, or **d**eoxyribo**n**ucleic **a**cid, appears as a very long molecule inside a cell nucleus. If we look at it closely, we see that the strand is made up of two chains linked by pairs of tiny molecules, called *bases*. There are four bases: adenine, cytosine, guanine and thymine. The whole structure of the DNA molecule looks like a ladder, and each rung is formed by a single base pair. Because of the way it twists into a spiral staircase-like structure, DNA is often described as a *double helix*.

▶ DNA is a molecule, shaped like a double helix, located inside the cell nucleus.

DNA contains genetic information in its base-pair sequence. Binding of the bases is very specific: adenine always binds with thymine and cytosine always binds with guanine. These base pairs are arranged in a sequence along the double-helix DNA, just like letters are arranged in a sequence to create words and sentences in language. The entire base-pair sequencing in an individual or species constitutes the individual's or species' genome. In the case of humans, the genome is made up of approximately three billion base pairs.

▶ A GENOME is the complete set of genetic information of an individual or species.

1920
1958

Rosalind Franklin

British biophysicist Rosalind Franklin was the first to obtain an indirect image of DNA structure using X-rays. Her work led to the description of the double-helix structure of the DNA molecule by Francis Crick and James Watson in 1953.

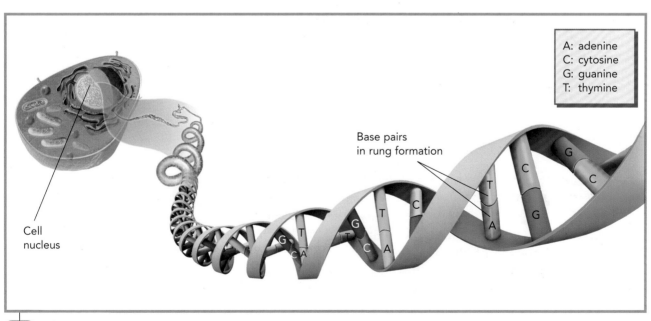

A: adenine
C: cytosine
G: guanine
T: thymine

Base pairs in rung formation

Cell nucleus

5.3 DNA has a double-helix structure.

Human and chimpanzee genes are 99 percent identical

It has been confirmed that humans and chimpanzees are indeed closely related. Decoding of the primate's genome has proven that genes of both species are 99 percent identical.

Results of this study—which involved 67 scientists from various universities in the United States, Israel, Italy, Germany and Spain— have recently been featured in the journal *Nature*. Genetic differences between humans and chimps are barely 10 times higher than between two humans.

What are the distinctions? Although humans do not possess the caspase-12 gene, which protects chimpanzees from Alzheimer's, our genetic baggage means we can walk upright and master language.

Adapted from Pauline Gravel, "Le décryptage du génome du chimpanzé confirme sa proche parenté avec l'humain," *Le Devoir*, September 2, 2005, p. A4. [*Translation*]

The chimpanzee is closely related to the human organism.

DNA is divided into genes, segments that contain the necessary information to manufacture proteins, such as enzymes, hormones and so on. Each of these types of protein has a specific job to carry out, from digesting nutrients and repairing wounds to making hair grow, giving eyes their colour and sending messages to other cells. The human genome is made up of about 25 000 genes. An individual's complete set of genes determines not only the way the body works, but his or her specific characteristics as well.

> ⊘ A GENE is a segment of DNA that contains the genetic information required to carry out a particular job.

1.3 GENETIC DIVERSITY

We are all unique individuals because our DNA is unique. Every gene can exist in different variations and forms. For example, genes responsible for eye colour can render the eyes blue, green, brown and so on, while the genes responsible for hair colour produce hair that is a particular shade of blond, brown, red or black. Because there are about 25 000 genes in each person, each with its own genetic variation, it is virtually impossible for two individuals to possess the same genetic information, with one exception: identical twins.

DOMINANT GENES

Why are there more people with brown eyes than blue eyes? It's because the genes responsible for the colour brown are *dominant*. If present in a person's genome, the genes for brown eyes express themselves at the expense of the genes that determine other eye colours.

The total number of possible genetic combinations make up the genetic diversity of a species.

▶ **GENETIC DIVERSITY includes all the possible genetic variations of a species.**

Sexual reproduction increases the genetic diversity of a species. On conception, the offspring receives certain genes from its mother and certain genes from its father. Each birth is therefore a new opportunity to combine the genes of two parents, allowing for new variations within a population. For example, the presence of a green-eyed person in a population of previously blue- and brown-eyed people enriches that population's genetic diversity. The greater the number of individuals in a population, the greater the genetic diversity.

On the other hand, a small or isolated population is more likely to be less genetically diverse, as are populations in which related individuals breed with one another. This inbreeding can result in a higher expression of a defective gene than one would normally expect. For example, close inter-marriages between some of the descendants of Queen Victoria, who ruled Great Britain from 1837 to 1901, caused hemophilia, a relatively rare genetic disorder, to spread more readily among members of the royal family than in the rest of the population.

McGill researchers identify the Andermann syndrome gene

Researchers from Montréal's McGill University have identified the gene responsible for a severe neurological disorder that confines hundreds of children in Québec to wheelchairs. This rare genetic disease, Andermann syndrome, named for its researchers, is present almost exclusively in the Saguenay–Lac-Saint-Jean and Charlevoix regions of Québec.

Four hundred French Canadians founded Charlevoix and some carried the gene. When those who carried the gene married and had children, the disease was passed on to future gene-rations. As the inhabitants of Charlevoix migrated to the Saguenay–Lac-Saint-Jean region, the disease appeared in that region as well.

Although the gene's discovery is significant, years of research are still needed before a treatment is possible. Couples from the affected regions, however, can be tested for the gene before deciding to have children.

Adapted from André Noël, "Des chercheurs de McGill identifient le gène du syndrome d'Andermann," *La Presse*, October 9, 2002, p. A1. *[Translation]*

The Andermann syndrome confines hundreds of children in Québec to wheelchairs.

Possible or impossible?

What is the probability of two people (who are not identical twins) possessing identical genetic information, that is, the same combination of 25 000 genes?

Let's solve this puzzle mathematically using bags of coloured marbles. Each bag represents a gene, while the coloured marbles inside a bag represent the possible genetic variations of the same gene.

Suppose we have five bags, each containing four marbles of a different colour. If we remove one marble from each bag, we obtain a particular combination of colours. If we return each of the marbles to its respective bag and then repeat the exercise, what are the odds of obtaining the same combination of marbles? Let's find out!

$$\frac{1}{4} \times \frac{1}{4} \times \frac{1}{4} \times \frac{1}{4} \times \frac{1}{4} = \left(\frac{1}{4}\right)^5$$

that is, a chance of 1 out of 1024.

Using 25 bags with four marbles each, the odds of obtaining the same combination are:

$$\left(\frac{1}{4}\right)^{25}$$

that is, a chance of 1 out of 1.13×10^{15}.

Now let's calculate the probability using 25 000 bags.

$$\left(\frac{1}{4}\right)^{25\,000}$$

that is, a chance of approximately 1 out of $1.13 \times 10^{15\,000}$.

When calculating probabilities, a chance of less than 1 in 10^{50} is considered an impossibility.

2 CELL DIVISION

Cell division occurs for three reasons:
- to increase an organism's cell count, thereby allowing the organism to grow
- to regenerate damaged or broken tissue
- to make sexual reproduction possible

▶ CELL DIVISION is a process that is essential to the production of new cells for the purpose of growth, tissue repair and sexual reproduction.

Cells, however, are not constantly dividing. Most of the time, they perform valuable functions to ensure that the human organism is in good working order. The period when they are not dividing is called *interphase*.

Toward the end of interphase, as a cell prepares to divide, it duplicates the DNA in its nucleus. This process of DNA duplication is referred to as *replication*. During this process, the double helix of the DNA unwinds, splitting into two strands (Figure 5.4.). Each strand serves as a template for building a new complementary strand. As a result, two helixes, each identical to the original DNA helix, are formed.

As cell division begins, the DNA strands coil and condense to form rod-like structures called chromosomes. Chromosomes are shaped like an X because they are made up of two rods joined together at the centre. Each rod, called a *chromatid*, is an exact copy of the other, since the cell has already replicated its DNA during interphase.

Chromosome comes from the Greek words *khrôma*, meaning "colour," and *soma*, meaning "body." (It is usually quite simple to colour, or stain, chromosomes to make them visible under an optical microscope.)

Chromosomes form pairs. Within each pair, one chromosome contains genetic material from the mother, while the other contains genetic material from the father.

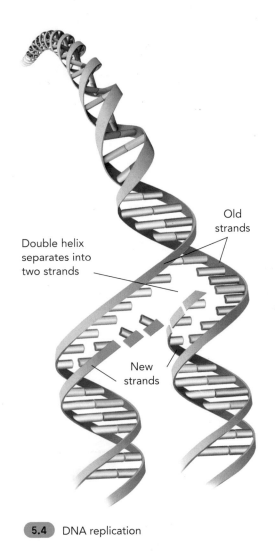

Double helix separates into two strands

Old strands

New strands

5.4 DNA replication

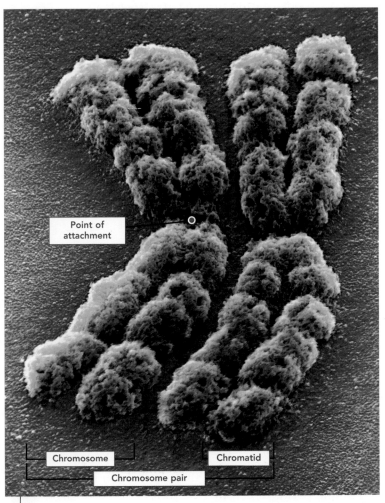

Point of attachment

Chromosome

Chromatid

Chromosome pair

5.5 In a chromosome pair, one chromosome is derived from the mother, the other from the father. Within a chromosome, each chromatid is the exact copy of the other.

The number of pairs of chromosomes in the genome of a species varies from one species to the next. Because of this, cells are said to contain *2n* chromosomes (where *n* represents the number of pairs). In humans, *n*=23; each person's genome contains 23 pairs of chromosomes.

Usually the first 22 pairs of chromosomes are numbered. The 23rd pair, which is the pair that determines an individual's gender, is labelled XX for females and XY for males.

There are two types of cell division. The first type is called *mitosis.* It increases the number of cells and replaces dead or worn cells (Section 2.1, below). During mitosis, the original cell (called the *parent cell*) divides, producing two identical cells (called *daughter cells*).

The second type of cell division is called *meiosis.* During meiosis, the parent cell divides twice, producing four daughter cells, each containing only half the DNA of the parent cell (Section 2.2, page 135). The daughter cells, which are also called *sex cells,* can now unite with another sex cell to produce a new individual with a complete set of DNA.

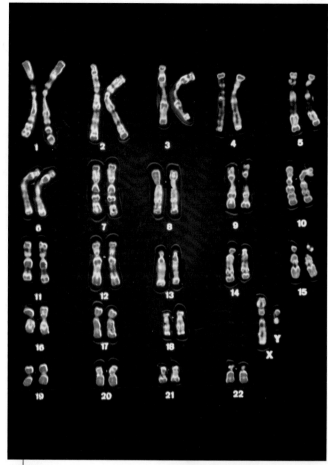

5.6 The human genome includes 23 pairs of chromosomes. The genome pictured here is of a male since the 23rd pair is XY.

LAB 39

2.1 MITOSIS

Mitosis results in the formation of what is known as diploid cells. Each diploid cell possesses two sets of chromosomes (that is, two copies of each gene): one from the father and one from the mother. All cells in the human body are diploid, except for sex cells.

> *Diploid* comes from the Greek word *diploos,* meaning "double."

> ▶ **MITOSIS is a process of cell division in which cells multiply in order to ensure growth and tissue repair.**

Mitosis consists of four phases: prophase, metaphase, anaphase and telophase. Figure 5.7, on the next page, provides an overview of the entire process.

PROGRAMMED TO DIE

If most of the cells in our body can divide in order to replace worn or damaged cells, why do we ever age? It is believed that cells can undergo mitosis only a certain number of times. Once that number is reached, cells lose their ability to divide, so they disintegrate and disappear.

Original DNA
Replicated DNA

End of interphase
The parent cell has grown and completely replicated its DNA.

Beginning of interphase
DNA appears as threads.

- DNA strands coil and condense to form chromosomes.
- The nuclear membrane disappears.

Metaphase – Phase 2
Chromosomes align at the centre of the cell.

Telophase – Phase 4
- A new nuclear membrane forms.
- DNA uncoils into separate strands.
- Organelles and cytosol are evenly divided.
- The cell divides into two daughter cells.

Anaphase – Phase 3
- Chromosomes separate from their point of attachment into chromatids.
- Chromatids move away from the centre; half go to one end of the cell, the other half go to the other end.

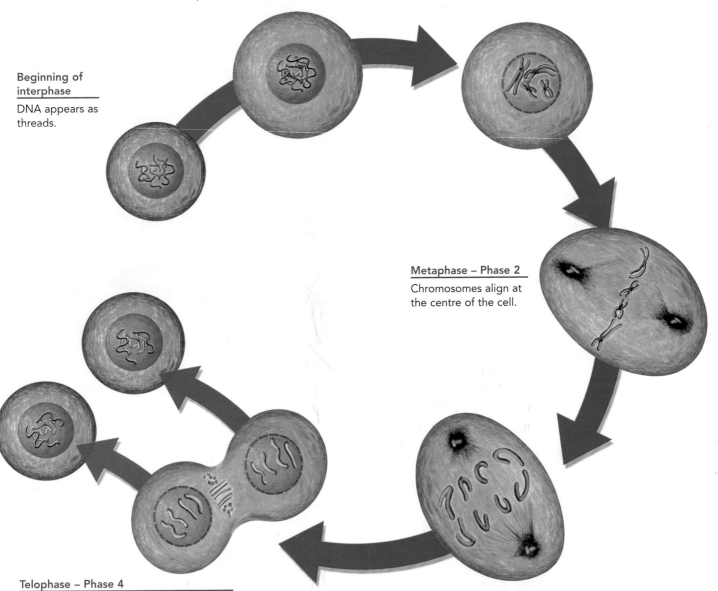

5.7 Interphase and the four phases of mitosis. At the end of cell division, the two daughter cells possess the same genetic material as that of the parent cell. (To simplify the illustration only four chromosomes are shown here.)

2.2 MEIOSIS

The purpose of meiosis, the second type of cell division, is sexual reproduction, that is, the union of two sex cells during fertilization. Sex cells are also called [haploid] cells: they contain only one set of chromosomes, that is, one member from each pair of chromosomes. Thus, haploid sex cells have only one copy of each gene.

Haploid comes from the Greek word *haploos*, meaning "simple."

There are two types of sex cells: male sex cells called *male gametes* or *spermatozoa*, and female sex cells called *female gametes, eggs* or *ova*.

▶ MEIOSIS is the process of cell division in which male and female gametes are produced in order for sexual reproduction to take place.

As Figure 5.8 indicates, meiosis and mitosis are somewhat similar. In both types of cell division, the parent cell is diploid. When the cell starts to divide, the DNA of the parent cell coils and condenses to form chromosome pairs, each containing two identical chromatids. The main difference is that in meiosis, the cell divides not once but twice. These divisions are known as *meiosis I* and *meiosis II*.

In the first meiotic division (meiosis I), chromosome pairs are separated, reducing their numbers by half. By the end of meiosis I, each cell ends up with 23 chromosomes.

In the second meiotic division (meiosis II), chromosomes split into two from their point of attachment. The result is four haploid daughter cells.

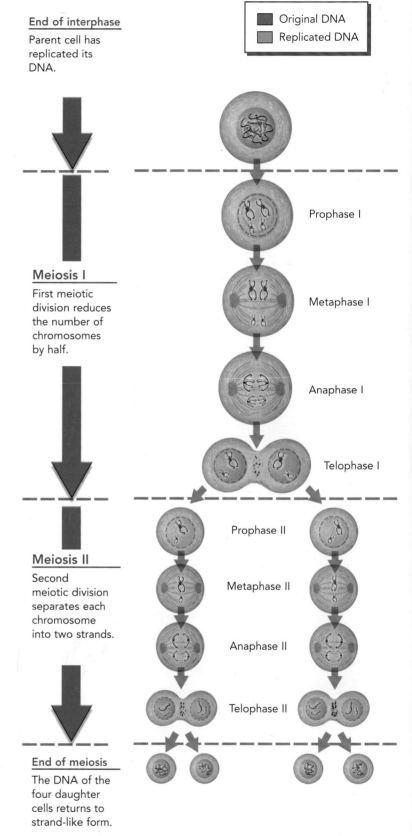

End of interphase
Parent cell has replicated its DNA.

■ Original DNA
■ Replicated DNA

Prophase I

Meiosis I
First meiotic division reduces the number of chromosomes by half.

Metaphase I

Anaphase I

Telophase I

Prophase II

Meiosis II
Second meiotic division separates each chromosome into two strands.

Metaphase II

Anaphase II

Telophase II

End of meiosis
The DNA of the four daughter cells returns to strand-like form.

5.8 Interphase and the phases of meiosis. At the end of cell division, the four daughter cells possess only half the genetic material of the parent cell. (To simplify the illustration, only four chromosomes are shown here.)

3 CELLULAR SPECIALIZATION

The immediate result of fertilization is the formation of a **ZYGOTE,** a single cell with a full set of DNA. The single cell then divides into two cells, which divide into four cells, which divide into eight cells, and so on, until a fully formed organism is created through mitosis. An adult human being is composed of approximately 60 trillion (6×10^{13}) cells. Cells, however, do more than just multiply. They also specialize in order to meet the multiple needs of the body.

In this section, we will learn that **SPECIALIZED CELLS** that perform a common function are called *tissues,* that various types of tissue can form an organ, and that groups of organs can form organ systems, which in turn form an organism, in this case, a human being.

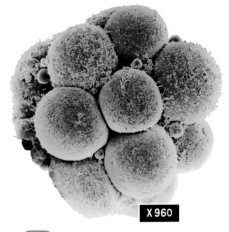

X 960

5.9 Four days after fertilization, the zygote has already become a small cluster of 16 cells.

3.1 TISSUE TYPES

Microscopes allow researchers to observe how specialized cells form groups in order to perform specific functions. The most basic level of cellular organization is the tissue.

> ▶ A TISSUE is a group of similar cells that have a common function.

There are four types of tissue: epithelial, connective, nerve and muscle.

EPITHELIAL TISSUE

Epithelial tissue covers and protects organs, both inside the body (e.g. digestive tract lining) and out (e.g. skin). Epithelial tissue also secretes, absorbs and filters substances.

5.10 The epithelial tissue of the skin covers and protects underlying tissue.

5.11 The epithelial tissue of salivary glands contains cells that secrete saliva.

5.12 The epithelial tissue of the small intestine contains cells that absorb nutrients.

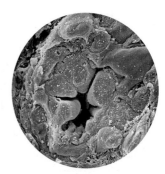

5.13 The epithelial tissue of the kidneys contains cells that filter blood.

CONNECTIVE TISSUE

Connective tissue binds and supports tissues and organs in the body, providing them with protection and nutrients. Connective tissue is the most abundant and widely distributed tissue in the body.

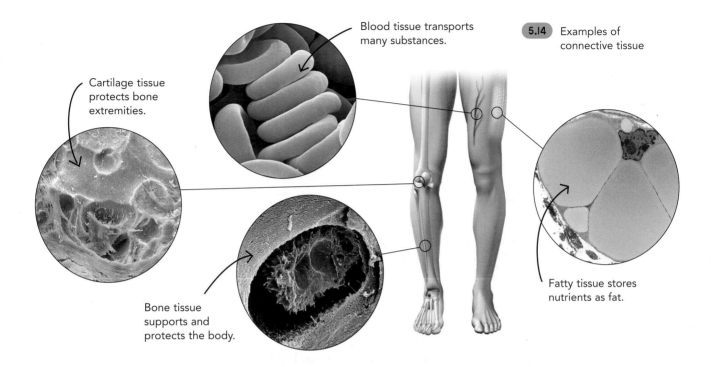

Cartilage tissue protects bone extremities.

Blood tissue transports many substances.

5.14 Examples of connective tissue

Bone tissue supports and protects the body.

Fatty tissue stores nutrients as fat.

NERVE TISSUE

Nerve tissue helps control and guide body activity, making it possible for messages to be received, processed and transmitted between the brain and other parts of the body. The nerves, spinal cord and brain are made up of nerve tissue.

MUSCLE TISSUE

Muscle tissue has the ability to contract and regain its shape like a spring, making it possible for the body to move. Muscle tissue can be controlled voluntarily, such as when we move our fingers, or involuntarily, such as when our heart beats.

There are three types of muscle tissue:

- skeletal muscle tissue, which makes up the muscles that are attached to the bones
- smooth muscle tissue, which makes up the lining of organs that contract, such as the stomach, bladder, uterus and some blood vessels
- cardiac muscle tissue, which is found only in the heart

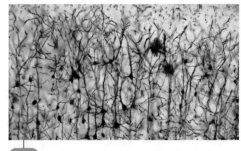

5.15 The brain is composed of nerve tissue.

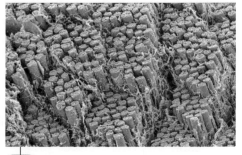

5.16 Muscle tissue is made up of thin elongated cells, which contract and then regain their shape.

3.2 FROM TISSUE TO ORGAN

A structure composed of tissues grouped together to perform one or more specific functions is called an *organ*. For example, the stomach is made up of epithelial, connective, muscle and nerve tissues. These tissues store, break down and digest food. The stomach is an organ because it is composed of different types of tissue that perform complementary functions. The skin, heart, lungs and brain are other examples of organs.

> ▶ An **ORGAN** is a structure composed of two or more tissue types performing one or more specific functions.

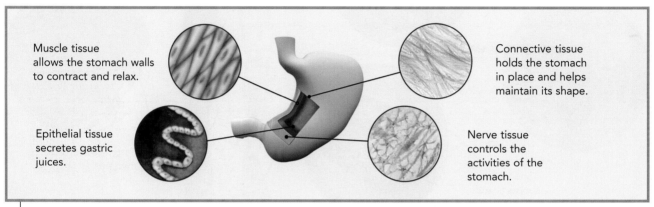

Muscle tissue allows the stomach walls to contract and relax.

Connective tissue holds the stomach in place and helps maintain its shape.

Epithelial tissue secretes gastric juices.

Nerve tissue controls the activities of the stomach.

5.17 The stomach is an organ made up of four types of tissue whose functions are to store, break down and begin to digest food.

Bio-engineered bladders

Urologists from Wake Forest University, North Carolina, have successfully "grown" bladders in their lab for seven children born with a congenital bladder defect. This was achieved by first taking a sample of existing cells from the patients, then growing those cells in a culture in the lab. When cells had increased sufficiently, they were placed into biodegradable bladder-shaped moulds. Once the new bladders formed, they were transplanted into the patients.

This revolutionary procedure should be available in a few years in Québec. Every year, dozens of patients in the province require bladder reconstruction surgery. The procedure has only been used on children, but experts believe it can be easily adapted for adult patients as well.

Adapted from Mathieu Perreault, "Vers des organes de rechange," *La Presse*, April 5, 2006, p. A6. *[Translation]*

Dr. Assaad El-Hakim, a urologist at the Royal Victoria Hospital in Montréal, has studied the bladder reconstruction procedure developed in the U.S. and is currently conducting tests to implement it in Québec.

3.3 FROM ORGAN TO SYSTEM

Tissues and organs must function together to ensure proper functioning of the human body. A *system* is a group of tissues and organs working together to accomplish a common purpose. The stomach, for instance, works with the intestine, esophagus and other organs of the digestive system in order to help the body nourish itself.

▶ A SYSTEM is a group of organs and tissues working together to accomplish a common function.

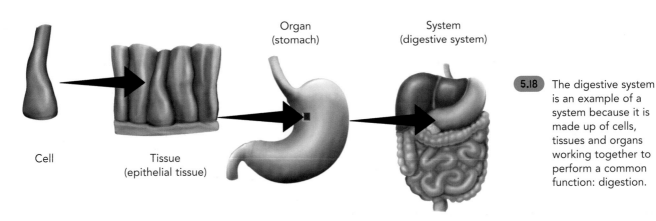

Cell

Tissue
(epithelial tissue)

Organ
(stomach)

System
(digestive system)

5.18 The digestive system is an example of a system because it is made up of cells, tissues and organs working together to perform a common function: digestion.

All organ systems together make up an organism, or a living body. The organism represents the highest level of cellular organization.

Figure 5.19 lists the functions of various systems, many of which will be covered in later chapters. In the next section of this chapter, we will study the human reproductive system.

5.19 ORGAN SYSTEMS AND THEIR FUNCTIONS

System	Function
Cardiovascular system	Circulates the blood, transports nutrients to cells and eliminates waste.
Digestive system	Breaks down and absorbs nutrients and eliminates waste.
Endocrine system	Uses hormones to control organ performance.
Excretory system	Ensures that the body's waste is excreted.
Lymphatic system	Works with the immune system to protect the body against foreign microorganisms.
Musculoskeletal system	Provides the body with support and mobility.
Nervous system	Controls the entire organism (thoughts, decisions, memories), relays information to the various body parts and interacts with the environment through the sensory organs.
Reproductive system	Directs sexual reproduction.
Respiratory system	Helps the body absorb oxygen and expel carbon dioxide.

4. THE REPRODUCTIVE SYSTEM

Every living being seeks to survive by meeting its basic needs, such as breathing, eating, sleeping and so on. When all these essential needs are met, the organism then seeks to ensure the survival of its species. It does this by producing offspring. Along with many animal and plant species, human beings share a method of reproduction that requires the participation of two individuals, one male and one female. This process is called *sexual reproduction*.

4.1 STAGES OF HUMAN DEVELOPMENT

Sexual reproduction involves the fertilization of an ovum (a haploid cell from the mother) by a spermatozoan (a haploid cell from the father). During fertilization, the genetic material in the ovum is fused with that of the spermatozoan. The result is a diploid cell, made up of 23 pairs of chromosomes, half of which come from the mother and half from the father. The resulting diploid cell, called a *zygote,* can subsequently reproduce by mitosis and transfer its DNA to the entire organism. This means that all the cells in the body end up with exactly the same genetic information.

> ▶ FERTILIZATION is the fusion of an ovum and a spermatozoan. It results in one complete cell, the zygote, which contains the genetic material of both the father and the mother.

Meiosis and fertilization represent the first two stages of the developmental cycle of sexual species. Table 5.21 lists the other stages of this cycle in humans.

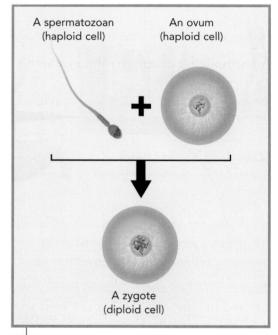

A spermatozoan (haploid cell)

An ovum (haploid cell)

A zygote (diploid cell)

5.20 During fertilization, the union of a spermatozoan and an ovum produces a zygote. Every zygote contains two complete sets of chromosomes, one set from the mother and one set from the father.

5.21 STAGES OF HUMAN DEVELOPMENT

	Stage	Approximate ages
Stages during pregnancy	Zygote	From fertilization to about 2 weeks
	Embryo	From about 2 to 9 weeks
	Fetus	From 9 weeks to birth
Stages after birth	Baby	From birth to 2 years
	Early childhood	From 2 to 6 years
	Childhood	From 6 to 10 years
	Adolescence	From 10 to 18 years
	Adulthood	From 18 to about 70 years
	Old age	From about 70 years to death

4.2 PUBERTY

Adolescence is the stage of development that marks a turning point between childhood and adulthood. It is a particularly important part of development because it includes puberty. During childhood, the reproductive system is inactive; in adolescence, the reproductive system becomes functional.

> ▶ **PUBERTY** is characterized by the changes that prepare the human body for the ability to reproduce. This stage generally occurs between the ages of 10 and 14 years old.

The beginning of puberty is marked by a progressive increase in the production of sex hormones.

A hormone is a chemical substance secreted by a specialized organ called a *gland*. These chemical substances are released

Hormone comes from the Greek word *hormân*, meaning "that excites, that arouses."

into the bloodstream and stimulate the activity of specific organs or tissues elsewhere in the body. Thus they work from a distance. Only those organs and tissues that are sensitive to these hormones react to their presence in the bloodstream.

> ▶ **HORMONES** are chemical messengers, which are transported by the blood and control the activity of one or more organs.

Hormones and hormone-producing glands are part of the hormonal system, more commonly referred to as the *endocrine system*. This system regulates the body's activities. It is responsible for the body's growth, for its ability to respond to stress, for reproduction and for the regulation of metabolic processes, among other things.

Puberty is triggered by two hormones that are secreted by the pituitary gland, a gland the size of a grape located at the base of the brain. The two hormones are follicle-stimulating hormone (FSH), and luteinizing hormone (LH).

FSH and LH are the hormones that stimulate the maturation of ova (in females) and the production of spermatozoa (in males). In women, they also stimulate the ovaries to produce female sex hormones (estrogens and progesterone). In men, they stimulate the testicles to produce male sex hormones (primarily testosterone).

The production of female and male sex hormones initiates significant physical and psychological changes. These are referred to as *primary* and *secondary sexual characteristics* (Figures 5.22–5.24, pages 142–143).

1866
1927

Ernest Starling

In 1902, with the help of William Bayliss (1860-1924), this English physiologist discovered the existence of chemical messengers in the body. Once secreted into the blood stream, these chemicals stimulate a remote organ into action. Three years later, Starling referred to these messengers as "hormones."

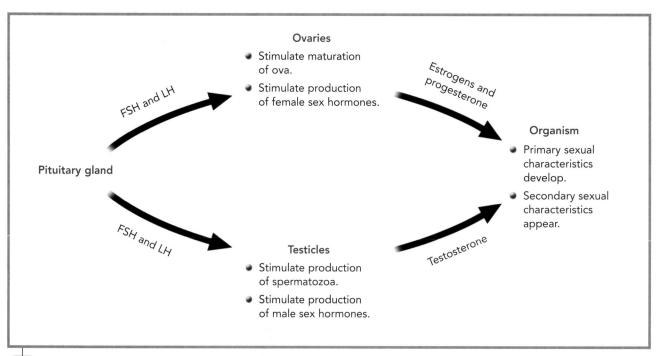

5.22 The effect of hormones secreted by the pituitary gland on the ovaries and testicles and the effect of sex hormones on the body

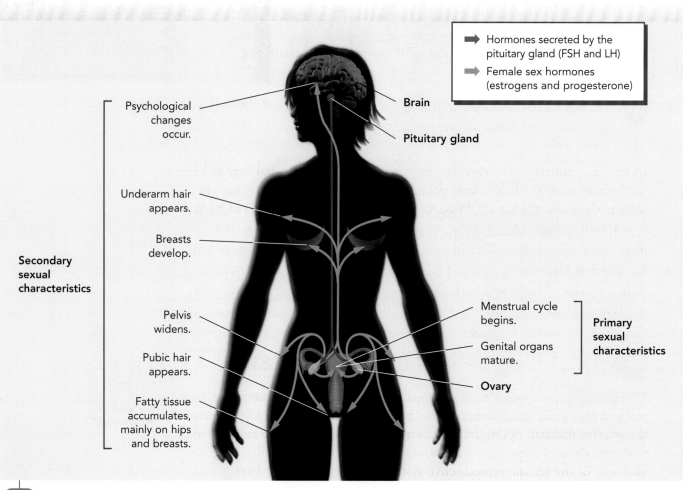

5.23 Hormone action promotes the development of sexual characteristics in teenage girls.

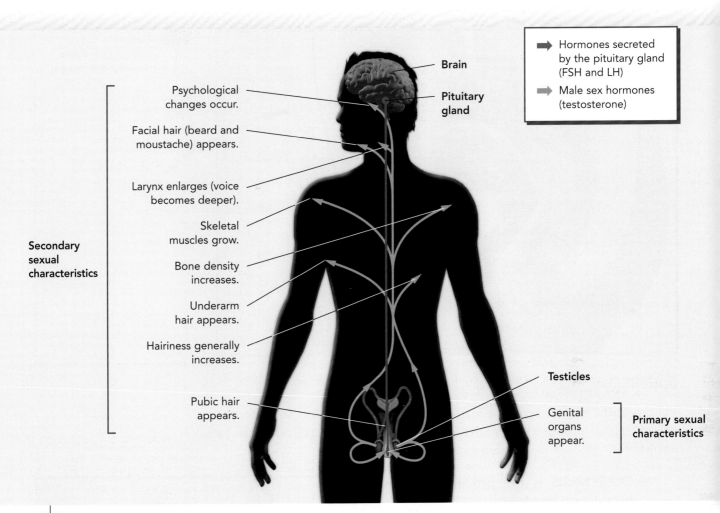

Brain

Pituitary gland

Psychological changes occur.

Facial hair (beard and moustache) appears.

Larynx enlarges (voice becomes deeper).

Skeletal muscles grow.

Bone density increases.

Underarm hair appears.

Hairiness generally increases.

Pubic hair appears.

Secondary sexual characteristics

Testicles

Genital organs appear.

Primary sexual characteristics

5.24 Hormone action promotes the development of sexual characteristics in teenage boys.

In women, puberty is marked by the maturation of the genital organs and the beginning of the menstrual cycle. This cycle begins at puberty and gradually ends at around age 50. Puberty in women is also characterized by the appearance and lasting presence of many secondary sexual characteristics (Figure 5.23).

In men, puberty is characterized by the maturation of the genital organs as well as the appearance and lasting presence of secondary sexual characteristics (Figure 5.24).

4.3 THE FEMALE REPRODUCTIVE SYSTEM

LAB
40

In this section, we will take a look at the role played by hormones in the maturation of ova (oogenesis) and in the periodic changes that take place in the ovaries (ovarian cycle) and the uterus (menstrual cycle). To gain a good understanding of these phenomena, you need to become familiar with the anatomy of the female reproductive system (Figure 5.25, page 144).

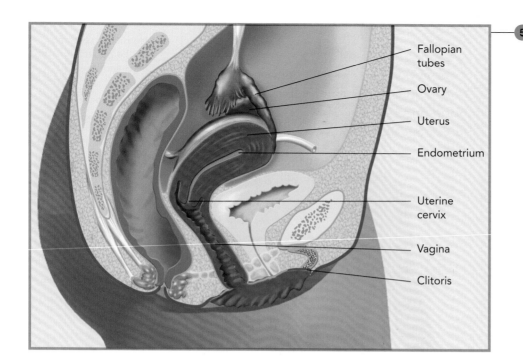

The pelvis contains most of the female reproductive organs.

Fallopian tubes

Ovary

Uterus

Endometrium

Uterine cervix

Vagina

Clitoris

OOGENESIS

Puberty is the beginning of the fertile phase of a woman's life. To be fertile, a woman must produce mature ova, that is, mature haploid cells that can be fertilized by spermatozoa. This process is called *oogenesis*.

▶ **OOGENESIS is the process of ovum production by meiosis.**

At puberty, a girl has approximately 700 000 cells in her ovaries capable of becoming ova. Called *oocytes*, these egg cells are diploid cells, each containing 23 pairs of chromosomes. Typically, under the influence of hormones, one oocyte per cycle develops into an ovum ready to be fertilized. Over the course of a woman's life, some 400 oocytes change into ova.

Each oocyte is surrounded by a layer of cells called an *ovarian follicle*. At the beginning of a cycle, one ovarian follicle begins to mature and its oocyte starts to undergo meiosis I, producing two haploid cells with 23 chromosomes each. One of these two cells ends up with almost all the cytoplasm provided by the parent cell and therefore has all the nutrients needed for an embryo to develop. The other haploid cell doesn't; it quickly dies.

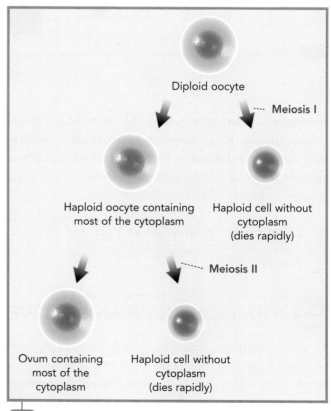

Diploid oocyte

---- Meiosis I

Haploid oocyte containing most of the cytoplasm

Haploid cell without cytoplasm (dies rapidly)

---- Meiosis II

Ovum containing most of the cytoplasm

Haploid cell without cytoplasm (dies rapidly)

5.26 Oogenesis

Around the middle of the cycle, the ovarian follicle bursts, releasing the oocyte into a fallopian tube. This process is called *ovulation*.

The oocyte now begins its trip to the uterus. As it moves along the fallopian tube, it undergoes meiosis II. Once again, two haploid cells are formed: one contains almost all the cytoplasm and the other, smaller haploid cell quickly dies. Each oocyte, therefore, can only give rise to one mature ovum.

If the ovum is not fertilized, it is expelled from the body during menstruation. If the ovum is fertilized, a zygote forms and implants itself in the wall of the uterus to develop into an embryo.

THE OVARIAN CYCLE

The series of changes that ovarian follicles undergo every month is referred to as the *ovarian cycle*.

> ▶ The OVARIAN CYCLE is the process whereby a single ovarian follicle matures (in order to release an ovum) and changes into a corpus luteum (in order to encourage the implantation of the ovum in the uterus).

At the outset of each cycle, the pituitary gland secretes more FSH, which stimulates the development and growth of an ovarian follicle. As the ovarian follicle develops, it secretes more and more estrogen.

This increase in the level of estrogens now stimulates the pituitary gland to secrete a second hormone, LH, in large quantities, along with even more FSH. The hormonal surge stimulates the mature ovarian follicle to rupture, tearing the ovary wall and releasing the ovum.

Subsequently, LH promotes the healing of the ruptured ovarian follicle, and transforms the follicle into the corpus luteum (pl. corpora lutea), a temporary structure in the ovary that secretes progesterone to ready the body to receive a fertilized ovum. Progesterone does this, for example, by inhibiting further production of FSH and LH and also by stimulating the thickening of the uterine wall (also known as the *endometrium*).

If the ovum is not fertilized, the corpus luteum disintegrates, producing less and less progesterone. The endometrium is sloughed off during menstruation. The body is now ready to begin another **cycle**.

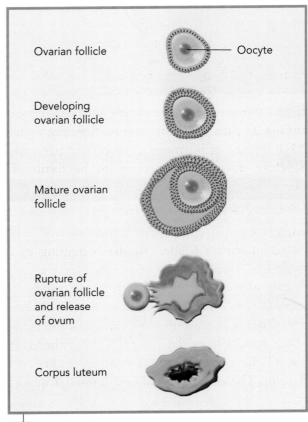

Ovarian follicle — Oocyte

Developing ovarian follicle

Mature ovarian follicle

Rupture of ovarian follicle and release of ovum

Corpus luteum

5.27 The ovarian cycle, based on a 28-day cycle

If the ovum is fertilized, the corpus luteum continues secreting progesterone until the **PLACENTA** is capable of taking over the job.

Figure 5.28 shows the development of the ovum and that of the ovarian follicle, while Table 5.29 summarizes the significant events of these two cycles and the role of various hormones.

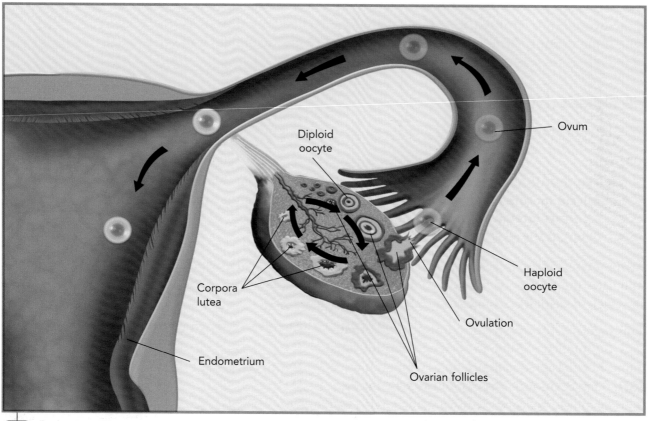

Diploid oocyte

Ovum

Haploid oocyte

Ovulation

Corpora lutea

Ovarian follicles

Endometrium

5.28 Oogenesis and the ovarian cycle result in the production of an ovum ready to be fertilized.

5.29 MAIN EVENTS OF OOGENESIS AND THE OVARIAN CYCLE, BASED ON A 28-DAY CYCLE

Period	Oogenesis	Ovarian cycle	Hormones
Days 1 to 13	• An oocyte undergoes meiosis I.	• An ovarian follicle completes maturation.	• The pituitary gland secretes a greater quantity of FSH, stimulating the development of an ovarian follicle. • The ovarian follicle secretes more and more estrogens, stimulating the pituitary gland to produce more and more FSH and LH.
Day 14 (ovulation)	• The oocyte is expelled from the ovarian follicle.	• The mature ovarian follicle bursts.	• The pituitary gland secretes LH in greater quantities as well as more FSH, producing a hormonal surge and thus initiating ovulation and the transformation of the ovarian follicle into a corpus luteum.
Days 15 to 28	• The oocyte moves into one of the fallopian tubes. • The oocyte undergoes meiosis II.	• The ovarian follicle is transformed into the corpus luteum. • If the ovum is not fertilized, the corpus luteum deteriorates.	• The corpus luteum secretes progesterone, inhibiting the production of FSH and LH by the pituitary gland. • As the corpus luteum deteriorates, progesterone production decreases, while FSH production increases again.

THE MENSTRUAL CYCLE

The ovarian cycle and hormone action produce the menstrual cycle in a woman. Sometimes the expression *menstrual cycle* is used to refer to all of the changes that a woman's body undergoes on a regular basis. In this textbook, however, we will use the term "menstrual cycle" to refer only to those events that occur in the uterus.

> ● The MENSTRUAL CYCLE represents all of the periodic changes in the uterine endometrium.

According to convention, the menstrual cycle begins with the first day of menstruation. If the ovum is not fertilized, the corpus luteum deteriorates, reducing its output of progesterone and thus triggering the menstrual phase. On the other hand, if the ovum is fertilized, the level of progesterone stays the same, menstruation does not occur, and the zygote implants itself in the endometrium.

The menstrual phase is followed by the proliferation phase, which lasts from the end of menstruation until ovulation. The endometrium begins to thicken again, stimulated by the production of estrogens by another developing ovarian follicle.

The menstrual cycle concludes with the secretory phase, which is also marked by a thickening of the endometrium, but in this case the thickening is stimulated by progesterone secreted by the corpus luteum.

5.30 PRIMARY EVENTS IN THE MENSTRUAL CYCLE, BASED ON A 28-DAY CYCLE

Phase	Event	Hormones
Menstrual phase (days 1 to 5)	Bleeding occurs, due to the expulsion of the endometrium and unfertilized ovum.	Production of progesterone decreases (due to deterioration of the corpus luteum).
Proliferation phase (days 6 to 14)	Endometrium begins to thicken.	Production of estrogens by a new ovarian follicle increases.
Secretory phase (days 15 to 28)	Endometrium continues to thicken.	Secretion of progesterone by the corpus luteum increases.

The duration of the menstrual cycle varies from woman to woman. What rarely varies, however, is the 14-day time period between ovulation and the beginning of menstruation.

Figure 5.32, on the next page, shows the relationship between the hormonal cycle, oogenesis, the ovarian cycle and the menstrual cycle.

An ovum lives from 12 to 24 hours; a spermatozoan lives from 24 to 72 hours. Therefore, a woman's fertile period, when she is most likely to become pregnant, lasts about four days: from three days before ovulation to one day after.

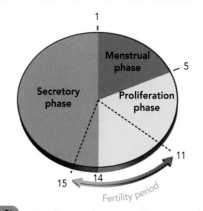

5.31 The phases of a woman's menstrual cycle and fertile period, based on a 28-day cycle

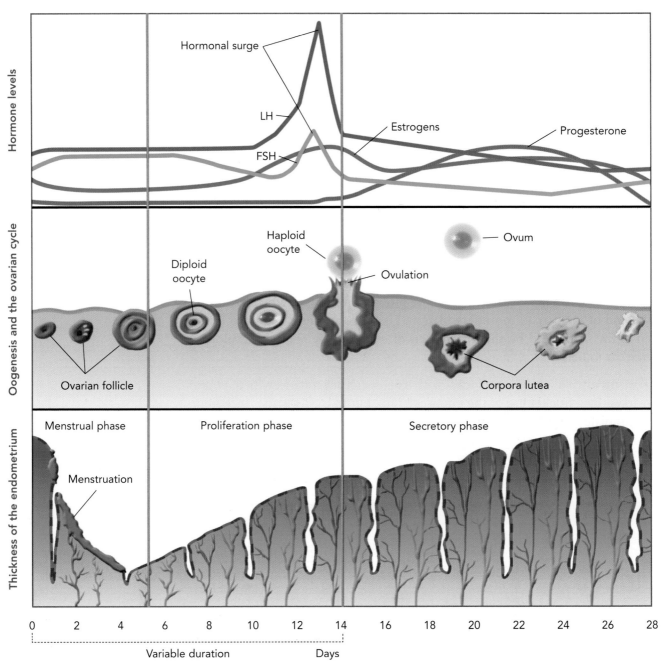

Menstruation **Before ovulation** **After ovulation**

Hormone levels

Hormonal surge

LH

FSH

Estrogens

Progesterone

Oogenesis and the ovarian cycle

Haploid oocyte

Ovum

Diploid oocyte

Ovulation

Ovarian follicle

Corpora lutea

Thickness of the endometrium

Menstrual phase   Proliferation phase   Secretory phase

Menstruation

0   2   4   6   8   10   12   14   16   18   20   22   24   26   28

Variable duration   Days

5.32 The ovarian cycle and the menstrual cycle are controlled by the hormonal cycle.

MENOPAUSE

A woman over 40 who has not menstruated for a year (apart from being pregnant or nursing) may well be starting menopause. This physical change occurs when the ovarian and menstrual cycles come to an end. The ovaries continue to produce estrogens for a certain period of time and then stop. As these hormones disappear, women may feel some discomfort such as hot flashes, mood swings and bone loss. Sometimes hormone supplements are prescribed to treat these symptoms.

Menopause comes from the Greek words *menos*, meaning "month," and *pausis*, meaning "cessation."

4.4 THE MALE REPRODUCTIVE SYSTEM

Hormones play an important part in the production of spermatozoa, called *spermatogenesis*. Before discussing this phenomenon, let's examine the anatomy of the male reproductive system (Figure 5.33).

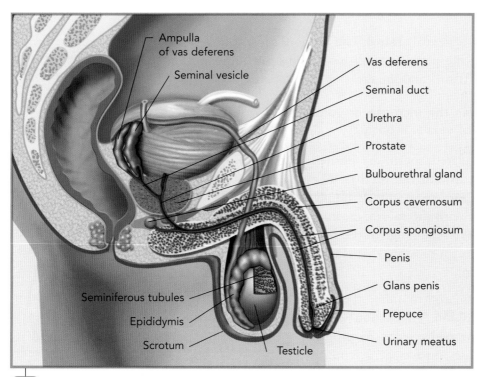

Ampulla of vas deferens
Seminal vesicle
Vas deferens
Seminal duct
Urethra
Prostate
Bulbourethral gland
Corpus cavernosum
Corpus spongiosum
Penis
Glans penis
Prepuce
Urinary meatus
Seminiferous tubules
Epididymis
Scrotum
Testicle

5.33 The pelvis contains most of the male reproductive organs.

SPERMATOGENESIS

When a boy enters puberty, the pituitary gland releases FSH, which stimulates spermatogenesis. Cells that cover the walls of the seminiferous tubules within the testicles are called *spermatogonia*. These cells undergo meiosis to form spermatozoa (sperm). Each spermatogonium gives rise to four spermatozoa. Given that spermatogonia are constantly being renewed, the testicles can produce vast quantities of sperm, roughly 120 million per day.

▶ **SPERMATOGENESIS** is the process of sperm production by meiosis.

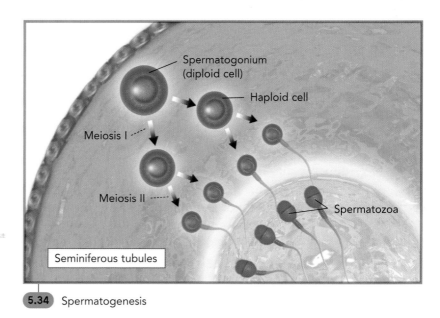

Spermatogonium (diploid cell)
Haploid cell
Meiosis I
Meiosis II
Spermatozoa
Seminiferous tubules

5.34 Spermatogenesis

ERECTION AND EJACULATION

Once formed, sperm are pushed into the ampulla of vas deferens. They collect there until they are expelled through the urethra.

The urethra is the canal through which both sperm and urine are expelled. Because urine kills sperm, it is vital that the two do not mix. Two ring-shaped muscles control the process. During an erection, these muscles contract, making it impossible to urinate.

A penile erection is the result of sexual arousal. The corpora cavernosa and spongiosa along the length of the penis fill with blood. This phenomenon brings about a swelling of the tissues and the erection of the penis.

> ◗ An ERECTION involves the increase in volume and rigidity of the penis as a result of sexual arousal.

When the erect penis is stimulated, sperm are pushed through the ejaculatory duct toward the urethra. The prostate and seminal vesicles secrete a whitish liquid, called *seminal fluid,* that mixes with the sperm, creating semen. The semen accumulates in the bulge of the urethra near the prostate, producing a pressure that is ultimately followed by ejaculation.

At the time of ejaculation, muscle surrounding the urethra contracts in rhythmic fashion. This action, combined with contractions in the penis, serves to project the semen. An ejaculation releases, on average, 3.5 mL of semen containing some 350 million sperm.

> ◗ EJACULATION is the expulsion of semen by the penis.

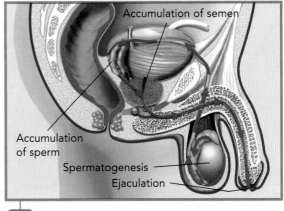

5.35 The life of spermatozoa, from formation to ejaculation

5.36 SEMEN COMPONENTS

Origin of semen components	% of semen	Description of semen
Epididymis	10% to 20%	Liquid containing sperm
Seminal vesicles	40% to 60%	Liquid rich in carbohydrates that provides essential energy to the sperm
Prostate	20% to 40%	Whitish liquid that contributes to the mobility of the sperm
Bulbourethral glands	5%	Mucus that lubricates the urethra and the tip of the penis

ANDROPAUSE

As men get older, hormone levels and sperm production decrease: this is called *andropause.* It is difficult to pinpoint with certainty when male andropause begins. Several physical and psychological changes occur, however, that are indications of hormonal variations. Contrary to menopause, andropause does not necessarily affect fertility in men.

4.5 BIRTH CONTROL

A greater understanding of the reproductive system and the role of hormones has enabled scientists to develop various methods of contraception. Figure 5.37 shows the processes that lead to the production of sperm and ovum and the methods that can be used to interrupt these processes at various points.

CYCLE ONE

└ Contraception
└ Methods of preventing the implantation of the zygote in the uterus

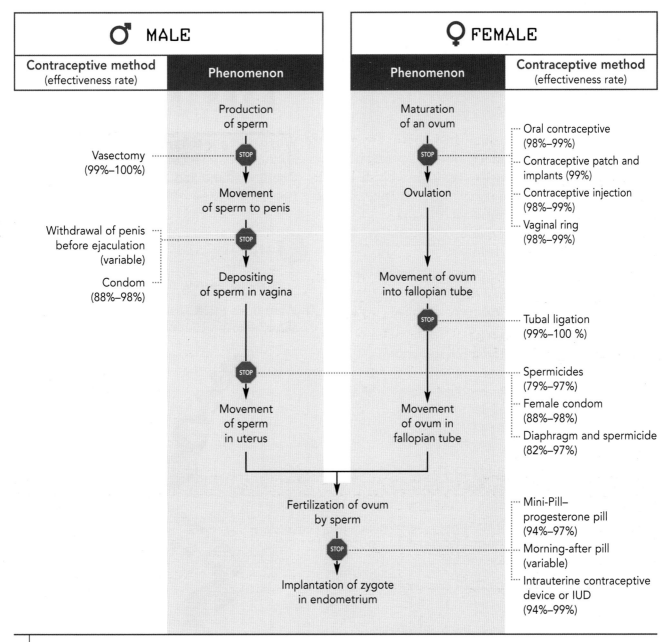

5.37 Processes that lead from the production of sperm and ovum to the implantation of the zygote in the uterus and the various contraceptive methods that can interrupt this process

Once a zygote is implanted in the uterus, the only way to interrupt the pregnancy is by abortion. Note that abortion is not a method of contraception.

ph2

ph3

ph4

ph5

ph6

ph7

ph8

THE PERPETUATION OF LIFE   151

CHECKUP

1 THE CELL (pp. 126–131)

1. Look at the following illustration.

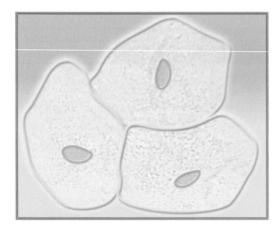

   a) What three cell components are visible under an optical microscope?

   b) What is the role of each of these components?

2. Cell organelles allow a cell to perform various functions.

   a) What organelles produce energy in the cell through cellular respiration?

   b) What organelles are responsible for digesting certain nutrients?

   c) What organelle transports material produced by the cell to the cell membrane?

   d) What organelle transports material produced by the cell from one place to another inside the cell?

3. Why do we say that DNA possesses a double-helix structure?

4. What is the difference between DNA, genes and genome?

5. What is the function of genes?

6. Complete the following DNA sequence.

7. Why are more children affected by the Andermann syndrome in the Charlevoix and Saguenay–Lac-St-Jean regions than elsewhere in Québec?

2 CELL DIVISION (pp. 131–135)

8. Give three reasons why cells divide.

9. What does the following illustration show? Explain your answer.

10. What are the two types of cell division?

11. Some human cells are said to be diploid while others are haploid.

   a) What distinguishes a diploid cell from a haploid cell?

   b) How many chromosomes does a human diploid cell contain?

   c) How many chromosomes does a human haploid cell contain?

12. During which phase of mitosis are chromosomes formed?

13. What kind of cells are formed during meiosis?

14. Look at the two following illustrations. They show a simplified version of the types of cell division.

a)

b)

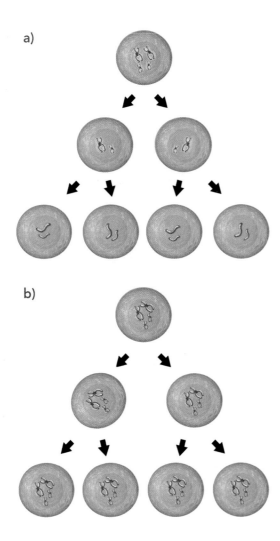

Name the type of division represented in a) and in b), then explain your answer.

15. Answer the following questions.

   a) What does a cell do when it is not dividing?

   b) Why do cells replicate their DNA?

   c) What is a gamete?

3 CELLULAR SPECIALIZATION
(pp. 136–139)

16. Look at the following illustration. It presents various tissue found in the arm.

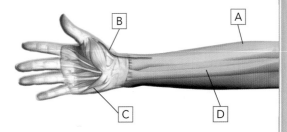

   a) Name each type of tissue indicated in the illustration.

   b) Indicate one function for each type of tissue.

17. What is a system?

18. Each of the following statements describes one of the body's vital functions. In each case, name the system that manages this function.

   a) Eating well is important to keep our bodies healthy.

   b) Nutrients carried by red blood cells provide energy for our cells.

   c) When we urinate, we eliminate certain waste products.

   d) Our sense of smell allows us to distinguish various odours.

4 THE REPRODUCTIVE SYSTEM
(pp. 140–151)

19. What is the name of the process that enables two haploid cells to produce a diploid cell?

20. Answer the following questions.
    a) What is a zygote?
    b) How is a zygote formed?

21. Name the chemical substances that are produced by the glands and secreted into the bloodstream.

22. What is the difference between adolescence and puberty?

23. Name three secondary sexual characteristics that appear in a boy and in a girl during puberty.

24. Name the two hormones responsible for the maturation of the ovarian follicle.

25. Name the two hormones responsible for the production of spermatozoa.

26. What distinguishes oogenesis, the ovarian cycle and the menstrual cycle?

27. The following illustration presents the various stages in the ovarian cycle. For each stage, indicate the hormone(s) involved and give a brief description of their action.

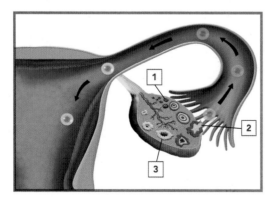

28. Julie, Sarah and Chloé have regular menstrual cycles: Julie has a 25-day cycle, Sarah a 30-day cycle and Chloé a 33-day cycle. If menstruation began for all three girls on the first day of the month, what will be the probable ovulation date for each one? You may use a calendar to help you.

29. Arrange the following events in chronological order:
    – maturation of the ovarian follicle
    – rupture of the follicle
    – meiosis I of the oocyte
    – menstruation
    – transformation of the ovarian follicle into the corpus luteum
    – meiosis II of the oocyte

30. Look at the following illustration. Each arrow represents an action by a hormone.

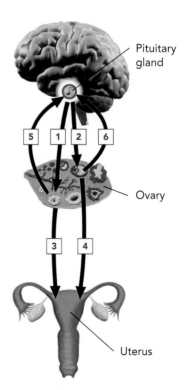

Arrow No.	Gland	Hormone(s)	Targeted organ	Action(s)
1				

a) Using a table like the one shown above, list the gland and hormone for each arrow involved as well as the organ targeted by the hormone.

b) In the last column of the table, arrange the following actions in the correct order:

- Inhibits further production of FSH and LH.

- Causes an increase in the level of progesterone, resulting in a thickening of the endometrium (secretory phase).

- Causes decreases in the level of progesterone, triggering menstruation.

- Causes a thickening of the endometrium (proliferation phase).

- Initiates ovulation.

- Transforms an ovarian follicle into a corpus luteum.

- Stimulates the maturation of an ovarian follicle.

- Stimulates the production of estrogens.

- Stimulates the production of FSH and LH in large quantities (hormonal surge).

- Stimulates the production of progesterone.

31. What changes occur in a woman's body during menopause?

32. What is spermatogenesis?

33. Name two differences between menopause and andropause.

34. Contraception makes it possible to stop the process that leads to the conception of a child. Name three contraceptive methods that prevent ovulation.

CONCEPT MAPS

HOW TO BUILD A CONCEPT MAP

Prepare your own summary of Chapter 5 by building a concept map using the following terms.

Map 1
- Cell
- Cell membrane
- Cytoplasm
- DNA
- Genes
- Nucleus

Map 2
- Diploid cells
- Cell division
- Chromosomes
- Haploid cells
- Meiosis
- Mitosis

Map 3
- Connective tissue
- Epithelial tissue
- Muscle tissue
- Nerve tissue
- Organs
- Specialized cells
- Systems
- Tissue

Map 4
- Fertilization
- Gametes
- Ovum
- Spermatozoan

Map 5
- Ejaculation
- Erection
- Female reproductive system
- Male reproductive system
- Menstrual cycle
- Oogenesis
- Ovarian cycle
- Reproductive system
- Spermatogenesis

CANCER, UNCONTROLLED CELL DIVISIONS

According to statistics published in 2006 by the Canadian Cancer Society, about 40 percent of Canadians will develop cancer in their lifetimes. Fortunately, the survival rate for several kinds of cancer has improved significantly, thanks to increasingly effective treatments and earlier detection methods.

Cancer develops when cells behave abnormally, dividing and multiplying out of control. Cancerous cells have lost their ability to specialize. They invade and destroy the healthy tissues around them by forming groups of cells called *tumours*. Sometimes cancerous cells break away from the tumour and spread throughout the body, forming what are called *metastases*.

There are several kinds of treatments for cancer. They can be used alone or in combination.

Surgery

DESCRIPTION

An operation that involves removing a tumour manually. This treatment is very common because it is usually effective, especially in the case of breast and prostate cancer.

Chemotherapy

DESCRIPTION

A treatment based on taking medication to kill the cancerous cells. Because this medication can also kill healthy cells, patients treated with chemotherapy often suffer side effects, such as hair loss.

Radiation therapy

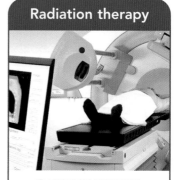

DESCRIPTION

A treatment consisting of killing cancerous cells by exposing a targeted area to very powerful radiation.

1. The earlier a cancer is detected, the better the chances that treatment will be effective. Therefore, screening tests are extremely important. Suggest some measures that could be helpful in the early detection of cancer.

2. The risk of developing cancer may be related to uncontrollable factors, such as heredity or the environment. Other factors, however, can be controlled. Suggest some healthy lifestyle habits that can help prevent cancer.

SCIENCE AT WORK

BARTHA MARIA KNOPPERS

Much hope is placed on genetic research. Unfortunately, researchers and institutions find themselves in fierce competition for ownership of the most recent discoveries in this expanding field. In the wake of the Human Genome Project (HUGO), which helped map the human genome, it is essential now more than ever before to protect the public's interest by studying the social, economic, environmental, ethical and legal issues surrounding genetic research. This is what Bartha Maria Knoppers has set out to do. Her passion has led her to take part in the HUGO project as well as other research projects. She was also involved in drafting the *Universal Declaration on the Human Genome and Human Rights,* under UNESCO.

NAME

Bartha Maria Knoppers

JOB

Canada Research Chair in Law and Medicine in the Faculty of Law at Université de Montréal

AREA WHERE SHE WORKS

Montréal

EDUCATION

Doctor of Laws

PROUDEST ACHIEVEMENT

Presided over the international ethics committee with regard to the mapping of the human genome (HUGO project)

5.38 A DNA sequence

5.39 OCCUPATIONS CONNECTED TO KNOPPERS' WORK

Occupation	Education	Length of study	Main tasks
Legal secretary	AVS* in secretarial studies (legal)	450 hours	● Provide secretarial services in a legal environment
Medical archivist	DCS in medical records management	3 years	● Code, store and inventory medical data for statistical and research purposes
Statistician	Bachelor's degree in statistics	3 years	● Collect, analyze and interpret data

* Attestation of Vocational Specialization

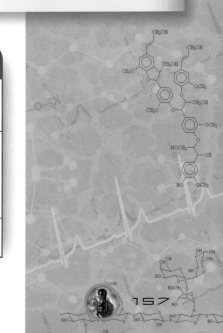

1997 — Creation of a plant that produces human hemoglobin

1970 — Development of the cardiac defibrillator

1958 — First successful organ transplant (kidney)

1952 — Invention of the respirator

1941 — Discovery of the Rhesus factor in blood

1928 — Discovery of vitamin C

1902 — First description of blood types

1887 — First cardiogram

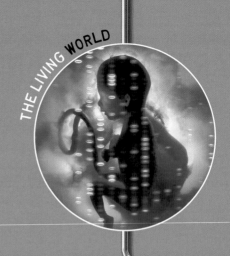

THE LIVING WORLD

CIRCA 1830 — Discovery of protein groups

1807 — Invention of the stethoscope

1661 — Discovery of blood capillaries

CIRCA 560 — First treatment of anemia using iron powder

CIRCA -270 — Discovery of the valves in the heart

CIRCA -400 — Discovery of sugar in the urine of diabetics

CIRCA -1600 — Publication of the first textbook on human anatomy

THE HUMAN ORGANISM

AND THE IMPORTANCE OF NUTRITION

T he human body is a marvellous machine composed of several interrelated systems. When we put food in our mouths, we trigger a series of mechanisms in our bodies similar to what happens when you press the "on" button on a computer. These mechanisms choose what our bodies require, transport the substance to where it is needed, and get rid of any surplus. And this happens without our knowledge as we go about our daily business. To find out what exactly happens when we ingest food, read this chapter, which explores the important mechanics of nutrition.

The first thing that usually comes to mind when we hear the word *nutrition* is food. Actually, nutrition is more than that; it covers all the processes involved in the absorption, use and elimination of substances needed to keep our bodies in good working order. The following is a brief description of the major systems that come into play in the process of nutrition:

CYCLE ONE

Inputs and outputs
(energy, nutrients, waste)

- The digestive system: The food we eat is absorbed and transformed into substances—**NUTRIENTS**—that our cells can use.

- The respiratory system: Our cells need oxygen in order to use the nutrients we eat. That's why, in addition to eating, we also need to breathe at least 12 to 15 times a minute.

- The cardiovascular system: The body contains five litres of blood, which circulate nutrients and oxygen to our cells.

- The urinary system: Once our cells have used what they need from the nutrients and oxygen, what's left is discarded in the blood. The urinary system filters the blood and eliminates the waste in liquid form.

This chapter is devoted to the study of these systems.

1 FOOD AND ITS USE BY THE BODY

LABS
41–49

Human beings must eat food and drink water regularly to stay alive. There are many kinds of food, including meat, fish, nuts, grain products, fruits and vegetables.

Food comes from the Old English word *foda*, meaning "to tend, to feed."

▶ FOOD is any substance that is ingested and sustains life.

6.1 Examples of food include fruit, vegetables, grain products, nuts and fish.

1.1 NUTRIENTS IN FOOD

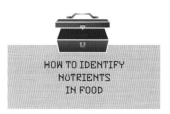

HOW TO IDENTIFY NUTRIENTS IN FOOD

Not all foods fill the same nutritional requirements. For example, eating an orange gives us sugar and vitamin C, while a steak gives us protein and iron. Each food can contain up to six types of nutrients.

> ▶ A NUTRIENT is a substance found in food that is used by the body to meet important needs.

There are six types of nutrients:

- proteins
- carbohydrates
- fats
- water
- vitamins
- minerals

Each type of nutrient plays a specific role in the human organism. Table 6.3 on page 162 describes the six types and provides examples of the foods that contain significant amounts of them.

THE ENERGY VALUE OF FOOD

Eating is one of life's greatest pleasures. But it is also a need. Our bodies must balance the energy they gain from food and drink with the energy they expend carrying out our daily activities.

Energy requirements

The amount of energy required for a human organism to undertake all its daily activities depends on a variety of factors, such as age, sex, weight, level of physical activity and overall state of health. Figure 6.2 shows the range of energy requirements of adolescents.

Although a *joule* (J) is the measurement unit for energy adopted by the International System of Units, *dietary calorie* (Cal) is the more common term. One dietary calorie equals about 4000 J or 4 kilojoules (kJ).

1861
1947

Frederick Gowland Hopkins

The importance of proteins, fats and carbohydrates in nutrition was already known by the end of the 19th century. In 1906, Frederick Hopkins, a British physician and biochemist, discovered that food contained other substances that were essential to good health: vitamins.

Adolescent girl	Adolescent boy
Between 1800 and 2400 Cal	Between 2200 and 3200 Cal
Between 7200 and 9600 kJ	Between 8800 and 12 800 kJ

6.2 The daily energy requirements for an adolescent vary from one individual to another and are dependent on such factors as sex and level of physical activity.

Nutrient	Description	Function
Proteins	Proteins are large molecules composed of chains of amino acids. Amino acids	• Build and repair cells and tissues. • Provide energy.
Carbohydrates	Carbohydrates are composed of a single sugar molecule or a chain of sugar molecules. Sugars Polysaccharides/ complex sugars (e.g. starch) Disaccharides/ double sugars (e.g. lactose) Monosaccharides/ single sugars (e.g. glucose)	• Are the body's main source of energy. Nutrients with names ending in -ose are usually carbohydrates.
Fats	Fats, also called lipids, are generally composed of fatty acids and a glycerol. Cholesterol is a fat. Fatty acids Glycerol Limit your intake of saturated fatty acids and trans fatty acids.	• Store and provide energy. • Are the building blocks of hormones and cell membranes. • Protect organs and insulate the body from the cold.
Water	Water is a simple molecule. Its chemical formula is H_2O. Water makes up about 70% of the weight of the human body.	• Transports nutrients and waste products. • Regulates body temperature. • Is essential in numerous chemical reactions in the body.
Vitamins	Vitamins are substances that the human body requires in small amounts.	Each type of vitamin (e.g. A, B1, B2, C, D, E) has a different function in the body, including: • contributing to chemical reactions • helping in energy production • helping fight off infections by strengthening the body • repairing damaged tissue
Minerals	Minerals are substances of mineral origin that make up about 4% of the weight of the human body. A certain amount must be ingested daily.	Each group of minerals (e.g. calcium, phosphorous, potassium) plays a different role in the body, includin • building tissue (e.g. bones and teeth) • maintaining fluid balance in the body • helping muscles contract • transporting oxygen in the blood

- Dairy products (e.g. milk, cheese), meat, fish, eggs, nuts, legumes, tofu

- Monosaccharides and disaccharides: fruits and fruit juice, pastries, sweets, carbonated drinks, granulated sugar, milk
- Polysaccharides (also called starch): breads, cereals, pasta, potatoes, rice, legumes, cassava (tapioca)

- Dairy products (except skimmed), vegetable oils, butter, fatty meats and fish, croissants, French fries, eggs, nuts

Choose unsaturated over saturated fats.

- Fruits and fruit juice, vegetables and vegetable juice, soups, milk, energy drinks

- Fruits, vegetables, dairy products, whole grains, eggs, liver

- Dairy products, legumes, seafood and fish, fruits, vegetables

Why do we expend energy during our daily activities? What is it used for? We use energy to maintain the temperature of our bodies at 37°C and to sustain its respiratory rhythm and heart rate. Our energy helps us carry out various activities such as running, talking or even just concentrating. Table 6.4 shows how much energy we use for certain activities.

6.4 APPROXIMATE ENERGY OUTPUT FOR VARIOUS ACTIVITIES

Activity (one hour)	Energy output	
	kJ	Cal
Sleeping or resting	240	60
Sitting (while watching TV, playing computer games, reading)	360	90
Standing (while getting dressed, washing dishes)	480	120
Weightlifting, gardening, walking	680	170
Sports (skiing, playing soccer, cycling)	Over 1200	Over 300

6.5 Soccer calls for a lot of energy.

Energy value

Because we constantly use energy, we need to replace it regularly. We get the energy we need from several sources.

- Carbohydrates and fats are the body's major sources of energy.
- Proteins, which are mostly used to build and repair body tissue, may sometimes be used as energy sources, if there aren't enough carbohydrates and fats to meet our energy needs, or if there is too much protein in the body.
- Water, vitamins and minerals are not sources of energy.

Table 6.6 indicates the amount of energy contained in one gram of nutrient.

OUR GREEDY BRAINS

The human brain alone consumes nearly one quarter of the energy we get from carbohydrates, even though it only represents two to three percent of our body weight. This explains why carbohydrate deficiency can cause fatigue and drowsiness, making concentration a challenge.

6.6 AVERAGE ENERGY CONTENT IN NUTRIENTS

Nutrient	Energy content	
	kJ/g	Cal/g
Carbohydrates	17	4
Fats	37	9
Proteins	17	4
Water	Nil	Nil
Vitamins	Nil	Nil
Minerals	Nil	Nil

We often hear about dietary fibre and how important it is. Dietary fibre comes from the carbohydrates in the vegetables we eat. Since we cannot digest dietary fibre, it has no energy value. Nevertheless, dietary fibre plays an essential role in digestion: it helps keep the intestines healthy by stimulating muscular contractions that ease food through the intestines.

Nutrition facts

One way of finding out the energy value of foods is to read the Nutrition Facts label on the package. Since December 12, 2005, nutrition tables have been mandatory on most prepackaged foods in Canada. As Figure 6.7 shows, the Nutrition Facts table contains the following information for a given serving size:

- amount of energy in calories (or in kJ)
- nutrient content (e.g. fat, carbohydrates)
- the percentage of the Recommended Daily Intake (RDI) for each nutrient (in the "% Daily Value" column)

If we read the label on the right, we can see that:

- One serving of two cookies provides 150 calories.
- Two cookies contain 21 g of carbohydrates (each cookie contains 10.5 g of carbohydrates).
- The 21 g of carbohydrates correspond to 7 percent of the total amount of carbohydrates we should eat in one day.
- Of these carbohydrates, 8 g come from simple and double sugars (the term *sugars* on the Nutrition Facts label applies to both types of carbohydrates).

THE FOOD GROUPS

As indicated in *Canada's Food Guide,* most of the food we eat can be broken down into four food groups. To meet our daily nutritional requirements, it is recommended that we eat a variety of foods from the four groups every day.

| Vegetables and fruits | Grain products | Milk and alternatives | Meat and alternatives |

6.7 The Nutrition Facts label on food packaging provides information on nutrient content.

6.8 The four food groups

Table 6.9 includes several recommendations (including the number of servings per day) from *Canada's Food Guide*.

6.9 RECOMMENDATIONS FROM *CANADA'S FOOD GUIDE* FOR 14- TO 18-YEAR-OLDS

Food groups	Number of servings per day		Servings	Other recommendations
	Females	Males		
Vegetables and fruits	7	8	• 1 orange • 250 mL lettuce • 125 mL juice • 125 mL broccoli	• Eat at least one green and one orange vegetable each day. • Choose vegetables with little or no fat, sugar or salt. • Eat vegetables and fruits more often than juice.
Grain products	6	7	• 1 slice of bread • 125 mL rice • 30 g cold cereal	• Make at least half of your grain products whole grain each day. • Choose grain products that are low in fat, sugar or salt.
Milk and alternatives (e.g. yogurt, cheese, fortified soy beverages)	3-4	3-4	• 250 mL milk • 175 g yogurt • 50 g cheese	• Drink skim, 1% or 2% milk each day. • Select low-fat milk alternatives.
Meat and alternatives (e.g. eggs, beans, lentils, tofu)	2	3	• 75 g fish, lean meat or cooked poultry • 175 mL cooked legumes • 2 eggs • 60 mL shelled nuts	• Have meat alternatives such as legumes and tofu often. • Eat at least two servings of fish each week. • Select lean meat and alternatives prepared with little or no added fat or salt.

Food fit for an athlete

It's hard not to notice how incredibly fit our Olympic athletes are. When we look at their impressive physiques we can't help but wonder what they could be eating to reach such record-breaking performances.

Contrary to common belief, the eating habits of a high-performance athlete are not much different from those of any other healthy person. Athletes are encouraged to eat foods that are rich in complex carbohydrates (e.g. brown rice, whole-wheat pasta, multigrain bread), and to avoid foods that are high in saturated fats (e.g. fatty meats, cheese) and trans fats (hydrogenated oils and products made from hydrogenated oil).

The main difference between an athlete and the average person is quantity. During intense training sessions and competitions, athletes can sometimes consume up to 8000 calories per day!

Adapted from Jacinthe Côté, "Manger pour atteindre des sommets," *La Presse*, February 19, 2006, *Actuel*, p. 4. [*Translation*]

When Olympic athletes compete, they need up to 8000 calories (32 000 kJ) a day.

1.2 THE DIGESTIVE SYSTEM

LABS
50–52

The cells of the human organism cannot use most food directly for energy. Food must be transformed in the digestive system before the organism can put it to use.

The digestive system's role is to break down ingested food into molecules that are small enough to be absorbed by the body. It also eliminates undigested food from the body in the form of solid waste.

ANATOMY OF THE DIGESTIVE SYSTEM

The digestive system can be divided into two parts:

- the digestive tract
- the digestive glands

The digestive glands produce the chemical secretions that are needed to digest food as it travels along the digestive tract.

The digestive tract is made up of the following components:

- the mouth
- the pharynx
- the esophagus
- the stomach
- the small intestine
- the large intestine (which terminates in the rectum and anus)

Glands in the digestive system include:

- the salivary glands
- the gastric glands (located in the stomach lining)
- the liver (the gallbladder stores fluids from the liver until they are released into the digestive tract)
- the pancreas
- the intestinal glands (located in the lining of the small intestine)

Figure 6.10 illustrates the different components of the digestive system.

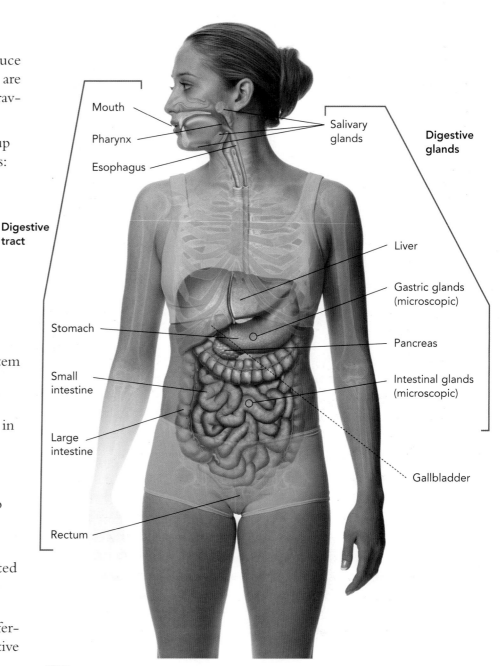

6.10 The digestive system consists of the digestive tract and the digestive glands.

THE IMPORTANCE OF NUTRITION 167

The digestion of food is a complicated process that involves the following functions:

- ingestion and propulsion of food along the digestive tract
- digestion of food
- absorption of nutrients
- elimination of fecal matter

These activities are covered in the following sections.

INGESTION AND PROPULSION OF FOOD ALONG THE DIGESTIVE TRACT

Ingestion is the act of taking substances (e.g. food, drinks, medication) into the body through the mouth. Two mechanisms then move the substances along the digestive tract:

- deglutition, more commonly known as *swallowing* (Figure 6.11)
- peristalsis, muscular contractions of the esophagus, stomach, small intestine and large intestine that propel substances through the digestive tract (Figure 6.12)

Peristalsis comes from the Greek word *peristellein*, meaning "to wrap around, to compress."

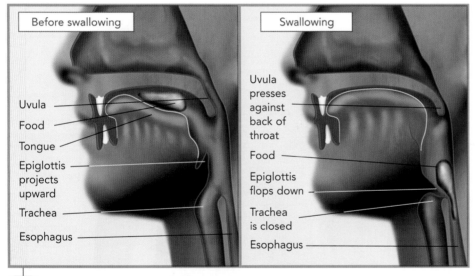

Before swallowing

Uvula
Food
Tongue
Epiglottis projects upward
Trachea
Esophagus

Swallowing

Uvula presses against back of throat
Food
Epiglottis flops down
Trachea is closed
Esophagus

6.11 When we swallow, the epiglottis closes the trachea (a tube that allows air to reach the lungs), and the uvula closes the nasal cavity. Food can thus travel to the esophagus without getting into the respiratory tract.

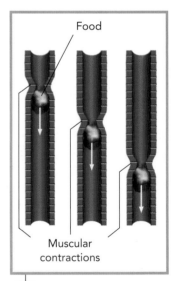

Food

Muscular contractions

6.12 Peristalsis propels food along the digestive tract.

DIGESTION

As food travels along the digestive tract, it is broken down so that it can be absorbed by the body. This is known as *digestion*.

> ◉ DIGESTION involves the transformation of food into nutrients that can be used by the body.

Food undergoes two types of transformation in the digestive process: mechanical and chemical.

Mechanical transformation

Mechanical transformation consists of mixing and breaking down food into smaller fragments without changing its nature. It prepares food for the next step: chemical transformation.

> ⬤ MECHANICAL TRANSFORMATION consists of physically breaking down food into smaller substances in preparation for subsequent chemical transformation.

There are two processes involved in the mechanical transformation of food: chewing and churning.

- Chewing is the process of crushing and grinding food, using teeth and the muscles of the mouth.
- Churning is produced by muscle contractions, which mix food with secretions from the digestive glands. It takes place primarily in the stomach and the small intestine (Figure 6.14).

6.13 Chewing makes it possible to cut, crush and grind food, for easier digestion.

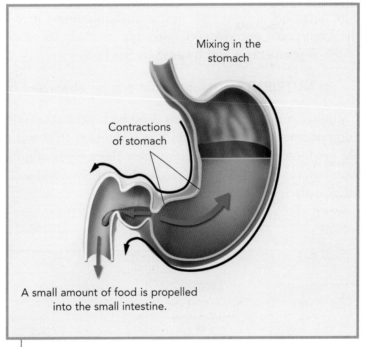

Mixing in the stomach

Contractions of stomach

A small amount of food is propelled into the small intestine.

6.14 Churning in the stomach helps mix food with gastric secretions.

Chemical transformation

Chemical transformations occur with the help of substances secreted by the digestive glands as food passes into the digestive tract. The secretions contain chemicals that break down complex molecules into simple ones that can be absorbed by the body.

▶ CHEMICAL TRANSFORMATION in the digestive tract breaks down the complex molecules of food into simpler molecules. These changes occur with the help of secretions from the digestive glands.

Table 6.15 lists the secretions produced by various digestive glands, their location in the digestive tract, and their targets.

6.15 DIGESTIVE GLANDS AND SECRETIONS

Digestive glands	Secretions	Location	Targets
Salivary glands	Saliva	Mouth	Starch (complex carbohydrate)
Gastric glands	Gastric juice	Stomach	Proteins
Intestinal glands	Intestinal juice	Small intestine	Proteins, carbohydrates, fats
Pancreas	Pancreatic juice	Small intestine	Proteins, carbohydrates, fats
Liver	Bile	Small intestine	Fats

The digestion of food ends in the small intestine. Once broken down into their molecular components, nutrients are ready to pass through the lining of the digestive tract and be used by the body.

▶ NUTRIENTS are foods that can be absorbed by the body.

Carbohydrates, fats and proteins must be broken down into their molecular components in order to be absorbed. Figure 6.16 shows the molecules that are produced by the digestion of these three types of nutrients. Meanwhile, vitamins, minerals and water can be directly absorbed and do not need to be chemically transformed first.

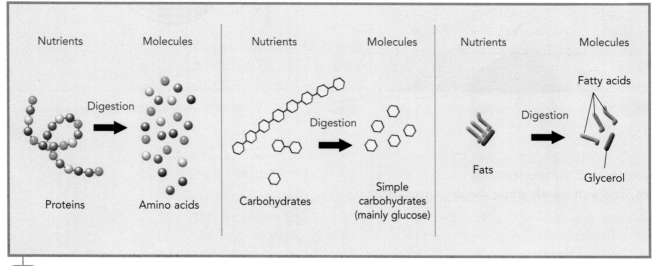

6.16 The digestion of proteins, carbohydrates and fats produces different kinds of molecules.

THE ABSORPTION OF NUTRIENTS

The process that moves nutrients through the lining of the digestive tract of the human organism into the blood or lymph is known as *absorption*.

> ⟩ **ABSORPTION** is the passage of nutrients from the digestive tract into the blood or lymph.

Most food absorption occurs in the small intestine, which has many folds called **VILLI**. These folds increase the surface area available for the absorption of nutrients. Each villus houses blood and lymph vessels through which nutrients flow into the body.

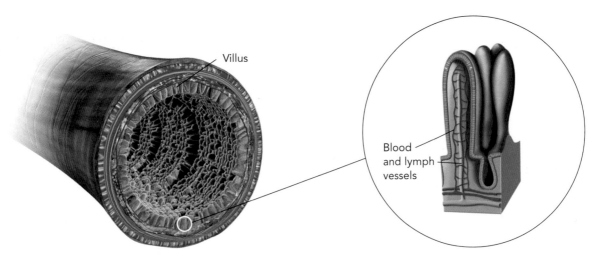

Villus

Blood and lymph vessels

6.17 The numerous folds in the small intestine are called *villi*. Nutrients are absorbed through the villi into the body.

THE ELIMINATION OF FECAL MATTER

As most absorption takes place in the small intestine, the digestive residue that enters the large intestine contains very little nutrient matter. It arrives in the large intestine in liquid form. Here, the water in the residue is gradually absorbed. By the time the residue has reached the rectum at the end of the large intestine, there is very little water left, which is why our feces are typically solid. From the rectum, the feces are expelled through the anus.

OVERVIEW

Each component of the digestive system plays a role in processing food. Figure 6.18 on the next page shows the main stages of the transformation of food as it travels along the digestive tract.

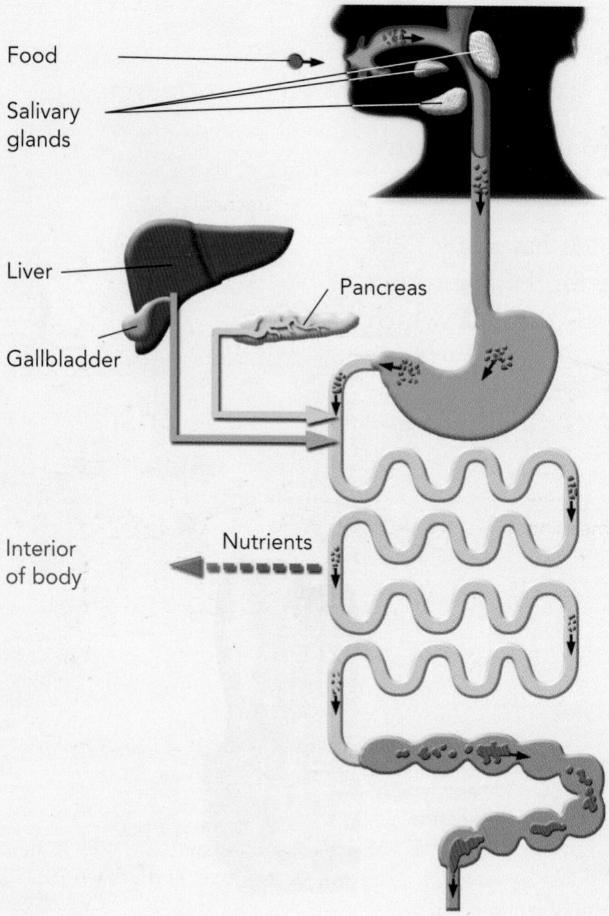

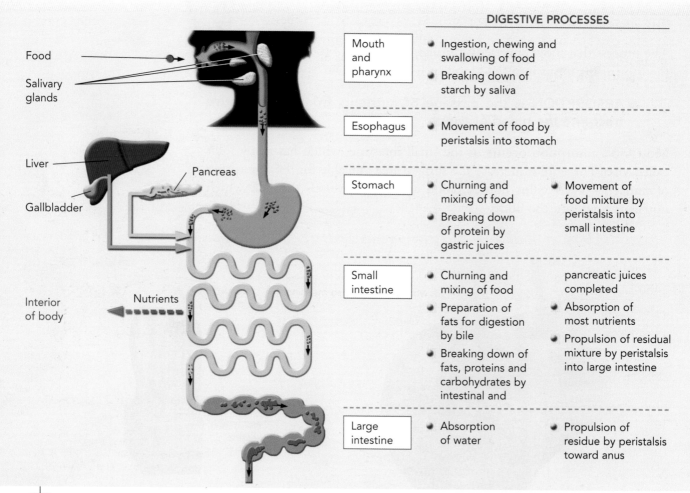

DIGESTIVE PROCESSES	
Mouth and pharynx	• Ingestion, chewing and swallowing of food • Breaking down of starch by saliva
Esophagus	• Movement of food by peristalsis into stomach
Stomach	• Churning and mixing of food • Breaking down of protein by gastric juices • Movement of food mixture by peristalsis into small intestine
Small intestine	• Churning and mixing of food • Preparation of fats for digestion by bile • Breaking down of fats, proteins and carbohydrates by intestinal and pancreatic juices completed • Absorption of most nutrients • Propulsion of residual mixture by peristalsis into large intestine
Large intestine	• Absorption of water • Propulsion of residue by peristalsis toward anus

6.18 Diagram of the digestive system and digestive processes

2 RESPIRATION

LABS 53–55

Human organisms not only need to eat, they also need to breathe. One of the components of air, dioxygen (O_2), or what we usually call *oxygen*, is indispensable for us to live. Without oxygen, our cells would be unable to efficiently extract the energy they need from nutrients. This reaction between the nutrients and oxygen is called **CELLULAR RESPIRATION.** It takes place at the cellular level, inside the cells' mitochondria. The equation for cellular respiration is shown below.

Respiration comes from the Latin word *respirare*, meaning "to come back to life."

CYCLE ONE
- Cellular respiration
- Air (composition)

Nutrients + oxygen ⟶ energy + carbon dioxide + water

6.19 The equation for cellular respiration

The carbon dioxide (CO_2) that is formed during cellular respiration is a waste product. It must be eliminated from the body; this is what we do when we exhale.

Human organisms take a breath an average of 12 to 15 times a minute. Breathing allows oxygen to enter the body and carbon dioxide to leave. The respiratory system is responsible for the exchange of these two gases between the body and the external world.

2.1 THE RESPIRATORY SYSTEM

The respiratory system can be divided into two parts:

- the respiratory tract
- the lungs

The respiratory tract is composed of:

- the nasal passages
- the pharynx
- the larynx
- the trachea
- the bronchi (that branch out into bronchioles)

> Pharynx comes from the Greek word pharuggos, meaning "throat."

> Larynx comes from the Greek word laruggos, also meaning "throat."

It is through the bronchi that air exits the respiratory tract and enters the lungs.

Table 6.22 on the next page outlines the functions of each structure in the respiratory system.

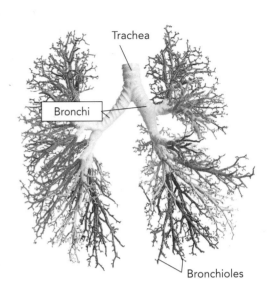

6.20 The trachea is divided into bronchi, then into many bronchioles.

6.21 The respiratory system is made up of the respiratory tract and the lungs.

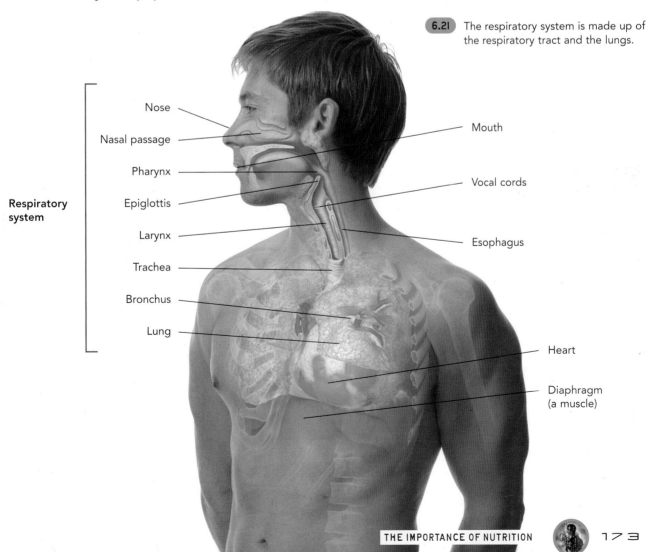

Structure	Description	Function
Nasal passages	Passages that open to the outside through the nostrils and end inside at the pharynx	• Filter air with hairs that coat lining of cavities. • Warm and moisten air with mucus, a viscous substance secreted by glands in nose lining.
Pharynx (throat)	Section that serves as a common passageway between the respiratory and digestive tracts	• Carries air toward trachea and food toward esophagus. When swallowing, epiglottis seals trachea (Fig. 6.11, p. 168).
Larynx	Upper section of the trachea composed of cartilage and housing the vocal cords	• Carries air. • Produces sounds (voice).
Trachea	Section measuring on average 11 cm in length, composed of cartilaginous rings to hold it open and located in front of the esophagus	• Further filters and purifies with sweeping motion of hair-like cilia on trachea walls toward pharynx. • Warms and moistens air with mucus secreted by glands in lining of trachea.
Bronchi	Tubes arising from a division of the trachea, composed of cartilaginous rings to hold them open, and branching into bronchioles once inside the lungs	• Carry air into lungs.
Lungs	Spongy, elastic organs on each side of the heart, enclosed in the rib cage and composed of millions of air sacs, called *alveoli*	• Ensure gas exchange between the body and the external world (Section 2.2).

RESPIRATION

The goal of respiration is to extract oxygen from the air and expel carbon dioxide. To understand how this mechanism works, you will need to apply the concepts that were presented in Chapter 3:

• Air is a mix of gases. Like all gases, it fills its container, which in this case is the lungs. Air is also a compressible fluid, and as such, its volume can increase or decrease.

• Variations in the volume of a compressible fluid produce changes in pressure. So if the volume of the lungs increases, the pressure decreases, and vice versa.

• Fluids always flow from an area of higher pressure to one of lower pressure. If the pressure is higher inside the lungs than it is outside, air exits the lungs. If the pressure is higher outside the lungs than it is inside, air enters the lungs.

Table 6.23 reviews the mechanics of respiration. The structures that play an important part in this process are:

• the intercostal muscles, situated between the ribs

• the diaphragm, a muscle that separates the rib cage from the abdomen

> *Diaphragm* comes from the Greek word *diaphragma*, meaning "separation, partition."

Inhalation	Exhalation

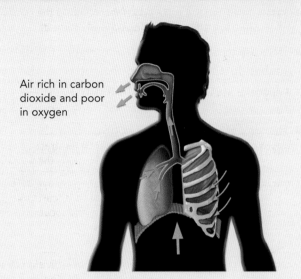

Inhalation — Air rich in oxygen and poor in carbon dioxide. Intercostal muscles. Diaphragm.

- Intercostal muscles and diaphragm contract.
- Ribs rise and diaphragm descends, which increases the size of the rib cage.
- Lung volume increases.
- Air pressure inside the lungs decreases. It becomes lower than the outside air pressure.
- Oxygen-rich air from outside flows into the lungs until the pressure inside and outside the lungs is equal.

Exhalation — Air rich in carbon dioxide and poor in oxygen.

- Intercostal muscles and diaphragm relax.
- Ribs descend and diaphragm rises, which decreases the size of the rib cage.
- Lung volume decreases.
- Air pressure inside the lungs increases. It becomes greater than the outside air pressure.
- Carbon dioxide-rich air inside the lungs flows outside until the pressure inside and outside the lungs is equal.

2.2 GAS EXCHANGE WITHIN THE LUNGS

In order for cellular respiration to occur, the oxygen that has been absorbed by the lungs must reach all the cells of our body. The circulation of the blood ensures that this distribution happens. Carbon dioxide, a waste product of cellular respiration that is also carried by the blood, must be expelled from the body. This gas exchange takes place in the alveoli of the lungs.

CYCLE ONE

└ Diffusion

Alveoli comes from the Latin word *alveolus,* meaning "little cavity."

Alveoli are miniature cavities filled with air that make up the bulk of the lungs. Each of the millions of alveoli is surrounded by tiny blood vessels, called *capillaries*. Gas exchange occurs by **DIFFUSION** between the air in the pulmonary alveoli and the blood circulating in the capillaries that surround them.

Figure 6.24, on the next page shows the alveoli and gas exchange within the lungs.

When the blood reaches the pulmonary alveoli, it is poor in oxygen and rich in carbon dioxide, while the air in the alveoli is rich in oxygen and poor in carbon dioxide. Gas exchange takes place as follows:

- Because the concentration of oxygen (O_2) is higher in the alveolar air than it is in the capillary blood, it diffuses from the alveoli to the blood.

- Because the concentration of carbon dioxide (CO_2) is higher in the capillary blood than in the alveolar air, it diffuses from the blood to the alveoli.

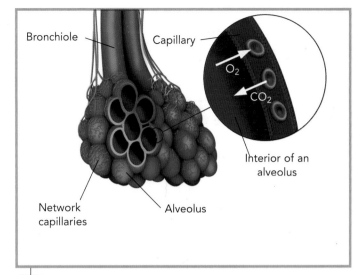

6.24 The gas exchange between the outside air and the blood occurs in the alveoli.

Tobacco could kill one billion people in the 21st century

When you smoke a cigarette, instead of breathing in fresh oxygen-rich air, you inhale smoke, which enters your respiratory tract and lung alveoli. Eventually carcinogenic substances and irritants contained in this smoke cause permanent damage to your health.

If current trends continue, smoking is likely to kill a billion people this century—10 times the toll it took in the 20th century, according to two studies published for the International Union Against Cancer Conference.

Currently, an estimated 1.25 billion men and women smoke. More than half of them will likely die of lung cancer (responsible for one in five cancer-related deaths) or cardiovascular and pulmonary diseases.

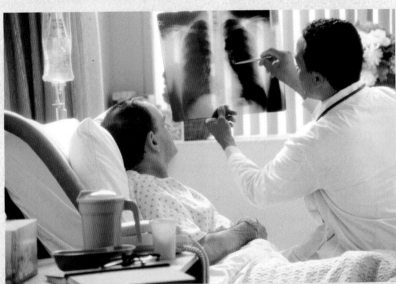

Smoking can cause many diseases, including lung cancer.

In China alone, where 300 million people now smoke, lung cancer could kill one million smokers every year.

Both studies will serve as references for doctors, political leaders, academics and lawyers working in public health.

Adapted from *Associated Press*, "Le tabac ferait un milliard de morts au cours du XXIe siècle," *Le Droit*, July 12, 2006, p. 21. *[Translation]*

3 BLOOD AND LYMPH
CIRCULATION

As we have learned, nutrients enter the bloodstream once they are absorbed by the body from the digestive tract, while oxygen enters the bloodstream from the pulmonary alveoli. Together, nutrients and oxygen travel throughout the body to nourish the cells. In the same way, waste products produced by the cells circulate in the bloodstream to be eliminated or used elsewhere in the body.

The blood and its circulation play vital roles in our bodies. This section takes a look at their functions, as well as the role of the lymph, a fluid derived from blood.

3.1 BLOOD CONSTITUENTS

Blood is the only fluid tissue in the body. It is red and viscous. A man's body may contain five to six litres of blood and a woman's four to five litres.

Although it seems homogeneous, blood is made up of cells suspended in liquid. Blood cells are called *formed elements*. The liquid that makes up the rest of the blood is called *plasma*. Table 6.27 on the next page describes the liquid and formed elements of blood.

When a blood sample is taken, the formed elements and plasma can be separated by **CENTRIFUGATION.** The formed elements, which account for about 45 percent of blood volume, collect at the bottom of the test tube and form a red deposit. The plasma, which is more transparent and golden in colour, rises to the top. Figure 6.26 shows what happens when blood undergoes centrifugation.

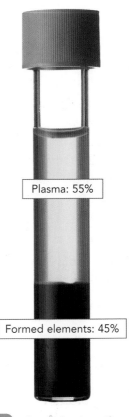

Plasma: 55%

Formed elements: 45%

6.26 Blood after centrifugation. The formed elements make up 45% of blood volume and the plasma makes up 55%.

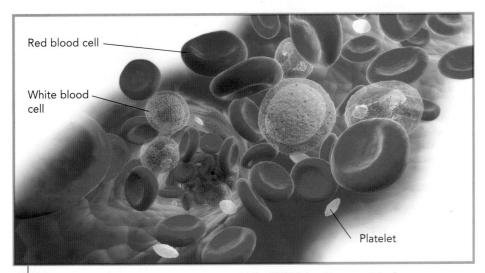

Red blood cell

White blood cell

Platelet

6.25 The formed elements of blood include red blood cells, white blood cells and platelets.

Liquid element	Description	Functions
Plasma	Yellowish liquid composed of 90% water, in which various substances are dissolved such as nutrients, antibodies, hormones and waste from cellular activity	• Transports nutrients to cells. • Transports waste products from cellular activity to excretory organs. • Transports hormones, antibodies, proteins and several other substances.

Formed elements	Number per mL of blood	Description	Functions
Red blood cells	4–6 billion	Red-coloured cells, in the form of biconcave disks, that have no nucleus and few organelles	• Transport oxygen with the help of a protein called *hemoglobin*, found in red blood cells. • Transport CO_2.
White blood cells	4–11 million	Transparent cells	• Defend against disease.
Platelets	150–400 million	Irregular fragments stemming from large cells in the bone marrow	• Help in blood-clotting process.

 Anemia is a disease that results in a lack of oxygen to the blood. This disease can have three causes: an inadequate number of red blood cells, an inadequate amount of hemoglobin in the red blood cells or abnormally formed hemoglobin.

3.2 BLOOD TYPES AND BLOOD TRANSFUSIONS

Most of us have heard of the four blood types, A, B, AB and O. But what distinguishes one type of blood from another type? Blood types are determined by the presence or absence of one of the following substances on the membrane of red blood cells:

• substance A

• substance B

In addition to substances A and B, red blood cells can carry another substance on their membrane:

• the Rhesus factor, commonly known as the *Rh factor*

The Rh factor makes it possible to further subdivide the four blood types A, B, AB and O into Rh positive and Rh negative.

Let's look at an example: If a person's red blood cells carry both substance A and the Rh factor, the blood type for that person will be A⁺. If the red blood cells carry only substance A, the type will be A⁻. Table 6.29 shows all the possible blood type variations based on the presence or absence of substance A, substance B and the Rh factor.

6.28 The Rhesus factor bears its name because it was first discovered on the red blood cells of a rhesus monkey, also known as *a macaque*.

	Blood type	A⁺	A⁻	B⁺	B⁻	AB⁺	AB⁻	O⁺	O⁻
Substance(s) present on the membranes of red blood cells	Substance A	💧	💧			💧	💧		None of the three substances is present.
	Substance B			💧	💧	💧	💧		
	Rh factor	💧		💧		💧		💧	
	Illustration of red blood cells	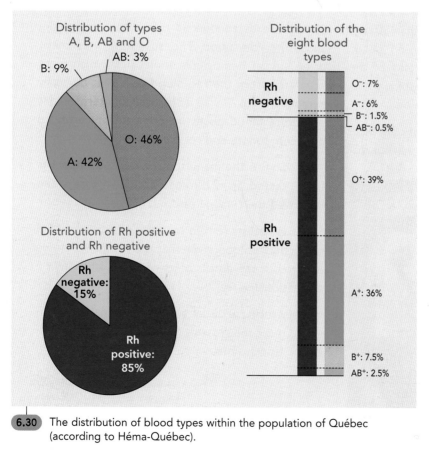							

Figure 6.30 illustrates the distribution of blood types within the population of Québec.

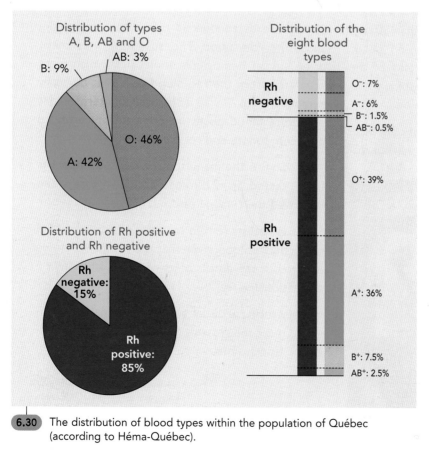

Distribution of types A, B, AB and O
- AB: 3%
- B: 9%
- O: 46%
- A: 42%

Distribution of Rh positive and Rh negative
- Rh negative: 15%
- Rh positive: 85%

Distribution of the eight blood types
Rh negative
- O⁻: 7%
- A⁻: 6%
- B⁻: 1.5%
- AB⁻: 0.5%

Rh positive
- O⁺: 39%
- A⁺: 36%
- B⁺: 7.5%
- AB⁺: 2.5%

6.30   The distribution of blood types within the population of Québec (according to Héma-Québec).

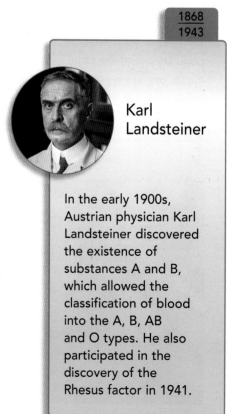

1868
1943

Karl Landsteiner

In the early 1900s, Austrian physician Karl Landsteiner discovered the existence of substances A and B, which allowed the classification of blood into the A, B, AB and O types. He also participated in the discovery of the Rhesus factor in 1941.

BLOOD TRANSFUSIONS

People with certain blood diseases must receive regular blood transfusions to stay alive. Transfusions may also be necessary in other cases, especially when someone has lost a lot of blood due to an injury or during surgery.

▶ A BLOOD TRANSFUSION entails the injection of blood into a person.

A blood transfusion requires a donor and a recipient. The donor and recipient may be the same person. This happens when people bank their own blood in preparation for surgery.

▶ A blood DONOR is a person who gives blood for the purpose of a transfusion.

▶ A blood RECIPIENT is a person who receives blood from a transfusion.

Before blood types were discovered in 1902, many transfusions resulted in recipients dying. Now we are well aware of the rules for blood transfusions.

A synthetic substitute for blood

Each year, there is a shortfall of more than 50 million litres of blood to meet transfusion needs worldwide. And what is more, the ageing of the population and the large increase in hospital treatments predict a growing demand for blood.

As a result, many researchers are at work developing artificial blood. One private American laborato-

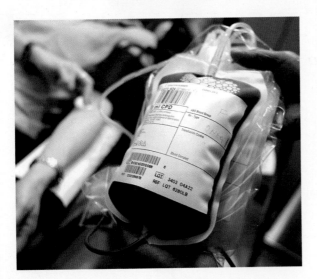

ry has already announced that it has perfected a substitute for blood. The substitute was made using human hemoglobin molecules, which were separated from the red blood cells that normally surround them. Unlike its natural counterpart, this substitute blood poses no compatibility problem between donors and recipients.

According to the manufacturer, the substitute has been tested in 720 road-accident cases and improved the survival rate.

Some specialists remain sceptical of the benefits of this artificial blood, given that the company refuses to give out the details of its research, labelling it a professional secret.

Manufacturing artificial blood could enable suppliers to meet the growing demand for blood intended for transfusions.

Adapted from Émilie Tran Phong,
"Sang pour sang artificiel," *L'Express*,
September 14, 2006. *[Translation]*

The primary rule governing blood transfusions is as follows:

- The donor's red blood cell membranes must not carry substances that differ from those on the red blood cell membranes of the recipient.

For example, a person whose blood type is B^+, that is, whose red blood cell membranes carry substance B and the Rh factor:

- **CAN** receive blood from a B^+, B^-, O^+ or O^- blood donor, because the donor's red blood cell membranes do not carry any other substances than substance B and the Rh factor.
- **CANNOT** receive blood from an A^+, A^-, AB^+ or AB^- blood donor, because the donor's red blood cell membranes carry substance A, a substance which is not found on the red blood cell membranes of the recipient.

Blood compatibility means that a person can receive blood from another person. By applying the blood-transfusion rules for all the blood types, it is possible to know all the possibilities of blood compatibility. Table 6.31 lists these possibilities.

> ▶ BLOOD COMPATIBILITY means that one person can receive blood from another person.

6.31 BLOOD COMPATIBILITY

Recipient \ Donor	O^-	O^+	B^-	B^+	A^-	A^+	AB^-	AB^+
AB^+	◊	◊	◊	◊	◊	◊	◊	◊
AB^-	◊		◊		◊		◊	
A^+	◊	◊			◊	◊		
A^-	◊				◊			
B^+	◊	◊	◊	◊				
B^-	◊		◊					
O^+	◊	◊						
O^-	◊							

◊ = Transfusion is possible

This blood-compatibility table allows us to draw the following conclusions:

- Transfusions are possible when both donor and recipient have the same blood type.
- People with Type O^- blood can donate blood to anybody (regardless of blood type). Thus individuals with O^- blood are called universal donors.
- People with Type AB^+ blood can receive blood from anybody (regardless of blood type). Thus individuals with AB^+ are called universal recipients.

Substances A and B, which are found on the membranes of the red blood cells, are called *agglutinogens.* When blood is transfused between incompatible blood types, the recipient receives red blood cells with foreign agglutinogens. These agglutinogens are seen as invaders and are recognized by antibodies, called *agglutinins,* in the recipient's plasma. These antibodies attach to foreign red blood cells causing them to clump. This phenomenon, known as *agglutination,* leads to the clogging of blood vessels and can kill the recipient.

3.3 THE CARDIOVASCULAR SYSTEM

We now know that the bloodstream carries substances throughout the human body. The transportation network used by the blood is called the cardiovascular system. This system includes the blood; the blood vessels, which carry the blood; and the heart, which pumps the blood, sending it throughout the body.

> *Cardiovascular* comes from the Greek word *kardia,* meaning "heart," and the Latin word *vasculum,* meaning "little vase, vessel."

By convention, diagrams of the cardiovascular system (as in Figure 6.32) depict:

- vessels carrying oxygen-rich blood in red
- vessels carrying carbon dioxide-rich blood in blue

6.32 The cardiovascular system includes the blood, the blood vessels and the heart.

BLOOD VESSELS

The body's blood vessels form a closed circuit in which blood circulates. This transportation network is enormous. If you placed all of an adult's blood vessels together end to end, they would measure about 100 000 km in total.

Blood vessels are divided into three categories:

- arteries
- capillaries
- veins

Vessels containing oxygen-rich blood (O$_2$)

Vessels containing carbon dioxide-rich blood (CO$_2$)

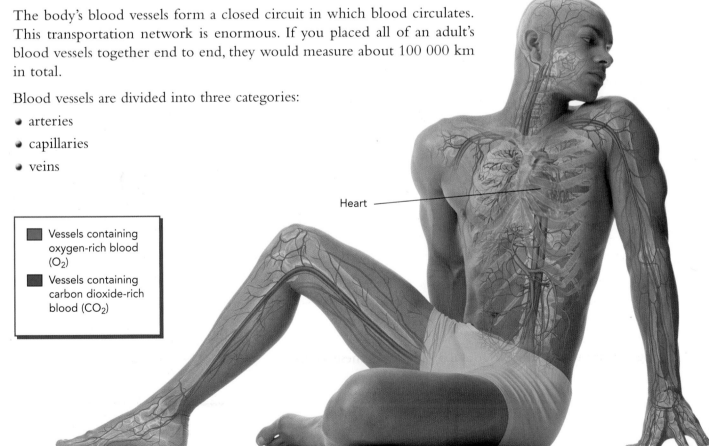

Heart

Arteries

Arteries are the largest blood vessels in the body. They carry blood from the heart to other parts of the body. Their walls are very thick, which enables them to withstand the high pressure of the blood they carry.

> ▶ An ARTERY is a blood vessel that carries blood from the heart to other parts of the body.

Capillaries

Arteries branch and narrow into smaller arteries, called the *arterioles*, which branch and narrow into capillaries, the smallest blood vessels that irrigate the body's tissues. Capillaries are so narrow that red blood cells travel through them in single file. Their walls are also very thin, made up of a single layer of cells. The thin walls ease the

> *Capillary* comes from the Latin word *capillus*, meaning "hair."

exchange of substances between blood and organ cells. It is in the capillaries that nutrients, oxygen and other substances pass to the cells and that blood picks up carbon dioxide and other cell waste.

> ▶ A CAPILLARY is a blood vessel with a small diameter and very thin walls in which exchanges between the blood and the cells of organs occur.

Veins

Once the capillaries have irrigated the organs, they unite to form venules which, in turn, join to form larger veins. Blood travels to the heart through the veins.

> ▶ A VEIN is a blood vessel that carries blood back to the heart.

Although the diameter of a single capillary is quite small, the pressure inside the veins is very low. To return to the heart, the blood moves forward, with the help of muscular contractions. These press against the veins, thereby causing the blood to circulate.

In the veins of the lower parts of our body, such as the legs, blood would normally be more likely to flow downward, due to gravity. But our veins have valves to keep blood from flowing downward and muscular contraction to keep blood flowing upward to the heart. Figure 6.35 illustrates these valves.

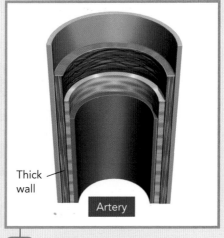

6.33 Arteries have very thick walls, which enable them to resist the high pressure of the blood.

Thick wall
Artery

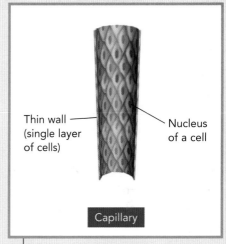

Thin wall (single layer of cells)
Nucleus of a cell
Capillary

6.34 The capillary walls are one-cell thick.

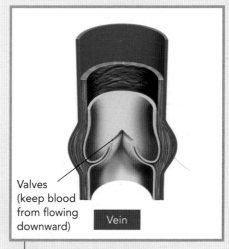

Valves (keep blood from flowing downward)
Vein

6.35 The veins in the lower parts of the body have valves to keep the blood from flowing back down.

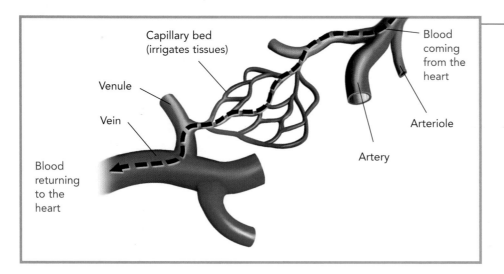

6.36 Blood circulates from the arteries to the capillaries, then from the capillaries to the veins. The blood returns to the heart, and begins the same cycle again.

All the blood vessels together form a closed circuit. Figure 6.36 shows the relationship between the various types of blood vessels in the cardiovascular system.

THE HEART

The heart is the organ that stimulates the movement of blood. It is considered the pump of the cardiovascular system. In an adult, it is the size of a fist and is located in the thoracic cage between the lungs. What does the inside of a heart look like and how does it work? We'll answer that question using Figure 6.37 and the information below.

Inside the heart

The heart is a hollow muscle with four cavities:

- the right atrium
- the right ventricle
- the left atrium
- the left ventricle

The right atrium is linked to the right ventricle, the left atrium to the left ventricle. The right and left sides of the heart do not communicate with each other, but are separated by a partition.

From both the right and left sides, the blood flows through valves to move from the atrium to the ventricle. The valves, called *atrioventricular valves,* keep blood from moving backward.

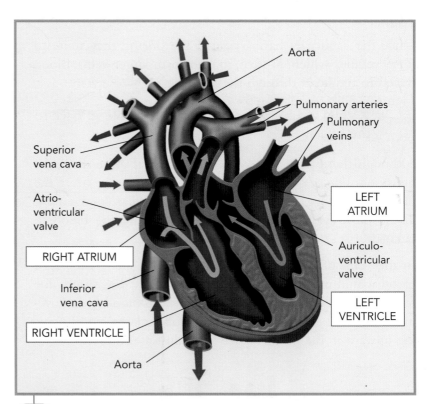

6.37 The heart is composed of two atria and two ventricles. A partition separates the heart into left and right.

Several blood vessels are attached to the heart. Veins (superior and inferior vena cavas and pulmonary veins) are attached to both atria, providing ways for blood to enter the heart. In addition, arteries (the aorta and pulmonary arteries) are attached to the ventricles to carry the blood as it exits these two cavities.

The function of the heart

The contraction of the heart muscle causes blood to circulate through the entire body.

- For blood to enter and fill the atria, the heart must be at rest, the muscles relaxed. This filling phase is called DIASTOLE.

Diastole comes from the Greek word *diastolê*, meaning "dilation."

- For blood to exit the atria, the atria must contract simultaneously, forcing the blood out and into the ventricles. Then, a few tenths of a second later, it's the ventricles' turn to contract, pushing the blood into the arteries attached to the heart. The contraction phase is called SYSTOLE.

Systole comes from the Greek word *systolê*, meaning "tightening, contraction."

The pulse that we can feel by pressing on our throat, wrist or temples corresponds to the contractions of the left ventricle. For a person at rest, the heart beats about 75 times per minute. Heart rate varies according to age, gender, physical fitness and intensity of physical activity.

CIRCULATION ROUTES

The heart works like a double pump. Because the right side of the heart is separated from the left by a partition, the blood can be pumped out of each side along two different routes:

LAB 59

- On the right side, the mechanism is called *pulmonary circulation*.
- On the left side, it is known as *systemic circulation*.

Figure 6.38 and Table 6.39 on the next page summarize the details of both circulation routes.

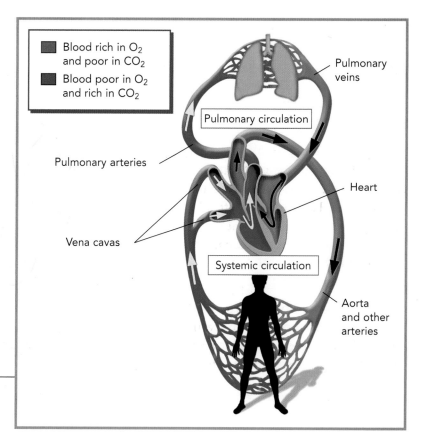

Blood rich in O_2 and poor in CO_2

Blood poor in O_2 and rich in CO_2

Pulmonary circulation

Pulmonary veins

Pulmonary arteries

Heart

Vena cavas

Systemic circulation

Aorta and other arteries

6.38 Blood can take two routes around the body: pulmonary circulation or systemic circulation.

Pulmonary circulation	Systemic circulation
Blood circulating through the lungs (pulmonary circulation) has a shorter route.	Blood circulating through the entire body (systemic circulation) has a longer route.
The right side of the heart is its pump.	The left side of the heart is its pump.
The blood travelling this route is rich in CO_2.	The blood travelling this route is rich in O_2.
• The blood exits the right ventricle through a pulmonary artery and flows to the capillaries of the lungs. • There the blood sheds its carbon dioxide and picks up oxygen. • Now rich in oxygen, the blood returns to the heart and enters the left atrium through a pulmonary vein.	• The blood exits the left ventricle through the aorta, the largest artery in the body. • The aorta divides into arteries that carry the blood to the capillaries of the body's organs. • There the blood sheds oxygen, nutrients and other substances—all are absorbed into the tissue cells—and picks up carbon dioxide and other waste. • Now poor in oxygen and rich in carbon dioxide, the blood returns to the heart and enters the right atrium through the vena cavas.

   CONNECTIONS PHYSICAL EDUCATION

How the heart benefits from physical activity

There are many health benefits to physical activity. Studies show that 30 minutes or more of moderate or vigorous exercise three times a week makes the heart work more efficiently.

A strong heart is bigger and its walls are thicker than a weak heart, thus increasing the force of its contractions. In addition, physically active people usually have a lower resting heart rate than sedentary people. The heart rate of certain athletes may be only 40 beats per minute at rest, while that of the general population is usually 75 beats per minute.

The heart of someone who exercises has a better recovery rate because its contractions are more efficient. This means that after a period of sustained effort, the heart of an active person returns to its normal rate more rapidly than that of a sedentary person.

Thus, a healthy, active lifestyle ensures a strong heart that can rise to the challenge of exercise with greater energy and efficiency, and help improve and maintain health.

3.4 THE LYMPHATIC SYSTEM

In this chapter we have learned that the role of blood circulation is to carry certain substances to the cells and carry other substances away from the cells to be eliminated. These exchanges do not occur directly between the blood and the cells. They take place in the liquid that surrounds our cells, called *extracellular fluid*. This liquid is the basis of another important system involved in the nutrition of our bodies—*the lymphatic system*.

Lymphatic comes from the Latin word *lymphaticus*, meaning "connected to water."

EXTRACELLULAR FLUID

Extracellular (also known as *interstitial*) fluid contains:

- water and other substances from blood plasma
- white blood cells

In a manner similar to that of soaker hoses, capillaries constantly leak water and other substances found in blood plasma through pores in their membranes. About three litres of liquid a day exit the capillaries through the tiny holes in their walls.

As for the white blood cells, they leave the capillaries using a process called **DIAPEDESIS**. Normally, white blood cells are too large to pass through the capillary pores. They can, however, alter their shape to squeeze through the pores. Figure 6.40 illustrates this.

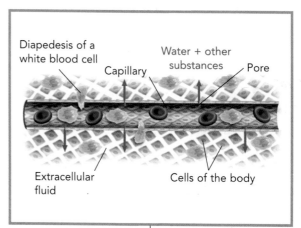

Diapedesis of a white blood cell · Capillary · Water + other substances · Pore · Extracellular fluid · Cells of the body

> **EXTRACELLULAR FLUID** is a clear liquid that surrounds our cells and contains water and other substances from blood plasma. It also contains white blood cells.

6.40 Diapedesis is the process whereby white blood cells are able to exit the capillaries by squeezing through the pores in the capillary membranes.

LYMPH AND LYMPHATIC CIRCULATION

If our cells were to keep the waste they produce, they would die. Waste products are therefore expelled into the extracellular fluid, where the lymphatic system returns them to the blood and transports them to the various organs that eliminate them from the body.

The lymphatic system is made up of vessels that transport extracellular fluid. Inside these vessels, this fluid is called *lymph*. The lymph circulates in vessels called *lymphatic vessels*. Their job is to carry the lymph to the blood.

> **LYMPH** is the fluid derived from extracellular fluid as it circulates inside lymphatic vessels to evacuate cell waste.

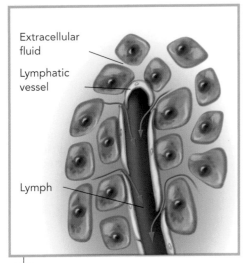

Extracellular fluid

Lymphatic vessel

Lymph

6.41 Extracellular fluid becomes lymph once it enters the lymphatic vessels.

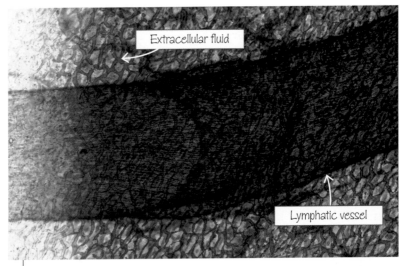

Extracellular fluid

Lymphatic vessel

6.42 Lymphatic vessels carry lymph to the blood. In this way, cell waste products travel to the organs that will expel them from the body.

The lymphatic system does not have a heart to pump the lymph. Like veins, it relies on muscular contractions to keep the lymph moving. The largest lymphatic vessels have valves to keep the lymph flowing in the right direction.

IN DEFENCE OF OUR BODIES

The human organism reacts to viruses and bacteria from the external world and considers them "invaders." Once these foreign entities successfully make their way inside our bodies, they can usually be found in the extracellular fluid, the lymph or the blood. All three of these liquids contain white blood cells, the body's "defenders."

As shown in Figure 6.43, the lymph circulates in the body, travelling through variously situated lymph nodes, which filter it. Inside the nodes, there are high concentrations of white blood cells. The lymph nodes are thus battlegrounds where the body fights its enemies.

6.43

The lymphatic system, like the cardiovascular system, extends throughout the body. Unlike the cardiovascular system, however, the lymphatic system is not a closed circuit.

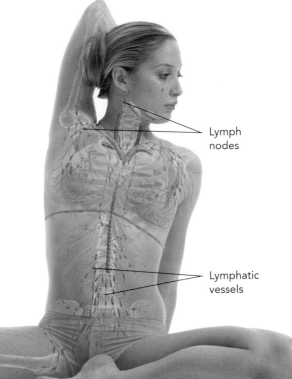

Lymph nodes

Lymphatic vessels

White blood cells can act in the following two ways to defend the body:

- They ingest invaders through phagocytosis.

- They neutralize invaders by secreting neutralizing substances called *antibodies*.

Phagocytosis comes from the Greek words *phagein*, meaning "to eat" and *kytos*, meaning "cell."

In phagocytosis, the membrane of a white blood cell engulfs the invader, as shown in Figures 6.44 and 6.45. Once inside the white blood cell, the invader is destroyed by a substance that is secreted by the white blood cell's lysosomes.

> ◗ PHAGOCYTOSIS is the mechanism whereby white blood cells ingest and destroy certain microorganisms.

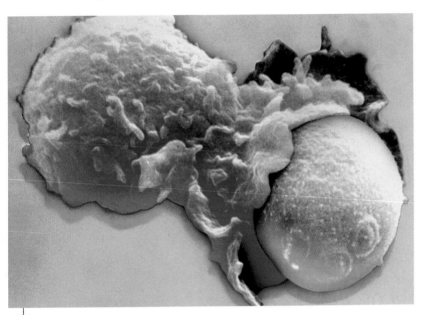

CHARGE!
If our white blood cells did not attack and destroy microorganisms, they would invade our body little by little, and a simple skin cut could be fatal.

6.44 This white blood cell is swallowing a microorganism so it can be destroyed. The action is called *phagocytosis*.

As was just mentioned, white blood cells can also produce antibodies as a defence against an invader. Figure 6.45 on the next page illustrates the action of antibodies:

- Antibodies recognize the antigens, elements which have attached to an invader.

- Antibodies then attache themselves to the antigens, thus neutralizing the invader and preventing it from reproducing or attacking other cells. Once neutralized, the invader is eliminated.

> ◗ An ANTIBODY is a substance secreted by white blood cells to neutralize invaders.

> ◗ An ANTIGEN is a substance recognized as foreign by the body and that triggers the body's white blood cells to produce antibodies.

1845
1916

Ilya
Ilyich
Mechnikov

This Russian zoologist and microbiologist is best remembered for his pioneering research into the human immune system. He successfully demonstrated that certain blood cells can defend our body by consuming foreign microorganisms. This process is now known as *phagocytosis*.

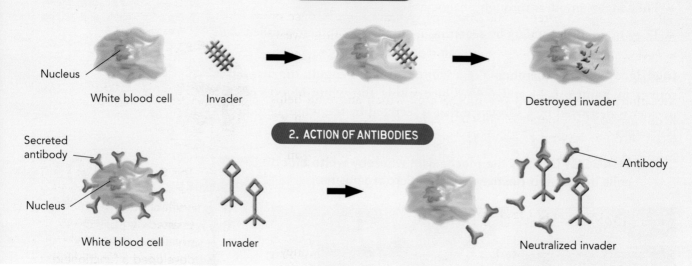

I. PHAGOCYTOSIS

Nucleus

White blood cell   Invader   Destroyed invader

2. ACTION OF ANTIBODIES

Secreted antibody

Nucleus   Antibody

White blood cell   Invader   Neutralized invader

The antibodies produced by the white blood cells have two features:

- They are specific: They can only recognize the antigens for which they were produced. This means that a different antibody needs to be produced for each new antigen.

- They are immunizing: The white blood cells remember, sometimes for a lifetime, how to produce a particular antibody. That is why we have certain diseases (like measles) only once in our lives.

6.45 Phagocytosis and the production of antibodies are strategies used by white blood cells to defend the body.

4 THE ELIMINATION OF WASTE

LAB
60

Cellular activity produces a lot of waste that is toxic to the body and must be eliminated. **EXCRETION** is the process by which waste products are eliminated from the body.

The elimination of waste is carried out mainly by our lungs, kidneys and sweat glands. If the lungs cannot excrete carbon dioxide, the body dies in just a few minutes. If the kidneys and sweat glands are unable to eliminate their respective waste products, the body can survive just a few days.

We have already seen how the lungs function during our study of the respiratory system. We shall now take a brief look at the way our sweat glands help maintain blood balance before moving on to the urinary system.

6.46 We must breathe in order to get rid of carbon dioxide, a waste product of the human organism.

THE SWEAT GLANDS

There are approximately 2 500 000 sweat glands on the surface of the human organism. These glands discharge their secretion, sweat, by means of channels that open to the skin surface (Chapter 7, page 217).

Sweating (or perspiration) is a mechanism, which above all helps keep our body temperature constant in hot weather or when we exert ourselves. Sweat is composed of water and waste materials from the blood. That is why sweat also plays a role in excretion.

4.1 THE URINARY SYSTEM

The urinary system in the human organism includes the kidneys, the ureters, the bladder and the urethra. Figure 6.47 and Table 6.48 (next page) illustrate this system.

1911
–

Willem Kolff

This Dutch doctor is considered the father of artificial organs. In 1943, assisted by the work of several scientists, he developed a functioning artificial human kidney. Throughout his career, Kolff devoted himself to developing artificial organs.

6.47

The urinary system is composed of the kidneys, the bladder and the tubes that carry urine (ureters and urethra).

Kidney

Ureter

Bladder

Urethra

Urinary system

Renal artery

Renal vein

Aorta

Inferior vena cava

Structures of the urinary system	Description	Functions
Kidneys	Two reddish bean-shaped organs	Eliminate waste and maintain blood balance through the production of urine (by excreting surplus water and toxic products, among them urea).
Ureters	Two tubes of about 25 cm in length; each links a kidney to the bladder	Transport urine produced in the kidneys to the bladder.
Bladder	Pear-shaped reservoir with elastic walls	Stores urine until it is released through urination; the bladder can hold about one litre of urine.
Urethra	Channel 3–4 cm in length in women and about 20 cm long in men	Transports urine from the bladder to the outside.

4.2 THE COMPOSITION OF URINE

The kidneys are the organs that filter blood; they remove waste products from the blood by producing a liquid called *urine*.

Urea is the chief waste product from the blood. It is created when cells use proteins to produce energy and amino acids are oxidized. The equation for this oxidation looks like this:

Amino acids + oxygen ⟶ energy + water + urea

6.49 The equation for the oxidation of amino acids

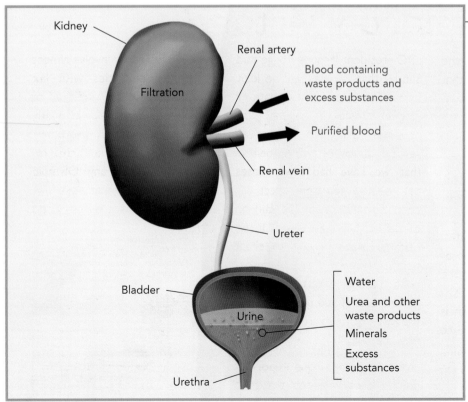

6.50 The filtration of blood and the composition of urine

Kidney

Renal artery

Blood containing waste products and excess substances

Filtration

Purified blood

Renal vein

Ureter

Bladder

Urine

Water

Urea and other waste products

Minerals

Excess substances

Urethra

The kidneys also help keep the blood in balance. They stabilize the amount of water in the blood, maintaining the concentration of minerals constant. If the blood contains an excess of water or minerals, the kidneys excrete them. Thus, urine is made up of the following components:

- water (95 percent)
- urea (2.5 percent) and other waste
- minerals
- substances that are in excess in the blood

Urine may also contain:

- protein, glucose, fats and/or blood cells. (Their presence is, however, an indication of a health problem.)
- traces of medications or drugs that the person has consumed. (This is why the urine of athletes is sometimes checked, in order to detect the presence of doping products.)

Note that the amount of urine produced by the body depends in part on the concentration of minerals in the blood and the amount of water in the body. If the concentration of minerals is too low, the kidneys excrete more water, thus raising the concentration of minerals. In this way, the amount of urine increases. On the other hand, if the body lacks water, or the concentration of minerals in the blood is too high, the kidneys excrete less water and we feel thirsty.

Is Beijing's win over doping a hollow victory?

The Beijing Olympics were the cleanest in history. It appears that athletes—from developed countries, at least—have decided never again to take forbidden substances. Or have they?

The doping record of Beijing 2008 would appear to suggest so. No athletes from Olympic giants China, the United States, Russia, Britain, Germany or Australia—who topped the medals table—are among the offenders. However, the truth is we will need to wait till 2016 to know whether the Beijing Games were as clean as the figures suggest.

IOC president Jacques Rogge said Sunday that samples will be kept frozen for eight years. Whatever illegal substances were not detected during the Games can yet be discovered. "We believe that we have had fewer cases because the deterrent effect has been augmented," Rogge said on the last day of the Games. "It has become more difficult to cheat because firstly, we have augmented the number of tests from 3 500 in Athens to 4 500 now. Secondly, we have also increased the penalties," he said.

However, there is one important point: the positive tests that have been known so far involve almost exclusively countries with lax testing or with a tradition of endemic doping. And in many cases the substances found are "prehistoric," substances that no sports star from any Olympic giant countries would dare use because they would easily be caught.

Adapted from DPA news agency, "Is Beijing's Win Over Doping a Hollow Victory?" *DW World* website, August 25, 2008.

CHECKUP

 1 FOOD AND ITS USE BY THE BODY
(pp. 160–172)

1. This is what Veronica ate for supper:

> 1 grilled Atlantic salmon steak
>
> 1 baked potato
>
> 5 mL of butter (on the potato)
>
> 3 boiled broccoli florets
>
> 2 glasses (500 mL) of 2% milk
>
> 125 mL of chocolate ice cream
>
> 60 g of strawberries (on the ice cream)

For each food item eaten by Veronica:

a) Name the food group to which the item belongs.

b) State the amount of energy provided by the item. (See Appendix 2, The nutritional value of certain foods, page 424.)

2. In a 250-mL glass of 2% milk:

a) How many grams (g) of proteins, carbohydrates and fats does this glass contain?

b) How many micrograms (μg) of vitamin A does it contain?

c) How much energy (kJ) is provided by the glass of milk?

3. Below is the Nutritional Facts table found on a bag of raisin bread.

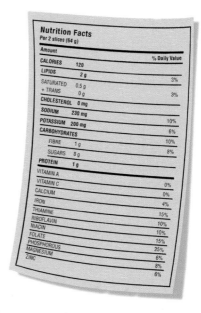

Nutrition Facts		
Per 2 slices (64 g)		
Amount		**% Daily Value**
CALORIES 120		
LIPIDS 2 g		3%
SATURATED 0.5 g		
+ TRANS 0 g		3%
CHOLESTEROL 0 mg		
SODIUM 230 mg		
POTASSIUM 200 mg		10%
CARBOHYDRATES		6%
FIBRE 1 g		10%
SUGARS 8 g		8%
PROTEIN 1 g		
VITAMIN A		
VITAMIN C		0%
CALCIUM		0%
IRON		4%
THIAMINE		15%
RIBOFLAVIN		10%
NIACIN		10%
FOLATE		15%
PHOSPHOROUS		25%
MAGNESIUM		6%
ZINC		8%
		6%

a) If you eat two slices of raisin bread, will you have eaten most of your recommended daily fat requirements? Explain your answer.

b) This raisin bread contains niacin (vitamin B3). What other vitamins does it contain?

c) This raisin bread contains zinc. What other minerals does it contain?

4. For each of the following statements, state whether it refers to a chemical or a mechanical transformation.

a) Teeth grind and cut food.

b) Saliva breaks down starch.

c) The stomach churns the food.

d) Gastric juices break down proteins.

5. For each structure of the digestive tract, indicate:

   a) the kind of conversion (mechanical or chemical transformation) that takes place

   b) the substances that are secreted for digestion, if applicable

   c) the glands that secrete these substances

   d) the nutrients that are broken down by these secretions

   You may write your answers in a table like the one below.

Structure	Type of conversion	Substances that are secreted	Glands that secrete these substances	Nutrients that are broken down

6. Digestion prepares nutrients so they can be used by the body.

   a) What do we call the transport of nutrients from the digestive tract into the blood and lymph?

   b) From which part of the digestive tract are most nutrients absorbed into the blood and lymph?

7. Our respiratory system enables us to extract a gas from the air, which we need in order to live.

   a) Name this gas.

   b) What is the general equation that summarizes the role of this gas in the nutritional process?

8. A student eating in the cafeteria starts to choke. Once he stops coughing, he wonders what made his body react this way. How could you explain it to him?

2 RESPIRATION (pp. 172–176)

9. Below are some statements about respiration. For each statement, indicate whether it refers to inhalation or exhalation.

   a) Intercostal muscles and diaphragm contract.

   b) Intercostal muscles and diaphragm relax.

   c) Lung volume increases.

   d) Lung volume decreases.

   e) Air pressure in the lungs decreases.

   f) Air pressure in the lungs increases.

   g) Air inside of the lungs flows outside.

3 BLOOD AND LYMPH CIRCULATION (pp. 177–190)

10. This is a photo of a drop of blood seen through a microscope.

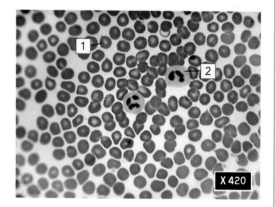

   a) Name element 1 and 2 and give their respective functions.

   b) What other formed element in the blood is not shown in the photo? What is its function?

   c) What percentage of blood volume is composed of formed elements?

11. a) What is the name of the liquid that contains the formed elements of the blood?

  b) What are the main constituents of this liquid?

12. Here are the blood types of four friends:
  - Joseph: AB^+
  - Karla: B^+
  - Maxime: O^-
  - Samir: A^-

  a) Draw the red blood cells of these four people while showing the substances found on each type of cell membrane.

  b) Samir is in a serious car accident and loses a lot of blood. He needs a transfusion. Which one of his friends could give him blood? Explain your answer.

  c) Which one of these four friends could be considered a universal recipient?

13. Name the type of blood vessel referred to in each of the following statements.

  a) This vessel carries blood back to the heart.

  b) This vessel is where most of the exchanges between the blood and the cells occur.

  c) In this vessel, blood circulates under high pressure.

  d) In this vessel, blood moves forward with the help of muscular contractions.

  e) In this vessel, red blood cells travel in single file.

  f) In this vessel, blood travels from the heart to the capillaries.

14. The diagram below shows the heart and the main vessels attached to it.

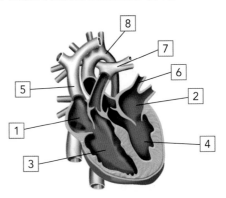

Name each of the numbered structures and state whether it contains oxygen-rich blood or carbon dioxide-rich blood. You may write your answers in a table like the one below.

Number	Structure	Oxygen-rich blood	Carbon dioxide-rich blood
1			

15. There are two blood circulation routes inside our body.

  a) Name the circulation route that carries blood to the lungs and then returns to the heart.

  b) Name the circulation route that carries blood to all the other parts of our body.

16. The blood, the extracellular fluid and the lymph are three liquids contained in our body.

  a) Describe how the elements in plasma and the white blood cells can leave the cardiovascular system and end up in the extracellular fluid and the lymph.

b) Draw a table like the one below and indicate where the blood, the extracellular fluid and the lymph circulate.

Liquid	Where it circulates
Blood	

17. While observing the lymph through a microscope, a microbiologist sees a white blood cell wrapped around a microorganism.

a) What is happening?

b) What other means can white blood cells use to defend the body?

4. THE ELIMINATION OF WASTE
(pp. 190-193)

18. a) What are the organs and structures involved in the formation, circulation and storage of urine?

b) Give the equation that summarizes how cells produce urea.

c) What organs help eliminate carbon dioxide?

19. For the following situations, state whether the amount of urine produced by the kidneys increases or decreases.

a) Nicole drank several glasses of water before going to class.

b) Jean-Philippe put a lot of salt on his fries.

c) Andrès forgot his water bottle and went on a bike ride during which he perspired a lot.

20. The presence of certain blood elements in the urine may indicate a health problem. What are these elements?

CONCEPT MAPS

HOW TO BUILD A CONCEPT MAP

Prepare your own summary of Chapter 6 by building a concept map based on the following terms.

- Amino acids
- Blood
- Carbohydrates
- Carbon dioxide
- Cardiovascular system
- Digestive system
- Fats
- Fatty acids
- Food items
- Glucose
- Glycerol
- Lymph
- Lymphatic system
- Minerals
- Nutrients
- Nutrition
- Oxygen
- Plasma
- Platelets
- Proteins
- Red blood cells
- Respiratory system
- Urinary system
- Urine
- Vitamins
- Water
- White blood cells

EATING DISORDERS

Eating disorders are serious conditions that affect a person's eating behaviour. There are three main disorders: anorexia, bulimia and binge eating. Table 6.51 describes these three disorders.

6.51 EATING DISORDERS

Eating disorder	Description	Possible complications
Anorexia	• Eat little • Eat foods low in calories • Obsess about maintaining a specific weight • Have powerful fear of getting fat • May experience bulimic attacks	• Cardiac problems • Blood imbalance • Lack of energy • Death
Bulimia	• Consume lots of food followed by purging (through vomiting, excessive physical exercise or taking laxatives) • Obsess about weighing as little as possible • Have powerful fear of getting fat • Have intense need to control self	• Stomach lesions • Cardiac problems • Blood imbalance • Lack of energy • Dental problems
Binge eating	• Occasionally consume massive amounts of food, without purging	• Obesity

Contrary to popular belief, people do not purposely acquire eating disorders; they are not controlled by willpower. As a matter of fact, people with eating disorders actually believe that they are eating properly. Several factors play a part in causing eating disorders, such as low self-esteem and a fixation or distorted view of body shape.

Eating disorders can be treated. Treatments include therapy to analyze and change inappropriate eating behaviour, nutritional advice and medication. The earlier treatment begins, the better the results.

1. Many experts believe that advertising, which uses very thin models, plays a role in increasing the risk of eating disorders.
   a) Why do such ads or commercials represent a risk factor for eating disorders?
   b) What solution would you suggest to help deal with this problem?
2. What advice would you give to a person who wants to have a healthy diet?

KATHERINE GAUDREAU-PROVOST

For most athletes, whether professional or amateur, diet is of great importance. Because athletes' nutritional needs vary and can be quite complex, athletes often consult sports nutritionists like Katherine Gaudreau-Provost. In her professional role, Gaudreau-Provost establishes what are an athlete's nutritional requirements and then puts together a suitable meal plan. To accomplish this, she learns everything about the athlete's training and competition schedules. She also must determine the athlete's muscle mass and body fat to adjust the diet. In addition, she is frequently called upon to give advice on good eating habits. In short, she analyzes all aspects of her client's nutritional profile in order to help her client reach peak athletic performance.

6.52

Jennifer Heil, who won in freestyle skiing (moguls event) at the 2006 Turin Olympics, made the most of Katherine Gaudreau-Provost's advice.

NAME

Katherine Gaudreau-Provost

JOB

Sports nutritionist

AREA WHERE SHE WORKS

Throughout Québec

EDUCATION

Bachelor's degree in kinesiology, with a specialization in clinical exercise physiology
Bachelor's degree in dietetics

PROUDEST ACHIEVEMENT

Designs diets for high-level athletes

6.53 OCCUPATIONS CONNECTED TO GAUDREAU-PROVOST'S WORK

Occupation	Education	Length of study	Main tasks
Professional cook	DEP in professional cooking	1350 hours	• Prepare and cook foods • Supervise and maintain kitchen equipment
Dietary technician	DCS in dietetics	3 years	• Ensure that menus correspond to needs • Ensure cleanliness in the meal-preparation process
Physiotherapist	Bachelor's degree in physiotherapy	3–4 years	• Help injured people regain their motor skills

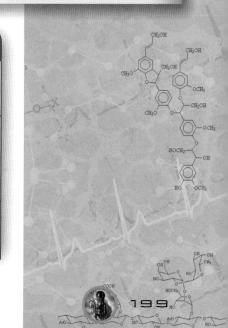

THE LIVING WORLD

1989	First graft of fetal brain tissue to treat Parkinson's disease
1949	First use of lithium to treat certain kinds of mental illness
1929	Invention of the electroencephalograph, a machine that records brain activity
1851	Invention of the ophthalmoscope for examining the retina
1837	Discovery of neurons
1795	Development of electrotherapy for the treatment of facial paralysis
1756	Discovery of the action of nerves on muscles
CIRCA 1160	Discovery of the retina's role in vision
CIRCA -375	Discovery of nerves
CIRCA -1300	First cataract operations
CIRCA -3000	First treatment of a broken bone by immobilization
CIRCA -12 000	First cranial surgery

THE HUMAN ORGANISM

AND THE EXTERNAL WORLD

Human beings are constantly interacting with their environment. No matter what they are doing—whether smiling at a friend, braking for a red light, eating when hungry or shivering when cold—human beings are constantly reacting to internal or external signals. They are able to do this because the human body is equipped with complex systems that are able to detect and analyze even the most subtle changes in their environment. This chapter deals with these systems.

1 THE NERVOUS SYSTEM

The human body is a symphony of activity, much of which is performed without our being aware of it. The heart pumps blood steadily through our blood vessels, the stomach digests our most recent meal, the muscles contract to maintain our posture, the eyes blink several times a minute to stay moist, the kidneys purify our blood. Meanwhile, we may also be studying or dreaming about weekend plans, chatting with friends or swimming in a pool. How does the body coordinate all these activities? Through the nervous system.

The human nervous system coordinates body functions so that they work in harmony. It receives, processes, stores and transmits information from both inside and outside the body:

- It receives information, thanks to specialized receptors located in various organs or tissues, such as the retina, the inner ear and the stomach.

- It transmits this information through the nerves to processing centres (the brain, for example). These centres process the information and decode its meaning. The brain, for example, receives a message and interprets it as a sound or a feeling of hunger.

- It stores the information for either short- or long-term use. The brain, for instance, is able to recognize a sight or sound it has heard before.

- It transmits the information it receives from these processing centres via nerves to various parts of the body in order to produce a particular action. For example, nerves transmit messages to the stomach muscles telling them to help in digestion or to the arm muscles, telling them to contract.

7.1 The nervous system is composed of the central nervous system and the peripheral nervous system.

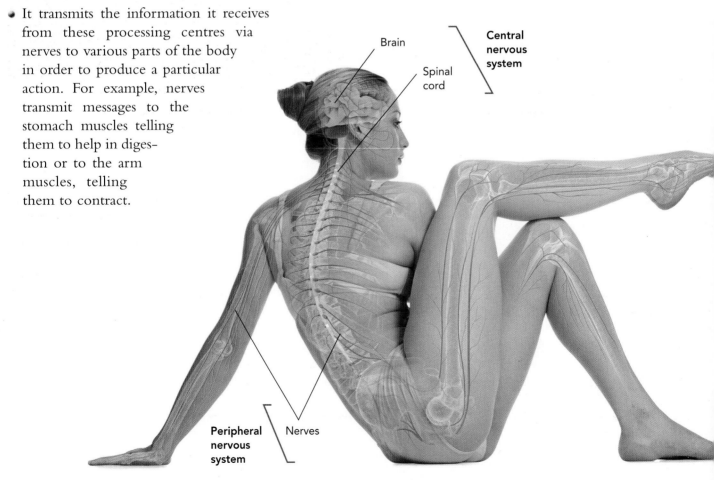

Brain

Spinal cord

Central nervous system

Peripheral nervous system

Nerves

▶ The NERVOUS SYSTEM receives, processes, stores and transmits information that comes from various parts of the body and the external world.

The nervous system is composed of the central nervous system (the brain and spinal cord) and the peripheral nervous system (the nerves).

1.1 THE NEURON

A human being possesses an average of 100 billion neurons, also called *nerve cells*. The entire nervous system functions with the help of neurons. They receive and transmit information.

> *Neuron* comes from the Greek word *neuron*, meaning "nerve, fibre."

▶ A NEURON is a specialized nerve cell in the nervous system that receives and transmits messages.

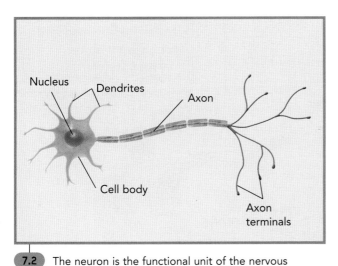

7.2 The neuron is the functional unit of the nervous system.

Labels: Nucleus, Dendrites, Axon, Cell body, Axon terminals

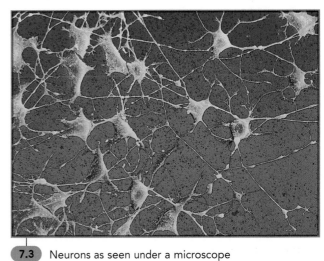

7.3 Neurons as seen under a microscope

As shown in Figure 7.2, a neuron is made up of four parts:

- dendrites
- cell body (containing the nucleus)
- axon
- axon terminals

> *Dendrite* comes from the Greek word *dendron*, meaning "tree."

The role of the neurons is to pick up stimuli, transform them into nerve impulses and transmit these impulses (next page).

▶ STIMULUS is anything that can be perceived by a living organism and that can trigger a reaction. Sound, light, heat, electrical shocks, odours and hormones are examples of stimuli.

▶ A NERVE IMPULSE is an electrical signal transmitted by a neuron.

CHARACTERISTICS OF THE NEURON

Neurons are specialized cells. The following characteristics distinguish them from other types of cells:

- A neuron can be stimulated: it reacts to a stimulus by changing it into an electrical signal (nerve impulse).
- A neuron is conductive: it transmits a nerve impulse from one neuron to another, until it reaches the target organ.
- A neuron consumes a great deal of oxygen and glucose. It can only survive a few minutes without oxygen.
- A neuron can live more than 100 years. People keep the same neurons their entire life.
- A neuron cannot reproduce itself; it cannot be replaced if destroyed.

1852
1934

Santiago Ramón y Cajal

This Spanish physician and physiologist published numerous articles describing nervous system structure and neuron communication. In 1906, he was awarded the Nobel Prize in medicine for his work on the nervous system.

TRANSMISSION OF NERVE IMPULSES

A nerve impulse travels from neuron to neuron until it reaches its target, for example, a muscle. It travels from dendrites to axon terminals, as shown in Figure 7.4.

- The dendrites of a neuron receive messages or stimuli and transform them into nerve impulses.
- The nerve impulses are then transmitted along axons to the axon terminals.
- Nerve impulses travel from one neuron to another via **NEUROTRANS-MITTERS** (chemical substances) secreted by axon terminals across the narrow space or transition zone, between two neurons. The transition zone between two neurons is called a *synapse*.

> ▶ A **SYNAPSE** is the transition zone between two neurons that allows a nerve impulse to be transmitted.

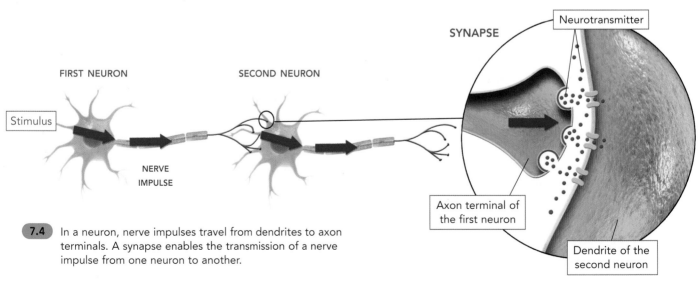

FIRST NEURON

SECOND NEURON

SYNAPSE

Neurotransmitter

Stimulus

NERVE IMPULSE

Axon terminal of the first neuron

Dendrite of the second neuron

7.4 In a neuron, nerve impulses travel from dendrites to axon terminals. A synapse enables the transmission of a nerve impulse from one neuron to another.

Nerve impulses move quickly from neuron to neuron and can reach a speed of 430 km/h, ensuring a rapid transmission of information among various parts of the human organism.

In the nervous system, axons of neurons sometimes combine to form nerves. As seen in Figure 7.5, the axons forming a nerve are covered by protective tissue and blood vessels.

> ▶ A **NERVE** is a structure that helps transmit information between the central nervous system and various regions of the body.

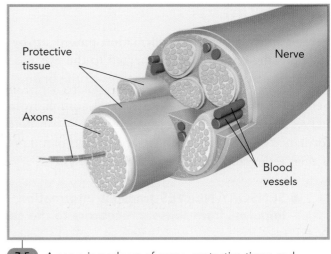

7.5 A nerve is made up of axons, protective tissue and blood vessels.

 ## THE PERIPHERAL NERVOUS SYSTEM

The peripheral nervous system connects different parts of the body to the central nervous system by means of nerve impulses. Sensory receptors detect internal and external stimuli. They send messages through nerves to particular parts of the organism in order to produce an action. The peripheral nervous system is made up of all the nerves that run throughout the body, as shown in Figure 7.1 (page 202).

> ▶ The **PERIPHERAL NERVOUS SYSTEM** connects different parts of the body to the central nervous system.

There are two types of nerves: *sensory* and *motor nerves*. Some nerves are mixed, meaning they have both sensory and motor capabilities. Before examining how sensory and motor nerves work, let's take a look at *sensory receptors*.

SENSORY RECEPTORS

Sensory receptors are specialized nerve cells. They pick up internal and external stimuli and transform them into nerve impulses. Sensory receptors are found throughout the organism, especially in the sensory organs (page 213). Organ-based receptors capture stimuli, such as smell and sound, from the external environment. Sensory receptors located elsewhere in the body capture information sent from the organs. For example, receptors located in muscles receive information that indicate the degree to which the muscles should stretch.

> ▶ A **SENSORY RECEPTOR** picks up stimuli and transforms the stimuli into nerve impulses.

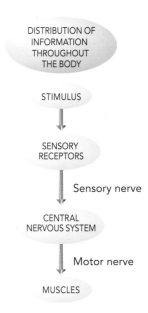

7.6 The peripheral nervous system distributes information throughout the body.

SENSORY NERVES

Sensory nerves transmit information picked up by sensory receptors. For example, the optic nerve, connected to the eye, is a sensory nerve. It transmits information captured by the eye to the brain.

Sensory nerves also pick up internal stimuli from vital organs. Sensory nerves surrounding the heart, for example, can detect changes in the performance of the heart, such as variations in blood pressure. This information is then redirected to the central nervous system.

> *Sensory* comes from the Latin word *sensitivus*, meaning "belonging to the senses."

> ▶ SENSORY NERVES transmit information, in the form of nerve impulses from sensory receptors to the central nervous system.

THE MOTOR NERVES

Motor nerves primarily transmit nerve impulses sent from the central nervous system to the muscles, as well as the glands. These nerve impulses stimulate the muscles to react and produce various voluntary and involuntary movements. For example, when light is too bright, the pupils in the eyes contract. When blood oxygen levels are too low, cardiac and respiratory rates increase. When we want to lift an arm, the brain sends a signal telling the muscles to contract.

> *Motor* comes from the Latin word *movere*, meaning "move."

> ▶ MOTOR NERVES transmit impulses from the central nervous system to the muscles in order to produce voluntary and involuntary movements.

1.3 THE CENTRAL NERVOUS SYSTEM

The central nervous system coordinates a major part of the nervous system activities. As seen in Figure 7.1 on page 202, it is made up of the brain and the spinal cord.

LABS
62 and 63

THE BRAIN

The brain is a large mass of nerve cells. It includes the cerebrum, hypothalamus cerebellum and brain stem. The cranium, or skull, and the meninges protect these soft parts of the brain.

> ▶ The BRAIN is composed of the parts of the central nervous system located in the cranium.

MANDATORY PROTECTION

Did you know that you have to wear a helmet in Québec's snow parks and ski hills? It has been required by law since the 2006-2007 ski season.

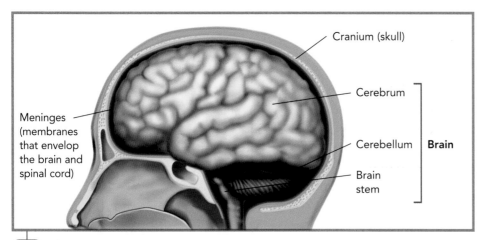

7.7 The brain is the part of the nervous system that is protected by the bones of the cranium.

The brain communicates with the entire organism through 12 pairs of nerves called *cranial nerves*.

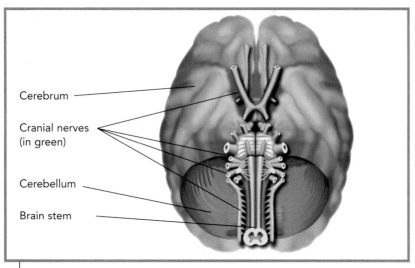

7.8 An inferior view of the brain and the 12 pairs of cranial nerves exiting from it

The cerebrum

The cerebrum is command central of all voluntary movements, of the interpretation of the senses and of intelligence. In addition, it is the centre of emotions. The average adult human cerebrum weighs about 1300 g (the brain itself weighs about 1600 g). It is divided into two hemispheres: the right hemisphere, which controls the left side of the body, and the left hemisphere, which controls the right side of the body.

As shown in Figure 7.9 on the next page, the cerebrum has an outer layer of grey matter, called the cerebral cortex, and an inner layer of white matter. The grey matter directs higher brain functions, such as planning, reasoning and logic.

Cortex is a Latin word also used in English, meaning "envelope, bark."

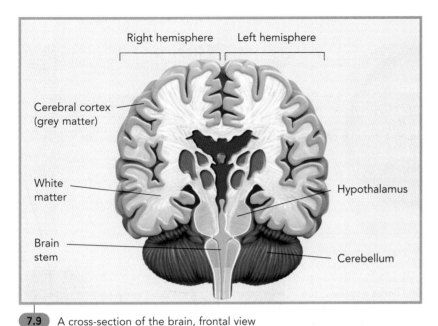

7.9 A cross-section of the brain, frontal view

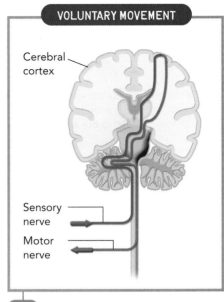

7.10 The route of the nerve impulse during a voluntary movement

▶ The **CEREBRUM** is the control centre of voluntary movement, sensory interpretation and intelligence. It is also the centre of emotion.

Table 7.11 describes the functions that are controlled by the cerebrum.

When music has no meaning

Ernesto "Che" Guevara suffered from amusia.

For the Latin American revolutionary Ernesto "Che" Guevara, hearing a symphony or a bus rattling along the streets of Havana amounted to the same thing. Lack of culture? Not at all. He was one of the five percent of people in the world affected by *amusia*. People with this condition are unable to remember a melody or to distinguish rhythms. For them, there is no difference in the tunes of *O Canada* and *Stairway to Heaven*. It has nothing to do with deafness or intellectual deficiency. On the contrary, "amusiacs" are as smart as the average person, if not more so. Researchers believe that amusia is the result of a brain malformation present at birth. It may also result from an injury to the temporal cortex (located near the temples.)

It makes sense because this part of the brain houses the structures essential to musical perception.

Adapted from Valérie Gaudreau, "L'amusie, ou quand la musique ne veut rien dire," *Le Soleil*, May 27, 2006, p. A5. *[Translation]*

Function	Description	Example
Controls voluntary movements	When we want to make a movement, such as raising our arm, the part of our cerebrum that is associated with motor control sends out a nerve impulse. The signal from the motor cortex travels to our arm muscles, stimulating them to contract.	
Interprets messages picked up by the senses	When one of the sense organs, such as our ears, eyes or skin, detects an external stimulus, it conveys the information to a particular region of the cerebrum in the form of a nerve impulses. The stimulated region of the cerebrum analyzes and interprets this information. For example, we hear a sound from the street and then identify it as a passing motorcycle.	
Controls intelligence	Problem-solving, reading, writing and speaking are all intellectual activities associated with intelligence. Although scientists have identified many regions of the brain that are responsible for various intellectual activities, it is still difficult to distinguish the actual limits of these regions, because several regions are involved at the same time in each activity. We do actually use 100% of our brain capacity, and not 10% to 15%, as some claim.	
Controls emotion	Managing emotions such as joy, sadness, anger and fear is very complex. As with intelligence, this function involves simultaneous activity in several regions of the brain.	
Regulates physiological functions	The hypothalamus, which lies below the cerebrum, is responsible for major functions of the body, including hunger, thirst, alertness and temperature regulation. It also controls the activity of the pituitary gland.	

Various brain functions are associated with a more intense level of activity in particular regions of the cerebrum, as can be seen in Figure 7.12.

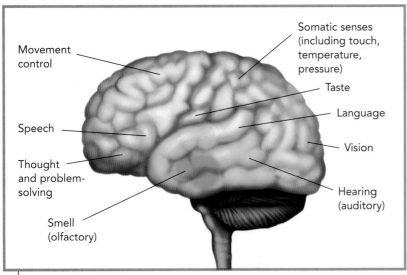

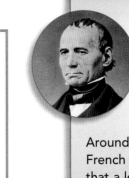

Movement control

Speech

Thought and problem-solving

Smell (olfactory)

Somatic senses (including touch, temperature, pressure)

Taste

Language

Vision

Hearing (auditory)

7.12 Each area of the cerebrum is responsible for a particular function.

1796
1881

Jean-Baptiste Bouillaud

Around 1850, this French physician showed that a lesion to a frontal area in the brain could result in loss of speech. He was thus the first to locate the region of the brain that controls speech.

An injury to any of these regions of the brain can cause a disturbance in the function connected with that region. For example, if the auditory region is damaged, a person may become deaf despite having perfectly healthy ears. By the same token, if a region connected to motor activity is damaged, the end result could be a loss of mobility or paralysis of one or several limbs. Indeed, paralysis is often caused by brain damage.

The cerebellum

The cerebellum is associated with balance. It coordinates movement according to the information it receives continuously from all parts of the body. Consequently, it helps maintain posture by constantly regulating the contraction of appropriate muscles. For example, the cerebellum enables us to walk in a straight line, dance without falling down, run, speak and play the piano.

> The CEREBELLUM is the centre of balance and movement coordination.

There are multiple balance disorders associated with the cerebellum. Motion sickness and vertigo, for example, occur when the cerebellum responds to contradictory signals. These conditions may be accompanied by nausea and dizziness.

7.13 The cerebellum enables this aerialist to walk on a tightrope without falling.

The brain stem

The brain stem is attached to the spinal cord, the cerebrum and the cerebellum. Ten pairs of cranial nerves exit from the brain stem. It processes all internal stimuli, detecting and analyzing changes taking place in the body. In this way, it controls the involuntary movement of the respiratory, digestive and circulatory systems. For example, when a person eats, the brain stem signals the organs and glands of the digestive system to make sure that digestion proceeds normally. The brain stem is also responsible for the movement of the esophagus as it pushes food toward the stomach.

> ▶ The BRAIN STEM is the control centre of internal stimuli as well as of involuntary movement.

THE SPINAL CORD

The spinal cord is similar to a large communication cable: it carries most nerve impulses (with the exception of those carried by the cranial nerves) between body and brain. In addition, it processes and conveys information involving reflexes, as we will see later.

> ▶ The SPINAL CORD is a nervous system organ that carries information from the various parts of the body to the brain. It is also the reflex centre.

The 31 pairs of nerves attached to the spinal cord transmit nerve impulses to all parts of the body. They are called *spinal nerves*. In Figure 7.15 we can see spinal nerves and a section of the spinal cord. Like the brain, the spinal cord is composed of soft tissue. It is protected by the meninges and the bones of the spinal column, called *vertebrae*.

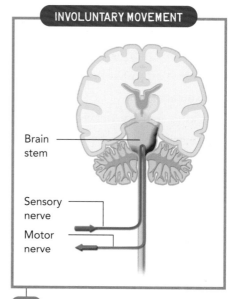

INVOLUNTARY MOVEMENT

Brain stem

Sensory nerve

Motor nerve

7.14 The path taken by nerve impulses during an involuntary movement

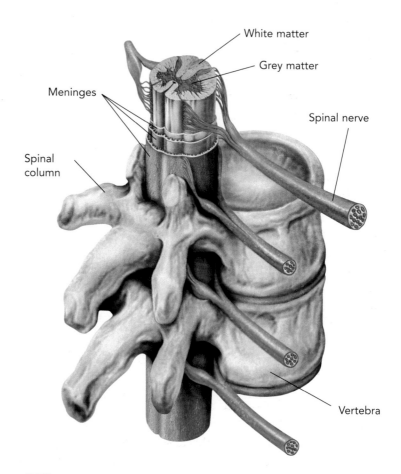

White matter

Grey matter

Meninges

Spinal nerve

Spinal column

Vertebra

7.15 There are 31 pairs of spinal nerves attached to the spinal cord.

The spinal cord is the reflex centre. A reflex is a rapid and involuntary reaction to stimu-

Reflex comes from the Latin word *reflexus*, meaning "reflect."

lus. When an insect bites us on the arm, we instinctively pull the arm away. The signal received and transmitted by the skin's sensory nerve cells is automatically redirected to the arm muscles by the spinal cord (see Figure 7.17). The brain only analyzes the event *after* the reaction has occurred.

Withdrawing a hand from a hot stove and blinking the eyes under a very bright light are both examples of reflexes. Reflexes allow us to react quickly in an emergency. Some reflexes also help re-establish normal body functions: goose bumps are the result of the body's attempt to maintain body heat by erecting body hair, trapping air as a layer of insulation.

▶ A REFLEX is a rapid and involuntary reaction to a stimulus.

The path taken by a nerve impulse during a reflex is called a *reflex arc*. As shown in Figure 7.18, the distance travelled by a nerve impulse in a reflex arc is much smaller than if it had to go to the brain. It is a shortcut taken in an emergency.

▶ A REFLEX ARC is the path taken by a nerve impulse during a reflex.

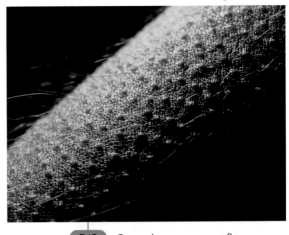

7.16 Goose bumps are a reflex.

AN INSIDIOUS POISON

Lead, a toxic metal, can be found in food, air, drinking water and paints, as well as in some cheap jewellery and cosmetics. It gradually accumulates in our body with every exposure and has a harmful effect on the nervous system, especially in young children.

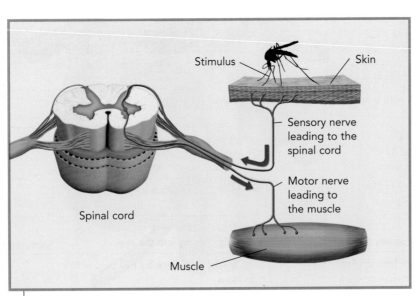

Stimulus — Skin

Sensory nerve leading to the spinal cord

Motor nerve leading to the muscle

Spinal cord

Muscle

7.17 A reflex occurs rapidly because the information received by the spinal cord is automatically redirected to the muscles.

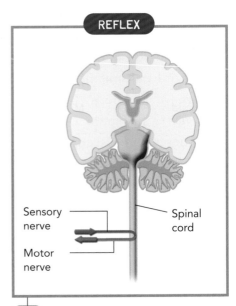

REFLEX

Sensory nerve — Spinal cord

Motor nerve

7.18 The path of a nerve impulse during a reflex (such a path is also called a *reflex arc*)

2 THE SENSORY ORGANS

This section deals with the organization and function of each sensory organ.

2.1 THE EYE

LABS
64 and 65

The eye is the sensory organ related to vision. It picks up light rays given off by light sources or reflected by objects. A normal eye can differentiate among 2000 or so colours, and can adapt to light intensity. The anatomy of the eye is shown in Figure 7.19, and Table 7.20 provides a brief description of the main structures in the eye.

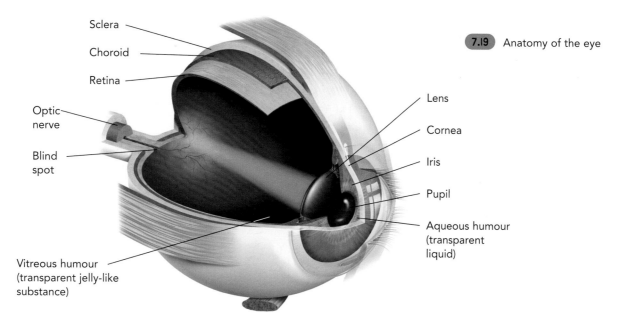

7.19 Anatomy of the eye

7.20 STRUCTURES OF THE EYE

Structure	Description
Sclera	Rigid, opaque membrane about 1 mm thick. It protects the eye from shock and gives it shape. It is called the *white of the eye*.
Choroid	Middle layer of eye, with blood vessels that nourish the eye.
Retina	Innermost layer at back of eye, thin and beige. Covered with millions of light-sensitive nerve cells that transform incoming data into nerve impulses. The junction point between the optic nerve and retina, called the *blind spot*, has no sensitivity to light.
Cornea	Clear and rigid membrane that is an extension of the sclera in front. It is slightly more dome-shaped than the rest of the eye.
Iris	An extension of the choroid, this pigmented membrane has an opening, called the *pupil*, in the centre, which serves to regulate the amount of light coming into the eye.
Lens	Flattened sphere that focuses light rays on the retina. It is held in place by muscles, which flatten it or make it more spherical, thus changing its focus.
Aqueous humour	Transparent liquid that fills the space between the cornea and the lens.
Vitreous humour	Transparent jelly-like substance that fills the space between the lens and the retina.

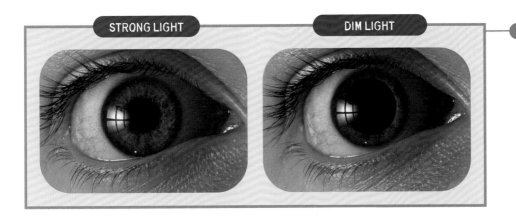

STRONG LIGHT   **DIM LIGHT**

7.21 The iris dilates and the pupil constricts when in bright light, allowing less light to enter the eye. The iris contracts and the pupil widens when it is dark, allowing more light to enter the eye.

The lens of the eye functions like a camera lens, changing its shape according to the distance of the object being looked at, to form a clear image on the retina. The lens is said to accommodate. Figure 7.22 shows the shape of the lens according to its distance from an object. (See Chapter 4 to learn more about how an image is formed in the eye.)

Accommodate comes from the Latin word *accommodare*, meaning "to adjust."

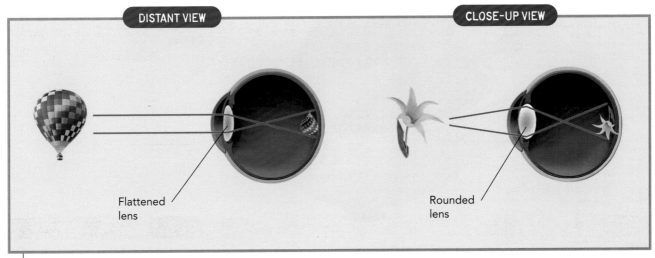

DISTANT VIEW   **CLOSE-UP VIEW**

Flattened lens

Rounded lens

7.22 The lens stretches and becomes flat when focusing on a faraway object. The lens shortens and becomes more spherical when focusing on a nearby object.

The nerve cells in the retina are photo-receptors: they convert light into nerve impulses. Some of these nerve cells, called *cones*, are only able to distinguish colours, while others, called *rods*, only distinguish variations in light intensity.

Nerve impulses from retina cells are sent to the brain through the optic nerve. The information is then processed and analyzed by the brain, which will superimpose the images received from each eye. This is how we are able to estimate distances and object contours.

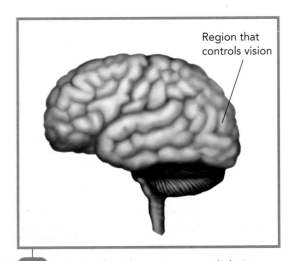

Region that controls vision

7.23 Nerve cells in the retina convert light into nerve impulses. These nerve impulses travel to the region that controls vision through the optic nerve, making sight possible.

  CHAPTER 7

2.2 THE EAR

The ear is the sensory organ associated with hearing. It picks up sounds and converts them into nerve impulses. The ear is divided into three sections: the outer ear, middle ear and inner ear. Figure 7.24 illustrates the anatomy of the ear, and Table 7.25 provides brief descriptions of the ear's main structures.

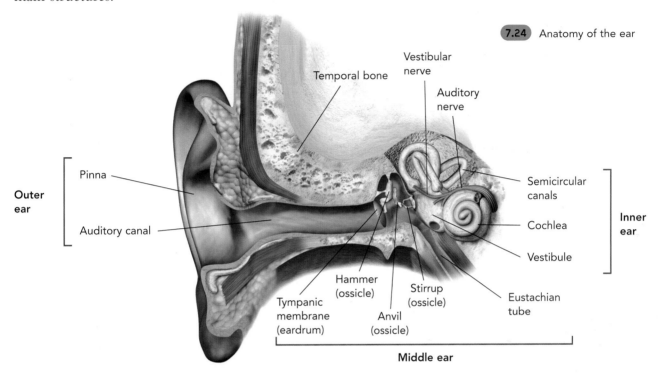

7.24 Anatomy of the ear

7.25 STRUCTURES OF THE EAR

	Structure	Description
Outer ear	Pinna (also called auricle)	Only visible part of the ear. It is shaped like a funnel to pick up sound vibrations easily from the air.
	Auditory canal	Slightly curved, about 2.5-cm-long canal that carries sound vibrations to the eardrum. It is lined with fine hairs and sebaceous glands (which produce wax), preventing foreign bodies from entering the ear.
Middle ear	Tympanic membrane (eardrum)	Thin, flexible and fibrous membrane about 1 cm in diameter, which moves to the rhythm of sound wave vibrations.
	Ossicles (bones)	Miniature bones located in the temporal bone. The three ossicles—the hammer, anvil and stirrup—can move in relation to one another.
	Eustachian tube	Canal that links the middle ear to the pharynx (throat). It equalizes the pressure on either side of the eardrum during swallowing.
Inner ear	Semi-circular canals	Canals that form a liquid-filled labyrinth in the temporal bone. They regulate balance when the body is in motion and are linked to the vestibular nerve.
	Vestibule	Liquid-filled structure that links the semi-circular canals to the cochlea. The vestibule plays a role in balancing the body in a static position. It is linked to the vestibular nerve.
	Cochlea	Liquid-filled structure, whose walls are covered with auditory nerve cells linked to the auditory nerve.

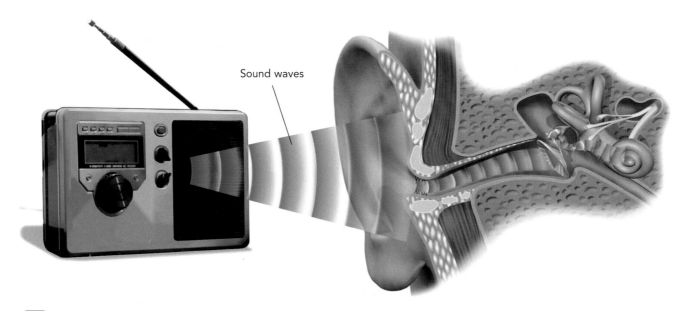

Sound waves

7.26 Sound vibrations travel to the liquid in the cochlea.

Sound is created by vibrations, usually in the air. The sources of sound (such as voices, musical instruments and motors) cause changes in air pressure, which create sound waves. The sound waves are channelled by the ear's pinna into the ear, through its various structures, until they reach the fluid-filled cochlea. Figure 7.26 illustrates the path sound waves take inside the ear.

The walls of the cochlea are lined with nerve cells, whose endings are sensitive to the vibrations in the liquid of the cochlea. These cells transform the information they receive into nerve impulses, which then travel to the cerebrum through the auditory nerve. It is at that point that the brain analyzes the waves and we "hear" the sounds.

The ear also plays an important role in balance. Specialized cells in the vestibule of the inner ear continuously monitor the position of the head. This monitoring allows a diver, for example, to find the water's surface. The cells also help maintain balance when the body is stationary: they stabilize our posture.

Other cells in the inner ear maintain balance when the body is in motion. They allow us to detect changes in speed and direction, helping us to walk and dance without falling over.

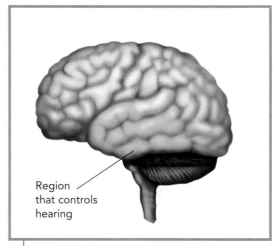

Region that controls hearing

7.27 The cochlear nerve cells convert sound waves into nerve impulses, which travel to the region of the cerebrum that controls hearing through the auditory nerve, enabling us to hear.

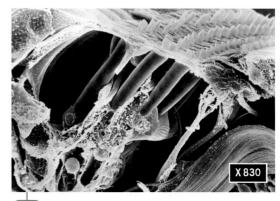

X 830

7.28 This photograph shows cochlear nerve cells viewed under a microscope.

THE SKIN

The skin is the sensory organ associated with touch. It is a very large organ as it covers the entire surface of the body. Figure 7.29 shows the structures located in one section of skin.

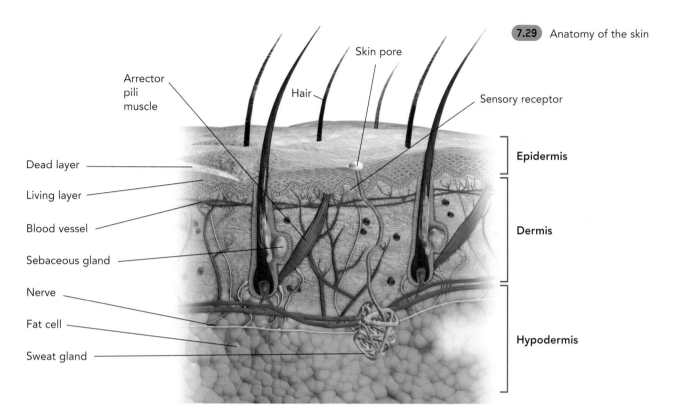

7.29 Anatomy of the skin

The skin is composed of three distinct layers: the epidermis, the dermis and the hypodermis. Table 7.30 provides a brief description of the main structures of the skin.

7.30 STRUCTURES OF THE SKIN

Layer	Structures	Description
Epidermis	Dead layer	Outer skin layer. Atmospheric pressure causes the cells to burst and die.
	Living layer	Layer of constantly dividing cells. New cells push old cells to the surface. They help the healing process.
Dermis	Sensory receptors	Structures that pick up stimuli.
	Blood vessels	Vessels that nourish the skin cells.
	Sebaceous glands	Glands that secrete *sebum*, an oily substance that waterproofs the skin.
	Sweat glands	Glands that produce sweat, which is carried to the skin surface through the pores.
	Hair	Structures arising from the dermis and partially covering the epidermis. An adjacent muscle (arrector pili muscle) can contract, making hair stand erect producing goose bumps.
Hypodermis	Fat cells	Layer of fat-containing cells that act as an energy reserve and a thermal insulator.

Sensory receptors in the skin allow us to experience the sensations of:

- tactile sensations (touch, pressure)
- thermal sensations (heat, cold)
- painful sensations (pain)

Each sensation is detected by receptors whose nerve endings are free or contained in a protective capsule. Figure 7.31 shows different types of nerve endings.

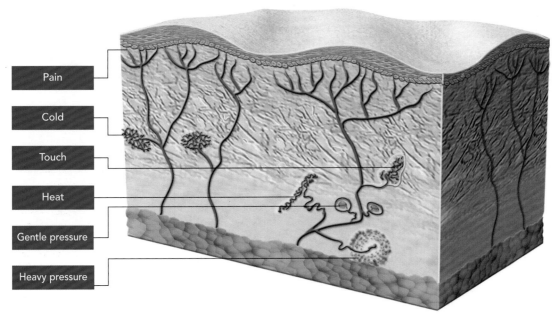

Pain

Cold

Touch

Heat

Gentle pressure

Heavy pressure

7.31 Each type of nerve ending specializes in its own type of sensation.

Sensory receptors are not spread out equally over the body. Some surface areas, such as the underside of the wrists and the cheeks, are more sensitive to heat, while others, such as the soles of the feet and the underside of the arms, have more receptors related to touch or pressure.

Sensory receptors combine to form sensory nerves that transport information to the cerebrum.

The skin is not only associated with touch, it also protects the body's internal organs and blocks the invasion of foreign bodies. In addition, it helps to eliminate waste by secreting sweat. Finally, it helps to produce vitamin D, which is needed to help the body absorb calcium.

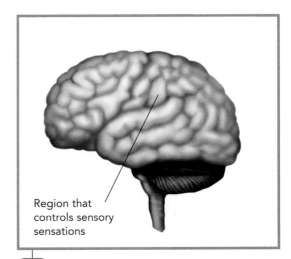

Region that controls sensory sensations

7.32 Sensory receptors combine to form sensory nerves that carry nerve impulses to the sensory region of the cerebellum, so we feel pain, cold, pressure and so on.

  CHAPTER 7

2.4 THE NOSE

The nose is the sensory organ associated with smell. Like the skin, it has multiple functions, such as inhaling and exhaling air. Figure 7.33 illustrates the anatomy of the nose.

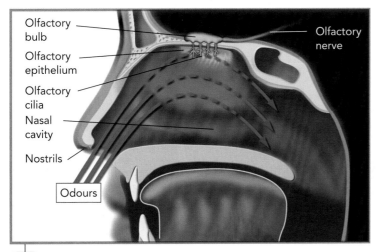

Olfactory bulb
Olfactory epithelium
Olfactory cilia
Nasal cavity
Nostrils
Odours
Olfactory nerve

7.33 Anatomy of the nose

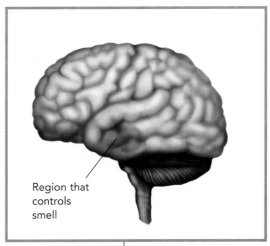

Region that controls smell

7.34 Nerve cells of the inner lining of the nose convert smells into nerve impulses, which then travel along the olfactory nerve to the region of the cerebrum that controls smell. This is how we experience smell.

Nerve cells sensitive to odours (arising from substances that smell) are located in the upper wall of the nasal cavity. They are concentrated on a small surface of about 5 cm^2 of the *olfactory epithelium*. About 15 million nerve cells are located in the olfactory bulb, at the tip of the olfactory nerve, the nerve that transmits impulses produced by the olfactory epithelium cells to the cerebrum.

Smell, a powerful but neglected sense

Although we are very good at detecting new smells and differentiating odours, we have a difficult time identifying them by name.

From our earliest years, we neglect our sense of smell. Although we are used to describing what we see and hear, we don't train ourselves to describe what we smell. Smell can be used not only to describe a perfume, but also to recognize various tastes. The proof: if you place a mixture of sugar and cinnamon on your tongue while holding your nose, you will only experience the sweet taste. Once you release your nose, the taste of sugar will be replaced with the taste of cinnamon.

Adapted from Pauline Gravel, "L'odorat, un sens négligé mais performant," *Le Devoir*, June 10, 2006, p. A8. [Translation]

Smell allows us to recognize the presence of cinnamon in a hot chocolate.

2.5 THE TONGUE

The tongue is a muscle scattered with sensory receptors for taste. The anatomy of the tongue is shown in Figures 7.35 and 7.36.

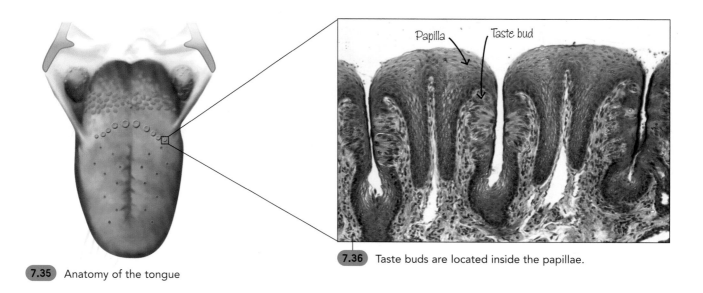

Papilla   Taste bud

7.36 Taste buds are located inside the papillae.

7.35 Anatomy of the tongue

The taste buds found inside papillae are the sensory receptors of the tongue. Three cranial nerves carry nerve impulses from the taste buds to the cerebrum.

Human beings can detect five different tastes:

- sweet (candy)
- sour (lemon)
- salty (table salt)
- bitter (endive or turnip)
- umami (a recently named taste associated with foods like aged meat

> *Umami* is the Japanese word for "yummy."

All taste buds experience all five tastes, regardless of their location on the tongue.

The sense of taste is only associated with the tongue. Yet, taste represents only 10 percent of the sensory information related with that sense. This is because taste and smell are interrelated, and smell encompasses 90 percent of the experience of taste. The smell of food, for instance, rises to the nose through the back of the throat and stimulates olfactory receptors, which then identify the food.

Other receptors found on the tongue are sensitive to temperature (hot or cold), discomfort (prickly feeling) and tactile properties (texture) of food.

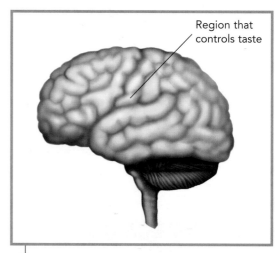

Region that controls taste

7.37 Taste buds change tastes into nerve impulses. The impulses travel to the region in the cerebrum that controls taste through the three taste-related nerves. It is at this point that we experience taste.

3 THE MUSCULOSKELETAL SYSTEM

As we have learned, the nervous system controls and coordinates the movements of our body. The system that makes movement actually possible is called the *musculoskeletal system*, and includes the bones, muscles and joints. Without this system, we would not be able to stand, walk, write or even smile.

3.1 BONES

Together, our bones make up the human skeleton. There are 206 different bones grouped into three anatomical regions: the head, torso and limbs. Figure 7.38 shows the human skeleton divided into these three anatomical regions.

LAB
68

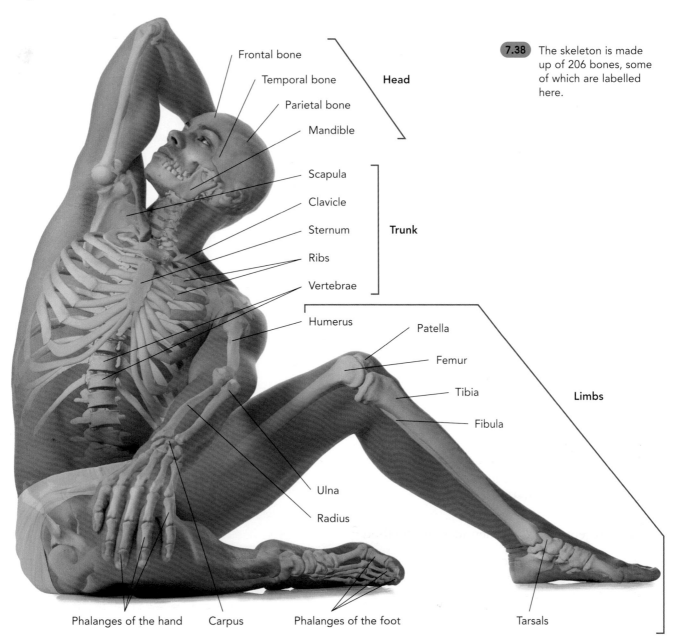

7.38 The skeleton is made up of 206 bones, some of which are labelled here.

Frontal bone

Temporal bone

Parietal bone

Mandible

Head

Scapula

Clavicle

Sternum

Ribs

Vertebrae

Trunk

Humerus

Patella

Femur

Tibia

Fibula

Limbs

Ulna

Radius

Phalanges of the hand   Carpus   Phalanges of the foot   Tarsals

▶ A BONE is a hard solid organ that forms part of the skeleton.

Bones are mostly made up of bone cells that are continuously renewed, even in adults. The bone tissue is the hardest material in the body. There are two types of bone: *spongy bone* and *compact bone*. They both can easily be distinguished with the naked eye. As illustrated in Figure 7.39, compact bone is dense, while spongy bone has numerous small cavities. Bones contain a variable proportion of both spongy and compact bone.

Bones come in a variety of shapes and sizes. For example, the thighbone, called the *femur*, is about 60 cm long, while the three ossicles in the ear are scarcely the size of a pea. Depending on their appearance, bones are divided into four categories (Figures 7.40 to 7.43, page 223):

● Long bones: Longer than they are wide, they have a thin body, or *diaphysis*, with two rounded extremities, called *epiphyses*. They are made up mainly of compact bone. The centre of long bones also contains bone marrow, a soft, fatty substance, and blood vessels. These bones are found mostly in the limbs.

● Short bones: Generally cubic in shape, they are mainly composed of spongy bone and are generally found in the wrists and heels.

● Flat bones: Thin, flat and generally curved, they are made up of two thin layers of compact bone separated by a layer of spongy bone. The skull, ribs, sternum and scapula are examples of flat bones.

● Irregular bones: These bones do not belong to any other group because they have an irregular shape. They are found mainly in the spine.

GOOD OL' BONES

According to Kino-Québec, engaging in vigorous physical activities like soccer, running, skiing or dancing during adolescence has a beneficial impact on bone mass and density. It also helps decrease the risk of developing osteoporosis in adulthood.

1514
1564

Andreas Vesalius

In 1543, this Flemish physician published a treatise on human anatomy that marked the beginning of modern anatomy. Furthermore, he developed a way of naming bones and muscles that we still use today.

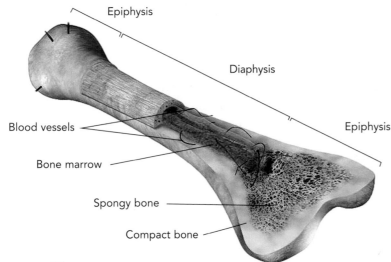

Epiphysis

Diaphysis

Epiphysis

Blood vessels

Bone marrow

Spongy bone

Compact bone

7.39 Inside a long bone

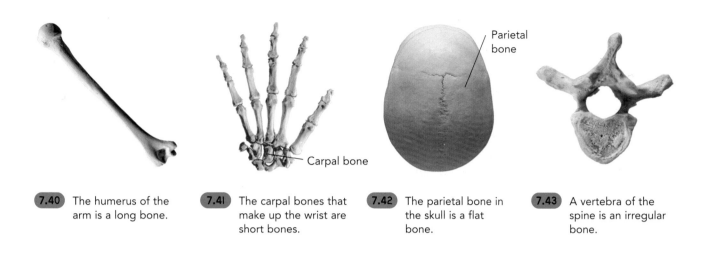

7.40 The humerus of the arm is a long bone.

7.41 The carpal bones that make up the wrist are short bones.

7.42 The parietal bone in the skull is a flat bone.

7.43 A vertebra of the spine is an irregular bone.

Table 7.44 describes various bone functions.

7.44 FUNCTIONS OF THE BONES

Function	Description
Support	Bones form a rigid structure that makes up the framework of our body. They allow us to hold our posture in standing, sitting or crouching positions, and also support or anchor soft organs, such as the muscles, heart and lungs.
Protection	Bones protect our internal organs. For example, the thoracic cage surrounds and protects vital organs contained in the thorax, such as the heart and lungs, and the cranial bones protect the brain.
Movement	Bones act as levers during muscle movement, allowing us to move around or to raise one part of our body. They form a structure that is both rigid and flexible.
Storage	The internal cavities of bones store fat, while the bony tissue stores minerals, mainly calcium and phosphorus. Regular exchanges occur between the bones and the blood to supply our bodies with the necessary minerals and maintain these at adequate levels.
Production of blood cells	The bone marrow found in the cavity of certain bones produces the formed elements of the blood, i.e. red cells, white cells and platelets.

3.2 JOINTS

The bones of the skeleton must be held together firmly and provide mobility when necessary. The joints make this possible. A joint is the junction between two or more bones. Almost all bones have at least one joint.

▶ A JOINT is the junction between two or more bones.

STRUCTURE OF JOINTS

Joints vary according to their makeup. For example, some joints hold bones together with a joint capsule filled with a lubricating liquid called *synovial fluid*. These joints are usually reinforced by fibrous bands of tissue called ligaments. This kind of joint offers great freedom of movement. To minimize wear, bone extremities are protected by cartilage, a whitish, elastic and perfectly smooth tissue. Figure 7.45 is an illustration of a joint.

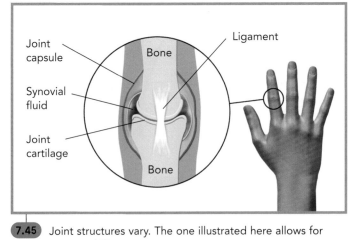

7.45 Joint structures vary. The one illustrated here allows for great mobility.

MOBILITY OF JOINTS

The degree of mobility varies greatly from one joint to another:

- Some joints are fixed, like those connecting the bones of the skull. Their solidity provides protection for the brain against blows to the head.
- Other joints are semi-movable, like those connecting all the vertebrae. They provide protection for the spinal cord and flexibility for the spine.
- Many joints are freely movable, such as those in the elbow or hip. There is a wide variety of movable joints.

Figure 7.46 provides some examples of joints.

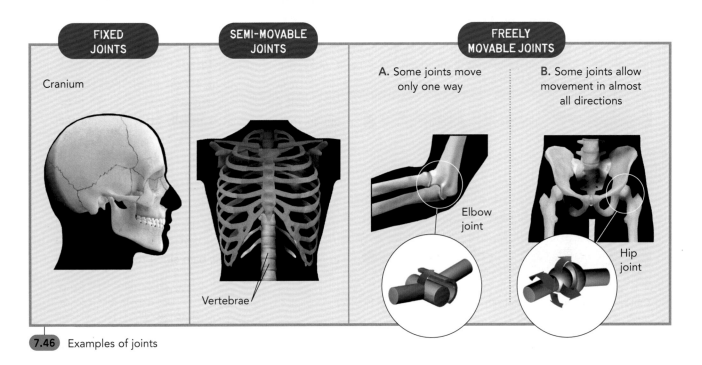

7.46 Examples of joints

MECHANICS OF JOINTS

Joint mobility makes it possible for our limbs to perform various movements, as illustrated in the figures below.

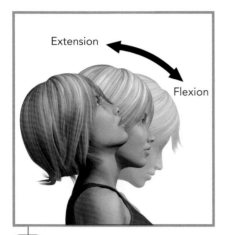

7.47 Extension increases the angle between two bones. Flexion decreases this angle.

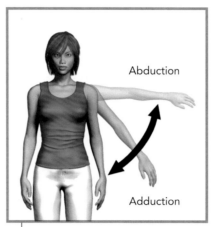

7.48 Abduction increases the distance between a limb and the body's midline position. Adduction decreases this distance.

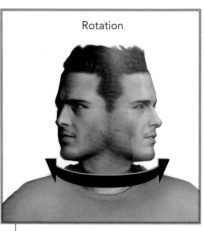

7.49 Rotation is the movement of a bone around an axis.

Shrimp in the knee

Former Montréal Canadiens defenceman, Serge Savard, is a great fan of shrimp, specifically of their shells. When the shells of these little crustaceans are ground up, one can obtain a useful natural product called *chitosan*. Thanks to this material, the former hockey star can now easily bend knees that were once damaged.

Repairing knee cartilage is like solving a puzzle. Cartilage cannot regenerate like skin and hair. It does not contain blood, nerves or enough cells to heal itself. On the other hand, stem cells are present in the bone that is usually attached cartilage, and once the bone cells are stimulated, they can transform into regenerative cells.

A company has developed a gel with a chitosan base. When injected into the knee, the chitosan prompts the stem cells to change. Serge Savard was one of the first to test the product and has experienced much less pain since then.

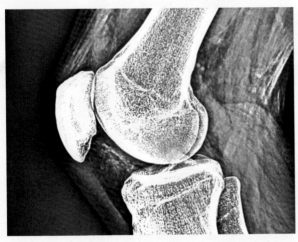

Chitosan, a material derived from shrimp shells, is used to repair knee cartilage.

Adapted from Isabelle Masinge, "Une crevette dans la rotule," *Québec Science*, September 2004, p. 13. [*Translation*]

3.3 MUSCLES

Muscles are the fibres found on bones and various organs. They help shape our figure. Examples of muscles are illustrated in Figure 7.50.

Muscle comes from the Latin word *musculus*, meaning "little mouse."

▶ **MUSCLES have the ability to contract causing our bodies or our internal organs to move.**

Although muscles are clearly associated with movement, they have additional functions (Table 7.51).

7.50 Examples of muscles that shape our body

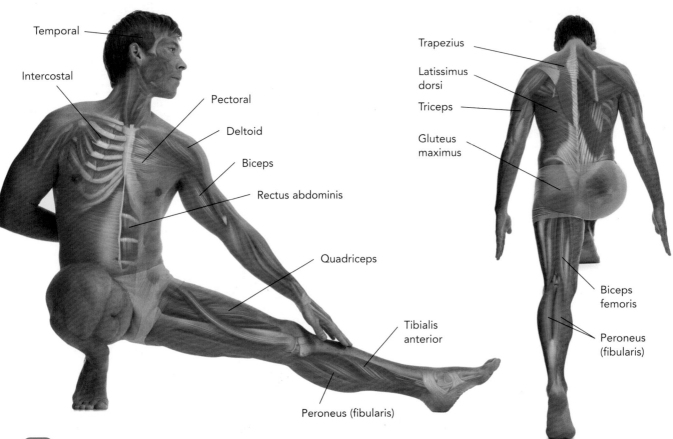

Temporal

Intercostal

Pectoral

Deltoid

Biceps

Rectus abdominis

Quadriceps

Tibialis anterior

Peroneus (fibularis)

Trapezius

Latissimus dorsi

Triceps

Gluteus maximus

Biceps femoris

Peroneus (fibularis)

7.51 FUNCTIONS OF THE MUSCLES

Function	Description
Movement	Muscles make the mobility of the body's limbs and organs possible. Some movements are controlled by thought (*voluntary*), such as raising an arm, while others occur without thought (*involuntary*), such as the contraction of the stomach walls when churning and mixing food. Each movement is the result of a muscle contraction followed by a release: the muscle shortens then resumes its original position.
Posture maintenance	Even when we do not move, our muscles contract and release. They must continuously work to maintain our posture.
Joint stabilization	Muscle movement supports and stabilizes joints. Without the muscles, some joints could not stay in place.
Heat release	During a muscle contraction, 75% of the energy expended is transformed into heat. The energy that is "lost" helps maintain body temperature at about 37°C.

Three types of muscles carry out the functions described in Table 7.51: skeletal muscle, smooth muscle and cardiac muscle. The photos below show what the muscle fibres look like under a microscope.

7.52 Skeletal muscles have characteristic striations. They provide the skeleton with mobility.

7.53 Smooth muscles are not striated. They make it possible for internal organs to move involuntarily.

7.54 Cardiac muscle is a very special striated muscle. It makes it possible for our heart to beat.

SKELETAL MUSCLES

The skeletal muscles are the only voluntary muscles. Attached to the bones of the skeleton, they contract and thus move the bones. They can react rapidly and with great force, but only for a short time. Skeletal muscles tire easily and must rest between periods of intense activity; they have little endurance.

A skeletal muscle is made up of several muscle fibres gathered into bundles. The muscle's power comes from the conjunctive tissue covering every muscle fibre and bundle. The muscle as a whole is also covered with conjunctive tissue, the ends of which fuse together to form a tendon. Tendons attach muscles to bones.

Tendon comes from the Greek word *tenôn*, meaning "pull, stretch."

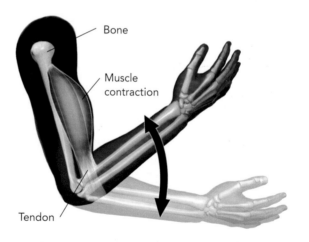

7.55 The muscle shortens when it contracts, then lengthens, resuming its original position.

SMOOTH MUSCLES

Smooth muscles make up the walls of certain internal organs, such as the bladder, stomach and uterus. They are involuntary. When they work they help substances to move from one place to another. Although smooth muscles are weaker than skeletal muscles, they have more endurance. They usually work slowly but tirelessly.

CARDIAC MUSCLE

As its name implies, this is the muscle that makes up the heart. It is a unique kind of muscle found nowhere else in the body. It is involuntary like the smooth muscles, with a structure similar to skeletal muscles and it has great strength and endurance.

The cardiac muscle forms the heart ventricles. When the heart is at rest, these cavities fill with blood. When the cardiac muscle contracts, the blood is propelled into the arteries and pumped into the rest of the body.

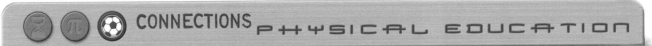

CONNECTIONS PHYSICAL EDUCATION

Fit muscles

Regular physical activity helps increase muscle strength and endurance.

A muscle's strength is determined by its tension during maximum contraction. You can see how strong your muscles are when you pick up a really heavy bag, move a piece of furniture or pull on the leash of a headstrong dog.

A muscle has endurance if it can repeat or maintain moderate contractions for a certain period of time. For example, the endurance level of your muscles will affect your ability to do sit-ups, ride a snowboard down an intermediate slope several times a day, or paint the walls of your bedroom with energy and enthusiasm.

A muscle that is strong and has stamina is said to be "fit" or "in shape." When your muscles are in shape, you can climb stairs, carry heavy objects or walk to school with more energy and less effort. You stand straighter and play sports better. All physical activities are improved, bone and tendon strength are increased, and the risk of injury and back problems is reduced. Last, but not least, when your muscles are in shape, you not only feel fit, you also experience a wonderful sense of well-being (improved body image and self-confidence).

When your muscles are in shape, you can do better in sports.

CHECKUP

 THE NERVOUS SYSTEM (p. 202–212)

1. The illustration below depicts the human nervous system. Name each of the structures indicated.

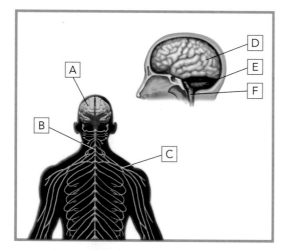

2. Relate each of the following examples to one or more functions of the nervous system, i.e. receiving, processing, storing or transmitting information.
   a) Feeling pain after being stung by an insect
   b) Sharing memories from a trip
   c) Raising your leg to avoid an obstacle
   d) Listening to your favourite music

3. The illustration below depicts two neurons. Name each of the structures indicated.

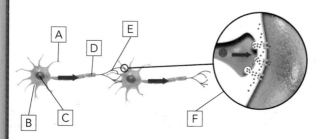

4. Name the chemical substances that help transmit nerve impulses from one neuron to another.

5. The brain communicates with the rest of the body via 12 pairs of nerves. Why are the nerves usually in pairs?

6. Name the region of the brain most likely responsible for each of the following activities:
   a) Singing a song
   b) Walking on a tightrope without falling
   c) Memorizing the script from a play
   d) Laughing at a funny joke
   e) Digesting a meal
   f) Walking to school

7. When the doctor taps your knee with a little hammer, he or she is testing your reflexes.
   a) Indicate the path taken by the nerve impulse during this procedure.
   b) Name the path taken by the nerve impulse.

8. Indicate whether the following examples refer to sensory nerves or motor nerves:
   a) The optic nerve conveys nerve impulses to the brain.
   b) Nerves transmit stimuli coming from the stomach.
   c) Certain nerves transmit nerve impulses to muscles surrounding the intestine.
   d) Certain nerves transmit stimuli coming from muscles.

2 THE SENSORY ORGANS (p. 213–220)

9. For each sensory organ:
   a) Name the sense associated with it.
   b) Name the structure where the related sensory receptors are located.
   c) Name the stimulus or stimuli detected by these sensory receptors.

   Write your answers in a table like the one below.

Organ	Sense	Structure where sensory receptors are located	Stimuli detected by sensory receptors

10. The lens accommodates according to the distance of the object observed. For each of the two illustrations below, indicate whether the object is near or far.

   a)    b)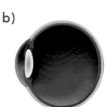

11. Name each structure indicated.

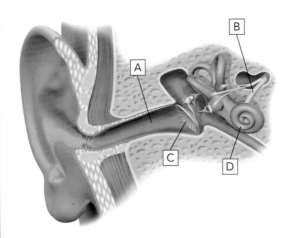

12. Why do we have the feeling that food has no flavour when our nose is congested?

13. What does each of the following phrases refer to?
   a) part of the retina where no image can be formed
   b) sensory receptors that detect tastes
   c) structures that play a role in balance
   d) organ that is responsible for vitamin D production
   e) transmitter of nerve impulses from the eye to the brain

3 THE MUSCULOSKELETAL SYSTEM (p. 221–228)

14. Name the type of bone for each of the following:
   a) cube-shaped bone, composed mainly of spongy bone
   b) bone that is longer than it is wide, composed mainly of compact bone
   c) bone of the spine
   d) bone that is flat

15. Describe the function of the bones referred to in each of the following cases:
   a) These skull bones surround the brain.
   b) Without bones, we would be as soft as a slug.
   c) Some patients with leukemia undergo a bone marrow transplant.
   d) Minerals are essential to the proper functioning of the organism.

16. What is the difference between a tendon and a ligament?

17. Indicate the joint movements illustrated in each example below.

a)

b)

c)

18. What function of muscles is described in each of the following situations?

   a) The members of the Royal Guard stand without moving for several hours at a time.

   b) The temperature of the body is maintained at about 37°C.

   c) Food moves into the esophagus.

   d) Muscles strengthen the junction between bones.

19. What type of muscle is involved in each of the following:

   a) the muscle that forms the ventricles of the heart

   b) the muscle that makes up the wall of internal organs

   c) the muscle that makes it possible to perform voluntary movements

CONCEPT MAPS

HOW TO BUILD A CONCEPT MAP

Prepare your own summary of Chapter 7 by building a concept map using the following terms.

- Bones
- Brain
- Brain stem
- Cardiac muscle
- Central nervous system
- Cerebellum
- Cerebrum
- Hypothalamus
- Joints
- Motor nerves
- Muscles
- Musculoskeletal system
- Nerves
- Nervous system
- Neurons
- Peripheral nervous system
- Sensory nerves
- Sensory organs
- Sensory receptors
- Skeletal muscles
- Smooth muscles
- Spinal cord

WHEN EMOTIONS OVERWHELM US

Our behaviour is often influenced by our emotions: joy, sadness, anger, fear or even surprise. We experience several of these emotions on a daily basis, but when a generalized feeling of sadness takes over, depression is imminent.

It is normal to feel depressed from time to time. Transitory feelings of depression can occur for various reasons. Some are psychological, related to our life experiences, such as the loss of someone we love or failure in school. Others are physiological in nature, meaning that they are related to our bodily function: for example, hormone levels, the number of hours of daylight, nutrition and sleep can affect our moods.

When dispirited feelings take over and prevent a person from leading a normal life, we speak of "depression." In people affected by depression, the neurotransmitters that should enable communication between the neurons are malfunctioning. The result is an imbalance in the central nervous system.

7.56 A person suffering from depression has difficulty leading a normal life.

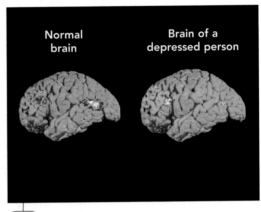

7.57 The brain activity of a person suffering from depression is less intense.

Depression is an illness that should be taken seriously. Treatment is generally two-fold and consists of:

- Medical treatment, which is based on taking medication that acts on the neurotransmitters to re-establish efficient communications between neurons.

- Psychological treatment, which is based on "talk therapy" that aims at correcting the way a person perceives his or her surroundings and at developing self-confidence.

1. A complete analysis of all the factors involved can produce a diagnosis of depression. Name some symptoms related to this illness.

2. Friends are often the first people to step in when someone is suffering from depression. Name some resources that could help them help a depressed friend.

ÉRICK VILLENEUVE

Érick Villeneuve designs and directs multimedia shows. When he creates a show, his main goal is to appeal to the audience's senses by communicating the emotions of the actors on stage. To do so, he uses special techniques that he has devised to create sound, olfactory and visual effects. One of these techniques involves the projection of slightly superimposed images to form a giant mosaic of very high resolution. Another uses motion detectors to synchronize the movements of an actor with music and image. Even smell plays a role in some shows designed by Villeneuve, where he uses the ventilation system to diffuse various scents throughout the theatre.

7.58 Érick Villeneuve staged and directed "Era, Intersection of Time," a permanent multimedia show performed in Shanghai, China.

| NAME |
| Érick Villeneuve |
| JOB |
| Multimedia designer, stage director and producer |
| AREA WHERE HE WORKS |
| Different parts of the world |
| EDUCATION |
| DCS in computer science (programmer-analyst) |
| PROUDEST ACHIEVEMENT |
| Developed staging techniques that appeal to all the senses of his audience |

7.59 OCCUPATIONS CONNECTED TO VILLENEUVE'S WORK

Occupation	Education	Length of study	Main tasks
Graphics designer	DPS desktop publishing	1800 hours	• Use technology and software to bring together various graphic elements
Designer of multimedia applications	DCS in Multimedia Integration Techniques	3 years	• Bring together and integrate multimedia content (texts, images, video, sound, etc.)
Building engineer	Bachelor's degree in building engineering	4 years	• Design, plan and supervise various aspects of construction

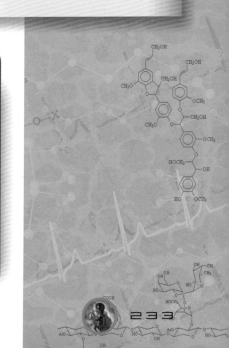

1998 — First culturing of human stem cells

1997 — First cloning of a mammal: Dolly the sheep

1978 — Birth of the first baby created through in-vitro fertilization

1972 — Creation of the first genetically modified organism (GMO): Genes are inserted into a bacterium

1939 — First culturing of plant cells

1928 — Discovery of penicillin

1907 — First culturing of animal cells

1897 — Discovery of the existence of viruses

1885 — First successful trials with rabies vaccine

1863 — Introduction of pasteurization

1798 — Creation of the first vaccine

1674 — Discovery of the existence of microorganisms

CIRCA **-3000** — Oldest evidence of yogurt production

6000 – 10 000 — Beginning of the production of cheese, leavened bread and wine, and the cultivation of wheat and barley

THE HUMAN ORGANISM

AND

BIOTECHNOLOGY

Biotechnology makes it possible to produce many things that we take for granted in everyday life. The bread, cheese and yogurt we eat and the milk we drink, for example, are produced through biotechnology, as are the pedigreed dog and the vaccines that protect us against disease. Someday our children may be conceived using the tools of biotechnology.

Today in our society, biotechnology is so widely found that some people say we are moving from the computer age to the age of biotechnology. Even as biothechnology's potential offers us hope, it also gives rise to fear. This is why it is so important to educate ourselves about the processes and applications of biotechnology. In this way, we can develop informed opinions about the risks as well as the benefits of this rapidly evolving field.

1 WHAT IS A BIOTECHNOLOGY?

As its name indicates, a biotechnology is a scientific method that relies on the study of living organisms (biology) and tools (technology). More specifically, biotechnologies use living organisms, such as bacteria, or substances derived from living organisms, such as genes, to meet a need or a want. For example, it is thanks to biotechnology that we can enjoy cheese and manufacture many medications, including antibiotics.

> *Biotechnology* comes from the Greek words *bios*, meaning "life," *teknê*, meaning "tools," and *logos*, meaning "study of."

CYCLE ONE
- Animal and plant cells
- Cellular components visible under a microscope
- Genes and chromosomes
- Asexual reproduction

▶ **BIOTECHNOLOGY** is the collection of technologies that are applied to living organisms or substances derived from living organisms in order to meet a need or a want.

Microorganisms are often used in biotechnology. Therefore, before describing the tools and applications of biotechnology, let's familiarize ourselves with some of the important terms related to microorganisms and microbiology (Figure 8.1).

Biotechnology uses many technologies. Those that were available early in human history are referred to as traditional biotechnologies (pages 237–238); those developed over the last three centuries or so are called modern biotechnologies (pages 239–248).

8.1 COMMON TERMS USED IN MICROBIOLOGY

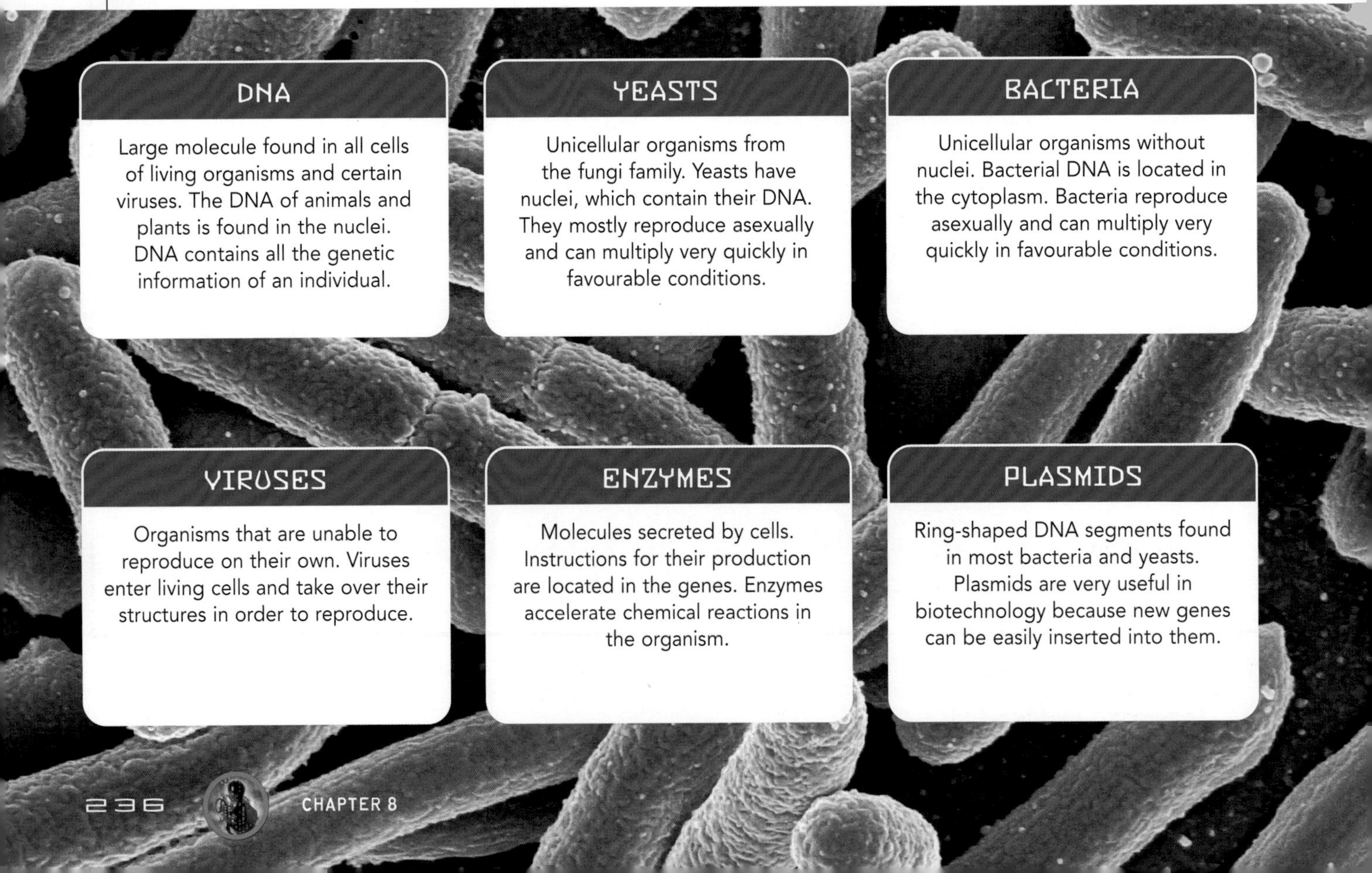

DNA

Large molecule found in all cells of living organisms and certain viruses. The DNA of animals and plants is found in the nuclei. DNA contains all the genetic information of an individual.

YEASTS

Unicellular organisms from the fungi family. Yeasts have nuclei, which contain their DNA. They mostly reproduce asexually and can multiply very quickly in favourable conditions.

BACTERIA

Unicellular organisms without nuclei. Bacterial DNA is located in the cytoplasm. Bacteria reproduce asexually and can multiply very quickly in favourable conditions.

VIRUSES

Organisms that are unable to reproduce on their own. Viruses enter living cells and take over their structures in order to reproduce.

ENZYMES

Molecules secreted by cells. Instructions for their production are located in the genes. Enzymes accelerate chemical reactions in the organism.

PLASMIDS

Ring-shaped DNA segments found in most bacteria and yeasts. Plasmids are very useful in biotechnology because new genes can be easily inserted into them.

2 TRADITIONAL BIOTECHNOLOGIES

Traditional biotechnologies were originally used in the fields of agriculture, breeding and food production.

CYCLE ONE
- Plant reproductive methods
- Animal reproductive methods
- Sexual reproduction
- Species
- Population

2.1 AGRICULTURE AND BREEDING

Traditional biotechnologies can be traced far back in human history. When our ancestors evolved from hunter-gatherers to farmers and breeders about 10 000 years ago, they noticed that the plants they used came in different varieties. Some had advantageous characteristics, or *traits*. Within the same species, for example, certain plants tasted better or produced more fruits and seeds, while others were more resistant to disease and drought.

Farmers selected and bred those plants that had desired traits. The selection and breeding processes were repeated with each new generation. After many generations, farmers were able to obtain a crop in which all plants had the desired traits.

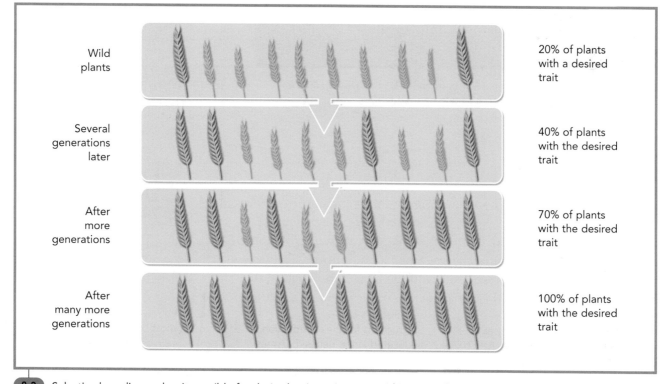

Wild plants	20% of plants with a desired trait
Several generations later	40% of plants with the desired trait
After more generations	70% of plants with the desired trait
After many more generations	100% of plants with the desired trait

8.2 Selective breeding makes it possible for desired traits to increase within a population. (Here we can see the increasing number of cereal plants with a desired trait produced over many generations.)

The technique of increasing the presence of desired traits within a population over many generations is called *selective breeding*; in this case, crop improvement is considered biotechnology since the technique involves manipulating living organisms to meet a specific need.

When humans first domesticated animals, they used these same methods of selective breeding to obtain cows that produced more milk, sheep that produced more wool and so on. They also developed new breeds of dogs.

Soft wheat

Durum wheat

8.4 Soft wheat and durum wheat are both varieties of the same wild species of wheat. Soft wheat was selected to produce flour ideal for baking. Durum wheat produces semolina, which is perfect for pasta.

Great Dane

Chihuahua

8.3 Although all dogs belong to the same species, selective breeding has produced striking differences among breeds.

2.2 FOOD

LABS 69 and 70

Humans have a long history of making important discoveries by accident. One such discovery came approximately 10 000 years ago, when people living in the Middle East noticed that the milk they stored in bags made from camel stomachs turned into cheese. Since they enjoyed the taste of the cheese, they continued to store milk in these bags. Subsequently, they diversified and improved on cheese-making techniques, resulting in the processes used today.

People did not really comprehend what was happening at the time. Now, we know that enzymes occurring naturally in the stomach secretions of camels help milk turn into cheese. Our ancestors were unknowingly using a type of biotechnology.

Nowadays, most enzymes used in cheese production are either synthesized in a lab or come from the stomachs of calves.

Cheese is not the only food item produced by traditional biotechnology, as shown in Table 8.5.

8.5 TRANSFORMATION OF VARIOUS FOODS

Base food	Organisms, or substances derived from organisms, that are used in food transformation	Transformed food
Milk	enzymes	cheese
Milk	bacteria	yogurt
Cereal (e.g. barley)	yeasts	beer
Cereal (e.g. wheat)	yeasts	leavened bread
Juice (e.g. grape juice)	yeasts	wine

8.6 By storing milk in camel stomachs, our ancestors accidentally discovered how to make cheese.

Although we still use methods from traditional biotechnology to manufacture various products, for the last three centuries we have come to rely more on new methods that have been developed in modern biotechnology.

3 MODERN BIOTECHNOLOGIES

Numerous technologies are used in modern biotechnology. They arise from a better understanding of biology, especially of cells and DNA, and are based on two methods in particular:

- Cell cultures involve the multiplication of strain(s) of cells that have been selected for specific purposes. The manufacture of vaccines, for example, is a biotechnology that calls for the use of many cell cultures.

- Genetic transformation involves the manipulation of genetic information. The technique is aimed at the cell nucleus or one or more genes. Clones are also produced by genetic transformation.

1881
1955

Alexander Fleming

In 1928, this Scottish biologist observed that all bacteria found near his mould samples died. He wondered whether the mould, a fungus from the *Penicillium notatum* species, secreted a substance that was able to kill bacteria. He isolated the substance, which he called *penicillin*, thus creating the first known antibiotic.

Modern biotechnology includes applications aimed not only at the chief targets of traditional biotechnology such as agriculture, breeding and food, but also at medicine, industrial production, the environment and so on. Table 8.7 contains some of the current uses of modern biotechnology that we will discuss in the following pages.

8.7 CURRENT USES OF MODERN BIOTECHNOLOGY

Targets	Examples	Techniques
Agriculture and breeding	Plants modified to resist sickness, insects, herbicides and harsh climatic conditions (such as cold and drought)	Genetic transformation
	Animals modified to accelerate growth or increase meat yield	Genetic transformation
Food	Foods transformed to provide higher nutritional value or to increase shelf life	Genetic transformation
Medicine	Viruses or bacteria transformed to make them harmless and cultivated to manufacture vaccines	Cell cultures and genetic transformation
	Embryos cultivated to treat infertility	Cell cultures
	Stem cells cultivated to engineer replacement tissue and organs	Cell cultures

To understand how these innovations are achieved, let's take a look at the techniques that are used, such as *cell cultures* and *genetic transformation*.

3.1 CELL CULTURES

Scientists have perfected cell culture techniques in order to cultivate the cells of microorganisms outside of their natural environment. Cell cultures allow scientists to control cell growth and obtain great quantities of the original microorganism or of related substances.

> ▶ A CELL CULTURE is a laboratory technique that involves growing or culturing cells outside of their natural environment.

Culturing cells refers to increasing the number of cells, not their size. Thus we say that there is a culturing of cells when the number of cells in a culture is increasing.

> ▶ CULTURING CELLS results in an increase in the number of cells in a cell culture.

METHOD FOR GROWING A CELL CULTURE

The principle of cell cultures is very simple: the cells are placed in favourable conditions and left to multiply.

LAB
71

The details of the technologies used to grow cells depend on whether the cells come from a unicellular or multicellular organism. The cells of unicellular organisms, such as bacteria and yeast, come from very diverse environments such as forest ecosystems, aquatic ecosystems or the digestive tracts of animals. In contrast, the cells of a multicellular organism play specialized roles inside a living organism (plant or animal). In each case, scientists must duplicate the growth conditions present in the environment of origin to ensure cell growth.

Unicellular contains the prefix *uni*, from the Latin *unus*, meaning "one."

Multicellular contains the prefix *multi*, from the Latin *multi*, meaning "many, much."

Figure 8.8 illustrates the process of culturing cells.

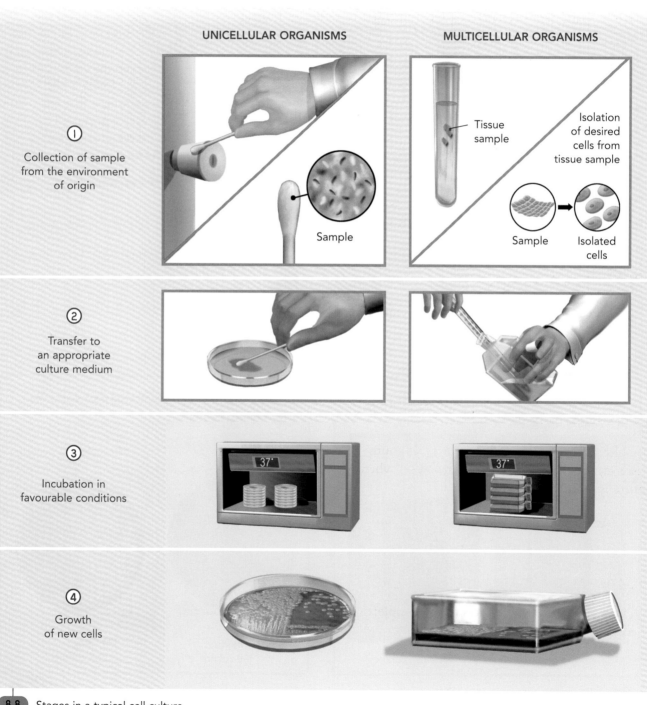

UNICELLULAR ORGANISMS   MULTICELLULAR ORGANISMS

① Collection of sample from the environment of origin

Sample

Tissue sample

Isolation of desired cells from tissue sample

Sample   Isolated cells

② Transfer to an appropriate culture medium

③ Incubation in favourable conditions

37°   37°

④ Growth of new cells

8.8 Stages in a typical cell culture

CELL CULTURE MEDIA

For cells to grow, samples must be placed in an environment that provides all the elements necessary to support growth. The environment is commonly referred to as a *culture medium* (pl. media).

> ▶ A CULTURE MEDIUM is an environment that contains all the necessary elements to promote cell growth in a culture.

The culture medium varies according to the nature of the cell sample. For example, a medium used to cultivate bacteria will not have the same constituents as a medium used to cultivate human cells.

The following parameters must be controlled in a culture medium:

- water level
- nutrient composition
- mineral level
- oxygen and carbon dioxide levels
- temperature
- pH
- amount of light (in the case of plant cells and bacteria, which require light to grow)

Culture media are usually either liquid or solid. A liquid medium can also be called a *broth*.

1843
1910

Robert Koch

In 1882, this German physician identified the microorganism responsible for tuberculosis, a disease affecting the lungs. Cell cultures enabled Koch to determine that the disease was caused by a bacterium, now called *Koch's Bacillus*.

LIQUID MEDIUM

A liquid medium is a broth in which all elements necessary for cell growth have been dissolved.

Before cell culture   After cell culture

SOLID MEDIUM

A solid medium is a broth containing a substance that has made it gelatinous.

Colony of microorganisms

Before cell culture   After cell culture

8.9 Liquid and solid media

Liquid media are most often used when rapid growth is desired, while solid media make it easier to inventory and identify certain microorganisms.

CELL CULTURE GROWTH AND PRESERVATION

Growth rate in a cell culture is not continuous; it follows a curve that can be divided into four phases:

1. Lag phase: Cells adapt to their new environment; there is little or no cell growth.

2. Logarithmic (log) phase: Cells rapidly divide and consume most of the nutrients contained in the culture medium.

3. Stationary phase: New cells are produced and other cells die at the same rate due to a depletion of nutrients, lack of space and/or too much waste.

4. Death phase: Cell numbers decrease due to a depletion of nutrients, lack of space and/or an accumulation of waste.

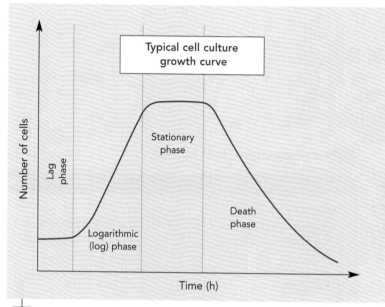

8.10 Cell cultures usually undergo four growth phases.

Cell growth rate begins to slow down at the end of the log phase.

If future analysis is planned, it is best to stop and preserve the cell culture at the stationary phase. Cell cultures that need to be preserved can be quickly frozen. There are companies that cultivate specific cell lines, freeze them and sell them to researchers, who need them for their work.

IMPORTANCE OF A STERILE ENVIRONMENT

When lab technicians grow a cell culture, they keep the culture medium and all materials in the laboratory sterile. The last thing they want is to contaminate the cultivated cells with other microorganisms.

Sterile comes from the Latin *sterilis*, meaning "barren, unproductive."

When lab technicians are finished with a cell culture, they destroy it thoroughly and carry out sterilization procedures to prevent any possibility of contamination.

▶ A STERILE ENVIRONMENT is one without any living microorganisms.

Anything left out in the open air, from tools and other equipment to work surfaces and floors, can become contaminated by microorganisms, as illustrated in Figure 8.11. The most common methods for sterilizing equipment are listed in Table 8.12.

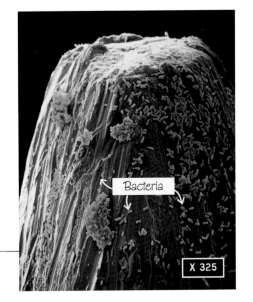

8.11

The tip of a needle can hold a large number of bacteria.

8.12 COMMON STERILIZATION METHODS

Method and description	Possible disadvantage
Dry heat Equipment is heated over a flame. The heat kills microorganisms.	Intense heat from the flame can melt material.
Hot air oven Equipment is heated inside an oven, killing microorganisms.	Equipment that is not heat-resistant can break.
Chemical Material is soaked in a chemical solution (e.g. hydrogen peroxide) or exposed to gas (e.g. ethylene oxide), killing microorganisms. An autoclave is used when sterilizing with gas.	Sterilizing substances are sometimes toxic to humans and difficult to manipulate safely.
Moist heat Usually carried out in an autoclave, a machine with a sealed chamber in which equipment to be sterilized is placed. The intense heat and pressure kill microorganisms.	Equipment not resistant to humidity cannot be sterilized with water vapour.
Irradiation Equipment is exposed to a radiation source (e.g. X-rays, ultraviolet rays and gamma rays) that kills microorganisms.	Exposure to radiation is harmful to humans.

8.13 Dry heat sterilization

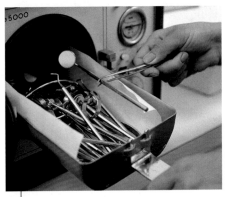

8.14 An autoclave

3.2 GENETIC TRANSFORMATION

All living organisms possess useful genetic adaptations. Today, it is possible to improve a species' ability to adapt to a particular environment by modifying its genetic information. This is done by adding one or more genes from another species or by removing or modifying its genes. This process is called *genetic transformation*.

The arctic flounder is a case in point. It lives at the bottom of the ocean where water is extremely cold (4°C). The fish can do this because its genes enable it to secrete a substance with anti-freezing properties that helps it resist the cold. On the other hand, salmon do not possess this resistance. Consequently, researchers isolated the arctic flounder's genes that help it resist the cold and inserted these genes into the salmon's DNA. The result? These salmon can now breed in cold waters.

> ▶ A GENETIC TRANSFORMATION is the modification of a species' genome either by removing or modifying one or more of its genes or by introducing genes from another species.

Genetic transformation can produce living organisms with traits they would not naturally possess.

8.15 The arctic flounder (above left) lives in frigid waters. Its genes enable it to secrete a substance that protects it from the cold. Researchers transferred those genes to salmon (above right.) The salmon is now able to resist the cold.

Living organisms produced through genetic transformation are called *genetically modified organisms,* or *GMOs*. They are increasingly referred to as *transgenic* organisms.

> ▶ A GMO (genetically modified organism) is a living organism that has had its DNA modified through genetic transformation to provide it with traits it would not otherwise possess.

In theory, all living organisms, whether bacteria, plant or animal, can be genetically modified. When traits acquired through genetic transformation are passed on to descendants, the latter are also GMOs.

PROCESS OF GENETIC TRANSFORMATION

To identify the stages of the most commonly used process of genetic transformation, we will use corn as an example. Corn is very important in agriculture since it is the most cultivated cereal plant in the world. Most of it is used for animal feed.

The European corn borer larva is an insect that can ravage corn crops. Researchers discovered that a bacterium, called *Bacillus thuringiensis,* or *Bt,* secretes a substance that kills the larva. Researchers added the gene that caused the secretion to the corn genome, creating a GMO called *Bt corn.* To date, this variety of corn appears to have no harmful effect on human or animal health.

Genetic transformations, like this one, basically follow the same steps. The steps are described in Figure 8.16.

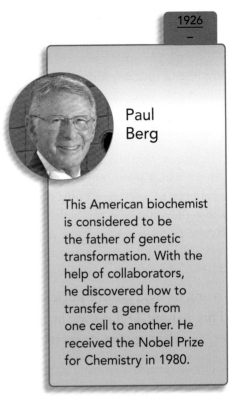

1926
–

Paul Berg

This American biochemist is considered to be the father of genetic transformation. With the help of collaborators, he discovered how to transfer a gene from one cell to another. He received the Nobel Prize for Chemistry in 1980.

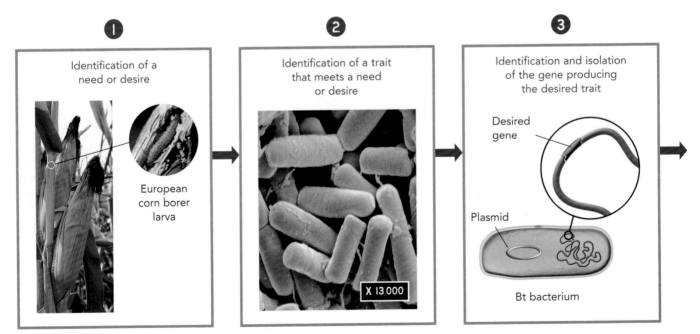

1 Identification of a need or desire

European corn borer larva

How to prevent the European corn borer larva from ravaging entire corn crops?

2 Identification of a trait that meets a need or desire

X 13 000

The Bt bacterium secretes a substance that kills the European corn borer larva.

3 Identification and isolation of the gene producing the desired trait

Desired gene

Plasmid

Bt bacterium

The gene responsible for producing the substance that kills the European corn borer larva is isolated.

8.16 Steps in a typical genetic transformation

CLONING

Living organisms that reproduce asexually produce genetically identical beings, essentially a natural cloning process. Most microorganisms and plants can reproduce this way. The results are called *clones*.

Other living organisms, such as humans, are incapable of reproducing asexually. The genetic transformation required to clone these organisms is called *artificial cloning*. The only exceptions are identical twins since they are basically natural clones of each other.

> ▶ **CLONING** is the process of producing a genetically identical copy of a living organism.

Artificial cloning consists of replacing the nucleus of an unfertilized ovum, or egg, with a nucleus from a cell of the organism to be cloned. This is how Dolly the sheep was created in 1997. Dolly was the first mammal cloned from a specialized adult cell.

The successful cloning of an adult mammal caused great controversy among many circles. Since we are also mammals, it is now theoretically possible to clone a human being.

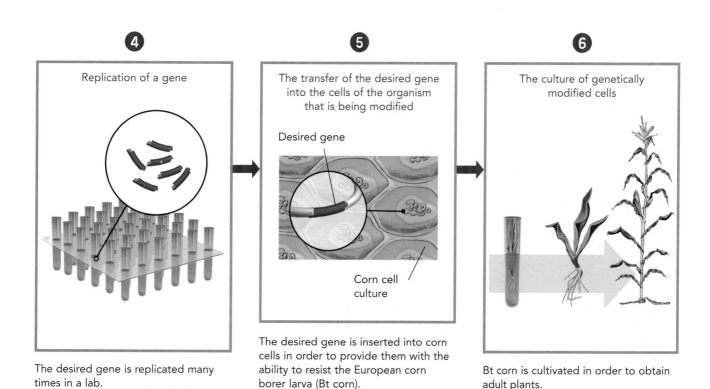

4 Replication of a gene

The desired gene is replicated many times in a lab.

5 The transfer of the desired gene into the cells of the organism that is being modified

Desired gene

Corn cell culture

The desired gene is inserted into corn cells in order to provide them with the ability to resist the European corn borer larva (Bt corn).

6 The culture of genetically modified cells

Bt corn is cultivated in order to obtain adult plants.

The cloning of a human being would serve the following two purposes:

- Reproductive cloning could be used to create an individual who is genetically identical to the one being cloned. In this case, the goal would be the birth of a child.

- Therapeutic cloning could be used to grow tissue or organs for a transplant. This kind of cloning would produce embryos whose cells could be cultivated to form a needed tissue or organ. Since the embryonic cells would contain the same genetic information as the person being cloned, it would avoid the problems of tissue or organ rejection that occur following a transplant.

In Canada, both types of human cloning are illegal.

8.17 Dolly the sheep

Starbuck II: made in Québec

In his holding pen at the Centre d'Insémination Artificielle du Québec in Saint-Hyacinthe, Starbuck II is an impressive bull weighing in at one tonne with a waist circumference measuring more than the height of a human being. What is most striking is not his stature, but his ancestry: he has neither mother or father.

Starbuck II is a clone, produced from a piece of the ear of the legendary bull Starbuck.

The original Starbuck fathered an estimated 200 000 cows and hundreds of bulls before his death in 1998. His sperm has been sold in more than 70 countries in order to expand the genetic lineage of this almost perfect bull specimen.

Although Starbuck's clone has also produced sperm, it remains in Saint-Hyacinthe, stockpiled in freezers. The reason: it is illegal in Canada, as in many other countries, to sell eggs, milk or meat from cloned animals.

Adapted from Philippe Mercure,
"Les animaux clonés dans votre assiette,"
La Presse, January 15, 2006,
Plus, p. 6. [*Translation*]

Starbuck II is a clone of the bull Starbuck.

4. APPLICATIONS IN THE AGRO-FOOD INDUSTRY

Modern biotechnology has many applications in the agro-food industry. Let's first examine how GMOs are used in agriculture and breeding, then we can take a look at a process, called *pasteurization*, that prolongs food conservation.

4.1 GMOs

Genetic engineering researchers have developed many genetically modified organisms. In Canada, the Canadian Food Inspection Agency, along with Health Canada and Environment Canada, manage the development of GMOs. Before approving the cultivation of a GMO or the production of a food product containing GMOs, the Canadian government ensures that there is no risk to human or environmental health. Producers are not yet required to indicate on labels whether their products contain GMOs.

GENETICALLY MODIFIED PLANTS

Farmers are forever searching for ways to improve their crops. Until the mid-20th century, they relied mostly on traditional biotechnologies, such as selective breeding. With the availability of modern biological techniques, farmers can now count on genetic transformation to improve their yield.

Listed below are some traits that improve either crop yield or shelf life and that have been added to plants worldwide through genetic transformation:

- resistance to herbicides (corn, soy, flax, canola, cotton, beets)
- resistance to insects (corn, potatoes, tomatoes, cotton)
- resistance to viruses (squash, papaya, potatoes)
- delayed ripening (tomatoes)

Genetic transformations have also improved harvests and the nutritional properties of certain cultivated plants. Here are a few examples:

- improvement of the quality of oils (soy, canola)
- increase in the quantity of certain nutritional substances (rice)
- reduction in allergic effects (peanuts, soy, rice, potatoes)

> **THE GOLDEN RICE CONTROVERSY**
>
> Swiss researchers have developed a variety of rice called *golden rice*. It can produce beta-carotene, a substance our bodies can transform into vitamin A. The goal of these researchers is to help people in developing nations who suffer from vitamin A deficiency and who rely on rice as a main staple. Some individuals, however, believe these people should be provided with diversified food sources instead of GMOs.

Already, large quantities of corn, soy and canola crops cultivated in Québec are GMOs. Most other crops in the province, however, are not.

The amount of corn cultivated in Québec in 2005: 3 450 000 tonnes

The amount of soy cultivated in Québec in 2005: 540 000 tonnes

The amount of canola cultivated in Québec in 2005: 11 800 tonnes

8.18 The proportion of GMO in Québec's corn, soy and canola crops in 2005
Source: Government of Québec

Non GMO
GMO

GENETICALLY MODIFIED ANIMALS

Scientific breakthroughs are not as frequent in the field of animal breeding as they are in plants because of higher research costs and the complexity of the modifications involved.

In addition, it is illegal in Canada to market a genetically modified animal.

Here are some results (potential or real) of genetic modification that could eventually be carried out or have already been carried out on animals:

- increase in growth rate (salmon)
- development of manure that is less harmful to the environment (pigs)
- production of lactose-free milk (mice, cows)
- production of milk more similar to human milk (cows)

8.19 The larger salmon pictured above is a GMO with a growth-accelerating gene. The smaller fish is a natural salmon of the same age.

ANIMAL TESTING: FOR OR AGAINST?

Research labs around the world often use animals when conducting various tests and trials, such as verifying drug toxicity. While it is sometimes possible to use tissue and organ cultures or computer models instead of animals, these methods are not yet frequently used.

Benefits	Concerns
• can produce desired results after only one generation • can transfer a useful gene from one species to another • could establish a gene bank • can improve harvests due to the development of GMOs that are resistant to herbicides or insecticides • can produce more nutritional foods • can produce less allergenic foods	• risk that GMOs hazardous to humans and other species could be accidentally created since gene behaviour is not yet fully understood • risk of creating new allergies • risk that biodiversity will be compromised by only cultivating transgenic plants • risk that insect pest resistance of certain transgenic plants could lead to the disappearance of useful insects • risk that the resistance of some GMOs to herbicides could be transferred to weeds • risk that GMO pollen could invade other crops and thus control over GMOs would be threatened

4.2 PASTEURIZATION

Culturing cells in a favourable medium makes it possible for them to multiply. By the same token, some foods can become culture media for undesirable microorganisms, whose proliferation could alter foods and turn them into health risks. The following are examples of media in which many microorganisms find ideal growth conditions: milk, cream, fruit juices, beer, wine and cider.

Pasteurization is often used to prevent the proliferation of harmful microorganisms in food.

During pasteurization, food is heated to a specific temperature for a particular length of time, determined by the nature of the product.

Heating time and temperature settings are established in order to kill most unwanted microorganisms without altering the taste or nutritional properties of the food.

1822
1895

Louis Pasteur

Pasteurization is named after this famous French scientist who developed the process in 1863. A group of merchants wanted to know why beer and wine acquired a vinegary taste with time. Pasteur discovered that microorganisms were the culprits, and that they could be destroyed when heated.

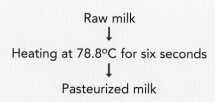

Raw milk
↓
Heating at 78.8°C for six seconds
↓
Pasteurized milk

8.21 Method for pasteurizing milk

The pasteurization of milk: putting children first

Stuart Foster, a doctor from the Hospital for Sick Children in Toronto, established the first milk pasteurization plant in Canada in 1908, 30 years before the process became mandatory in this country. Foster and his team wanted to maintain the health of children by destroying the bacteria that developed in milk during its transportation and preservation.

At the time, one out of four children in Québec died before age one. This was the highest infant mortality rate both in Canada and the rest of North America. The children were dying in part because they drank the milk that was delivered in uncovered bottles door-to-door. Such milk was prone to contamination, and thus encouraged the spread of diseases such as tuberculosis, cholera and typhoid fever. Pasteurized milk was available in Montréal, but only in privileged neighbourhoods.

In 1926, the government of Québec made the pasteurization of milk mandatory. But the legislation spurred debate among Québec politicians who found the process too expensive and potentially ruinous to small dairy farmers.

In the meantime, various health measures were established in the cities, the most effective being *Gouttes de Lait*, dispensaries organized in parishes for the distribution of quality milk to children. The most famous *Gouttes de lait* was located at Sainte-Justine Hospital in Montréal.

At the start of the 20th century, the practice of delivering non-pasteurized milk door-to-door encouraged the spread of harmful bacteria.

▶ **PASTEURIZATION** is a process whereby food is heated for a time in order to destroy harmful microorganisms.

Pasteurization is carried out for three main reasons:
- to provide healthier food
- to prolong the shelf life of food
- to preserve the nutritional properties of food

Food that has been pasteurized must still be refrigerated in order to slow the growth rate of any microorganisms left intact by the pasteurization process. Pasteurized milk left on the counter at room temperature, for example, should be discarded after several hours.

Canadian law requires that milk be treated prior to its consumption to eliminate any trace of harmful microorganisms. Of all available treatment methods, such as irradiation, ultracentrifugation and microfiltration, pasteurization is by far the most commonly used.

8.22 PASTEURIZATION : BENEFITS AND CONCERN

Benefits	Concern
• reduces risk of food contamination • reduces infant mortality rates	• can destroy useful elements in food, such as "good" bacteria and vitamins

5 MEDICAL APPLICATIONS

The medical field has greatly benefited from modern biotechnology. In the area of diagnostic medicine, for example, diagnostic procedures have become easier due to our ability to grow cell cultures of blood, urine and tissue samples. In addition, genetic transformation has resulted in innovative treatments that offer new hope for people suffering, for example, from genetic disorders, cancer or Alzheimer's. Numerous valuable medications have been produced with the aid of genetically modified bacteria, plants and animals.

This section focuses on three ways biotechnology has been applied in medicine: vaccination, infertility treatment and the production of engineered tissue and organs.

5.1 VACCINATIONS

Our body's immune system protects us from many disease-causing agents by producing white blood cells and antibodies. When we develop a resistance to a disease-causing infectious agent, it is said that we are immune to the disease caused by the agent.

> ▶ IMMUNITY is the capacity to resist a disease to which we have been exposed by being able to fight off the infectious agent that causes the disease.

White blood cells defend our bodies in two ways:

• by destroying infectious agents through **PHAGOCYTOSIS**

• by producing antibodies, which are able to neutralize the infectious agents and the antigens they produce (Chapter 6, page 189)

1749
1823

Edward Jenner

This British doctor observed that individuals who had come into contact with cows suffering from cowpox almost never contracted smallpox. The infected cows produced pus, a substance containing white cells and weak or dead infectious agents. He found that when he injected the pus into healthy people, they were immunized against smallpox. This was the first vaccine ever developed.

THE IMMUNE RESPONSE

When an infectious agent invades our body for the first time, our immune system produces antibodies to defeat it. It can take a few days, even weeks, before the right antibodies are produced in the amounts needed to neutralize the infectious agent. If the infectious agent is really dangerous, it may have enough time to reproduce and cause serious damage before being neutralized.

Once an infectious agent invades the body and is defeated by our immune system, the body is armed against another invasion: the immune system "remembers" how to produce the necessary antibodies. In addition, copies of the antibodies remain in our system even after the infectious agent is destroyed. Thus, if exposure to the infectious reoccurs, our bodies already possess the antibodies to fight the agent and are able to produce even more within 12 to 24 hours. Because the infectious agent is disarmed or destroyed quickly, the disease episode is much less severe.

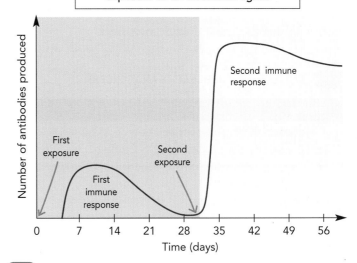

The immune response following exposure to an infectious agent

8.23 In this example, the individual took several days to react following the first exposure to an infectious agent. After the second exposure (and all subsequent ones), the response was not only faster, but also more intense (that is, a higher number of antibodies were produced).

THE ROLE OF VACCINATIONS

Vaccinations introduce weakened, also called *attenuated*, infectious agents of a disease into the body. An infectious agent that has been weakened cannot hurt us.

The attenuated agent in the vaccine is strong enough to "teach" our immune system how to fight the disease, but not strong enough to actually trigger a full-blown episode of the disease. Even if the immune system takes several days to respond, our health is not harmed.

If an infectious agent against which we have been vaccinated invades the body, it is defeated quickly because our immune system already has the necessary antibodies to fight it. The body is also able to produce additional antibodies quickly. This is how a vaccination protects an individual against disease.

> ▶ A VACCINE is a prepared substance that is able to immunize an organism against one or several diseases.

Although vaccines are usually administered by injection, there are a few that can be given orally.

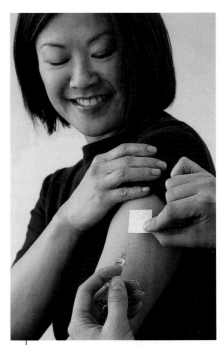

8.24 Most vaccines are administered through injection.

VACCINE MANUFACTURING

The manufacture of a vaccine begins with a massive cell culture of the infectious agent.

The cultured cells are treated to render them harmless. There are two treatment methods. Depending on the method chosen, the result is either a live vaccine or an inactive vaccine.

Live vaccines

To obtain a live vaccine, cultures of the infectious agent are chemically treated to remove its ability to cause illness. The cells of the now attenuated agent are then mixed with pharmaceutical products to improve their shelf life. The infectious agent is still alive, but it has lost its ability to cause disease.

Recently, new technologies using genetic transformation have also been developed to manufacture live vaccines. These methods transform the agent genetically to make it harmless. The infectious agent, therefore, no longer needs to be chemically treated in order to be used in a vaccine.

BIRD FLU:
QUÉBEC GETS READY

The government of Québec has stockpiled about 13 million doses of an antiviral agent for the treatment of its citizens should they become sick during an epidemic of bird flu. This reserve is part of a broader emergency plan, which includes the vaccination of the entire population of Québec. The vaccines have not yet been manufactured since any virus that could cause such an epidemic is still unknown.

Production of a live vaccine

TRADITIONAL METHOD	METHOD USING GENETIC TRANSFORMATION
Culture of infectious agent	Genetic transformation of infectious agent
↓	↓
Chemical treatment of infectious agent to render it harmless	Culture of modified infectious agent
↓	↓
Addition of agent to pharmaceutical products	Addition of agent to pharmaceutical products

 8.25 Two methods of manufacturing a live vaccine

Inactive vaccines

Inactive vaccines are developed using only a part or parts of an infectious agent that can still be recognized by antibodies. These part(s) are called *antigens*.

The first step is to identify the disease-causing antigens. Once these antigens are identified, they are isolated and chemically treated to render them harmless. The weakened antigens are then mixed with chemical products to improve shelf life. An inactive vaccine, naturally, does not contain any live infectious agents.

In 1985, genetic transformation produced the first inactive vaccine. The vaccine immunized people against the virus that causes hepatitis B. By transforming the genome of bacteria, yeasts or cells of animals, it is possible to produce antigens of an infectious agent in vast quantities.

Production of an inactive vaccine

TRADITIONAL METHOD	METHOD USING GENETIC TRANSFORMATION
Culture of infectious agent	Introduction of a gene causing production of desired antigens in a microorganism
↓	↓
Isolation of antigen	Culture of modified microorganism
↓	↓
Addition of antigen to pharmaceutical products	Isolation of antigen
	↓
	Addition of antigen to pharmaceutical products

 8.26 Two methods of manufacturing an inactive vaccine

Vaccine against cervical cancer

Experts say 60 percent of women under 25 are carriers of the human papilloma virus (HPV). Most of these women eliminate the virus naturally, while the unlucky ones risk developing cervical cancer. About 325 women are diagnosed with cervical cancer in Québec every year.

If the cancer is detected early, survival rates are 95 percent. Screening is done by Pap tests given during gynecological examinations.

Women and girls can now choose to get vaccinated against some forms of HPV. The vaccine for HPV has been available free of charge to Québec girls in Primary 2, Cycle 2 (grade 4) to Secondary 2, Cycle 1 (grade 9) since fall 2008. During these years, girls can be vaccinated if their parents request it. Parents have to sign a consent form for girls under 14, but the vaccine is free up to age 18.

Adapted from Marie Caouette, "Il existe un vaccin contre le cancer du col de l'utérus," *Le Soleil*, December 19, 2006, p. A8. *[Translation]*

Also, "Québec girls to be offered free HPV vaccine," *cbcnews.ca* website, April 11, 2008.

Cervical cancer is the only cancer that can be prevented by a vaccine.

Live vaccines generally cause a more agressive immune response than inactive vaccines. There is even a very slight risk for a weakened infectious agent to regain its **VIRULENCE**. On rare occasions, a live vaccine containing a weakened infectious agent could cause the disease, instead of immunizing against it.

VACCINATIONS IN QUÉBEC

To prevent potentially deadly infectious diseases, the government of Québec has established a vaccination schedule it recommends for all its citizens. The vaccines are not mandatory. Citizens, however, can pay for them through the Régie d'Assurance Maladie du Québec. Additional vaccines are sometimes recommended for at-risk populations. For example, the government recommends that all children under two receive the flu shot. Older people may also be vaccinated against the flu, but they have to pay a fee.

Table 8.27 includes certain vaccines, called *combination vaccines*, that immunize against several diseases at the same time. Some vaccines are given in multiple doses, called *boosters*. Boosters are given to stimulate the immune system into maximum effectiveness against serious disease.

EDIBLE VACCINES

Reasearchers are working to develop transgenic tomatoes, which are able to immunize humans against hepatitis B and perhaps AIDS. Should this research be successful, we might one day see edible vaccines on the market, available in even the poorest countries.

8.27 REGULAR VACCINATION SCHEDULE FOR QUEBECKERS IN 2008

Vaccine	Diseases prevented by vaccine	Types of vaccine	Age for first dose	Age for booster
DTaP-Polio-Hib	• diphtheria (D) • tetanus (T) • pertussis (whooping cough) (aP) • poliomyelitis (polio) • severe *Haemophilus influenzae* type b infections (Hib)	inactive	2 months	at 4, 6 and 18 months and between 4 and 6 years (without Hib)
Pneumococcus	• serious pneumococcal infections	inactive	2 months	at 4 and 12 months and at age 65
Influenza	• flu	inactive	between 6 and 23 months and at age 60	none
Chickenpox	• chickenpox	live	12 months	none
MMR	• measles (M) • mumps (M) • rubella (German measles) (R)	live	12 months	at 18 months
Meningococcus	• group C meningococcal infections	inactive	12 months	none
Hepatitis B	• hepatitis B	inactive	9 years	none
DTaP	• diphteria (D) • tetanus (T) • pertussis (whooping cough) (aP)	inactive	between 14 and 16 years (also indicated for all adults)	every 10 years

Source: Ministère de la Santé et des Services sociaux, Government of Québec

Benefits	Concerns
• protect against serious diseases	• can cause unpleasant side effects (e.g. allergic reactions)
• prevent contracting a disease before becoming immunized against it	• can cause new resistant strains of a disease to develop
• lower infant mortality rates and increase life expectancy	• risk that a weakened infectious agent could become virulent again
• help eradicate certain diseases (e.g. smallpox)	

5.2 TREATMENTS FOR INFERTILITY

From a medical standpoint, infertility is defined as the inability to conceive a child after 12 months of sexual relations without use of contraception. In Canada, between 10 and 15 percent of couples are infertile.

Certain couples turn to adoption or biotechnology to have a child. When biotechnology is used for procreation (to have children), the process is called *assisted reproduction*.

> ▶ ASSISTED REPRODUCTION refers to all medical procedures used to help women become pregnant.

Assisted reproduction techniques include ovarian stimulation, artificial insemination, in vitro fertilization and fertilization by microinjection.

OVARIAN STIMULATION

Ovarian stimulation involves the use of medication to stimulate ovaries into developing one or more mature follicles and eggs in a single ovarian cycle. Stimulation encourages one or more mature ova to be released at the same time, thus increasing the odds of fertilization. This technique is generally used for women who rarely or never ovulate.

CYCLE ONE
- Fertilization
- Gametes
- Pregnancy
- Reproductive organs

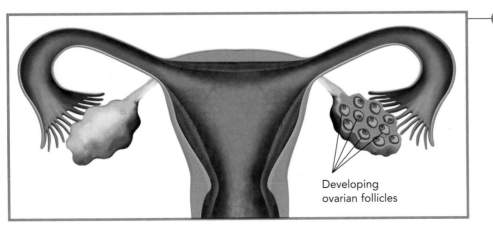

8.29 Ovarian stimulation

Developing ovarian follicles

ARTIFICIAL INSEMINATION

Artificial insemination is an option for women having difficulty conceiving because the sperm cannot pass through the cervix, or the sperm count or sperm motility (ability to move) are low. The technique consists of injecting semen directly into the uterus on the day of ovulation. The semen may be treated prior to insemination to increase sperm count.

> *Insemination* comes from the Latin *inseminare*, meaning "to sow."

IN VITRO FERTILIZATION

This technique involves the fertilization of an ovum by a sperm cell in a lab (using a test tube or petri dish), instead of in the fallopian tubes. After two to seven days of growth in a culture, the most viable embryos are implanted in the uterus to continue their development until birth. Babies conceived through in vitro fertilization are sometimes called *test-tube* babies, despite having spent only a few days in the lab.

In vitro fertilization is carried out in four steps:

> *In vitro* is a Latin expression meaning "in glass."

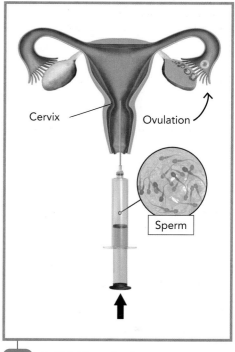

8.30 Artificial insemination

1. Ovarian stimulation

   The woman undergoes ovarian stimulation to develop multiple mature follicles and eggs at the same time. Numerous ova are produced as a result.

2. Retrieval of ova and collection of sperm

   Following ovulation, zygotes are retrieved from the follicles. The semen is usually collected the same day.

3. Fertilization in the lab

   Ova and sperm cells are placed together in a test tube or petri dish. Once fertilized, zygotes are transferred to a culture medium that is hospitable to embryonic development.

4. Transfer of embryos to the uterus

   After two to seven days of growth, the most developed embryos are transferred to the uterus. Two to four embryos may be transferred at a time to ensure at least one develops normally. Untransferred embryos may be frozen and later implanted in the uterus should the first attempt fail or the couple decide to have other children.

> ### IN VITRO FERTILIZATION AND PRENATAL SCREENING
>
> Couples with a high probability of passing on a severe hereditary disease to their children sometimes use in vitro fertilization despite being fertile. This means that their embryos can be screened and only those that are healthy are implanted.

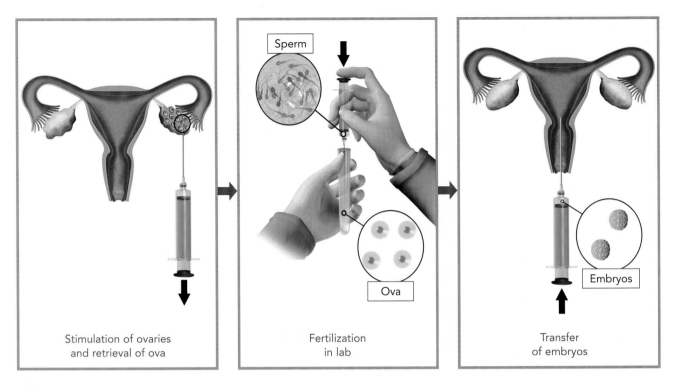

8.3l Steps of in vitro fertilization

FERTILIZATION BY MICROINJECTION

Fertilization by microinjection follows the same steps as in vitro fertilization. The difference here is that during fertilization in the lab, the physician injects the sperm cells directly into the ova with a microsyringe.

This technique is used when there is low sperm count or fertilization poses a problem. Should the semen contain little or no sperm, the physician may attempt to extract some directly from the testicles or epididymis.

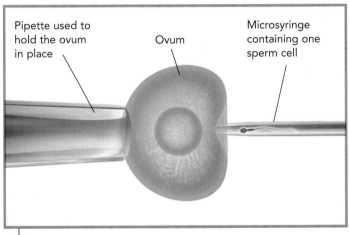

8.32 Fertilization by microinjection

8.33 INFERTILITY TREATMENTS: BENEFIT AND CONCERNS

Benefit	Concerns
• Infertile couples are able to have children.	• risk of multiple births (twins, triplets, etc.) • high cost of treatment (accessible only to wealthier couples) • risk that in vitro fertilization produces embryos that will not develop and could be frozen for stem cell use (see Concerns about stem cell culture, page 263) • risk of embryos being selected purely for desired traits (e.g. gender, eye colour)

Boy or girl?
Take your pick!

Thousands of couples from around the world are visiting a clinic in the United States where a cutting-edge technique provides them with a controversial $19 000 luxury of choosing the sex of their unborn child.

According to the clinic's director, Dr. Jeffrey Steinberg, more than half the couples who visit his Los Angeles-based fertility clinic are from China, Singapore, Thailand, Japan, Germany, Great Britain and other countries, where gender selection is banned.

The selection technique involves extracting several eggs from the woman and fertilizing them in vitro. A genetic test is then performed to determine which embryos will produce a boy or a girl and the selected embryos are then implanted in the uterus.

Bioethicists argue that the practice will reinforce gender imbalances. In countries like China and India, where couples prefer to conceive boys, a shortage of girls can already be seen.

Adapted from Agence France-Presse, "Choisir le sexe de son enfant: un luxe controversé," *Le Soleil*, May 14, 2006, p. 10. *[Translation]*

A Los Angeles clinic helps couples choose the sex of their unborn child.

5.3 TISSUE AND ORGAN ENGINEERING

Our bodies are made up of two types of cells: specialized cells and stem cells. Specialized cells play specific roles in the body. For example, cells in the liver produce substances that aid in digestion, while nerve cells transmit nerve impulses. These are just 2 out of 200 different types of specialized cells found in the human organism.

> SPECIALIZED CELLS play specific roles in the human body. When a specialized cell divides, it produces cells that have the same specialized functions as it does.

When a specialized cell is cultured, it produces cells with the same specialized functions. Cultured muscle cells only produce muscle cells, cultured skin cells only produce skin cells. In addition, specialized cells cannot divide indefinitely; the ability to divide varies from one cell type to another. For example, there would be no point in trying to culture neurons since most of them do not divide.

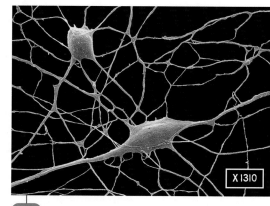

X 1310

8.34 Neurons are specialized cells that transmit nerve impulses.

Although stem cells have no specific function, they do have two important properties:

- They can divide almost indefinitely.
- They can become specialized under the right conditions.

> ▶ A STEM CELL is a cell that does not play any particular role in the human organism. It has the capacity, however, to divide many times and to transform into a variety of specialized cells.

Due to these two properties, stem cells can be used to engineer replacement tissue and organs.

An adult has more specialized cells than stem cells. Most stem cells are found in the blood and bone marrow, although the first embryonic cells are stem cells. As the embryo moves through various stages of development, these stem cells become specialized. It is possible to extract stem cells from the embryo, umbilical cord or placenta.

8.35 Stem cells from the blood of a human embryo

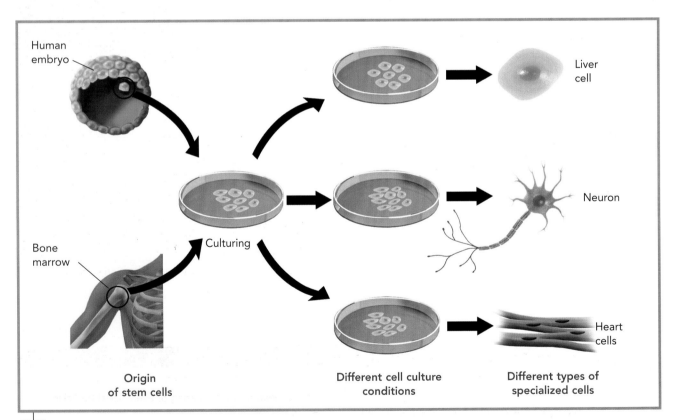

8.36 Stem cells can change into different kinds of specialized cells. Culturing them makes it possible to create replacement tissue and organs.

THE ETHICS INVOLVED IN CULTURING STEM CELLS

The culturing of stem cells has raised controversy because some people believe that human life begins when a sperm fertilizes an egg and, therefore, it is morally wrong to use embryos to culture stem cells.

The National Research Council of Canada has established ethical standards regarding the use of stem cell cultures. Scientists planning to use stem cells in cell cultures must adhere to these standards, which ensure that the moral principles reflecting our society's values are being respected.

▶ An **ETHICAL STANDARD** is a norm created to ensure that certain moral principles are being respected.

The following are a few of the ethical standards related to stem cell use:

- The embryos used must not be obtained through commercial transactions.
- A pregnant woman who donates her embryo must do so of her own free will.
- A pregnant woman who donates her embryo must be informed should the embryo be used for stem cell research.
- Stem cell research may use the umbilical cord and placenta if both parents consent.
- Embryonic stem cells may only be obtained with the consent of the donor. Consent of a parent or guardian is required in cases involving minors.

UMBILICAL CORD BLOOD

In addition to managing blood donations, Héma-Québec maintain the only public umbilical cord blood bank in the province. The blood is donated by consenting mothers who give birth to their babies at Sainte-Justine and Saint Mary's hospitals in Montréal.

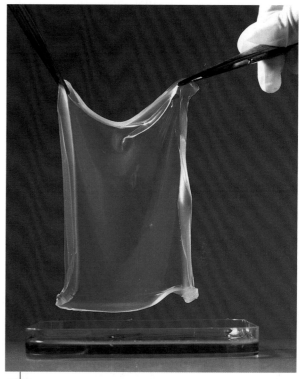

8.37 Epithelial tissue obtained through stem cell culturing

8.38 STEM CELL CULTURES: BENEFITS AND CONCERNS

Benefits	Concerns
• may lead to a cure for certain types of blood and lymph-node cancers • may lead to a cure for Alzheimer's, Parkinson's, multiple sclerosis and various heart diseases	• may lead to the destruction of human embryos • may lead to the marketing or even illegal trafficking of embryos

CHECKUP

① WHAT IS A BIOTECHNOLOGY? (p. 236)

1. What is the difference between technology and biotechnology?

2. What am I?
   a) To replicate, I have to get into a cell and use its structures.
   b) I help accelerate chemical reactions in the body.
   c) I am a unicellular organism without a nucleus.
   d) I am a unicellular mould.
   e) I am a ring-shaped segment of genetic information.
   f) I am a molecule containing an individual's genetic information.

② TRADITIONAL BIOTECHNOLOGIES (pp. 237–239)

3. When did human beings start using biotechnology?

4. How is selective breeding different from natural breeding?

5. Brittany retrievers are great in finding and fetching game because they have been selected for their sense of smell and for their calm and cautious nature. Provide two examples of desired traits used when breeding Malamute huskies.

6. Look at the photos below.
   a) Identify the product(s) made using enzymes.
   b) Identify the product(s) made using yeast.

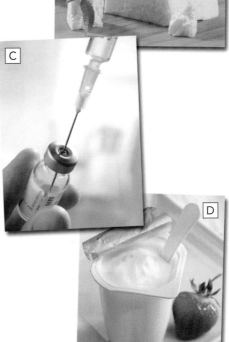

3 MODERN BIOTECHNOLOGIES
(pp. 239–248)

7. Give two reasons that explain the development of modern biotechnology.

8. What is the meaning of the term *cell growth* in a cell culture?

9. Illustrated below are the steps to follow when culturing unicellular organisms. The steps are not in the correct sequence. Name them and order them correctly.

A

B

C

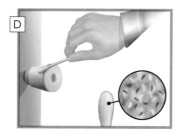
D

10. A culture medium must have all the elements necessary for cell growth.

   a) What are the seven main parameters that must be considered when preparing a culture medium?

   b) What are the two types of culture media?

11. The diagram below illustrates the growth curve of a typical cell culture. Name and describe each of the four phases.

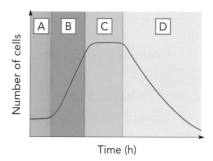

12. Why should lab equipment be sterilized before and after use in a cell culture?

13. The following statements describe various methods used to sterilize lab equipment. Name the methods described in each statement.

   a) This method destroys microorganisms using an oven.

   b) This method destroys microorganisms using irradiation.

   c) This method destroys microorganisms using a flame.

   d) This method destroys microorganisms using a liquid solution or gas.

   e) This method destroys microorganisms using pressure and high temperature.

14. GMOs are spoken of and written about frequently these days.

   a) What does GMO stand for?

   b) What process makes it possible to create GMOs?

   c) Describe the six steps needed to obtain a GMO.

15. Cloning is a controversial issue.
    a) What is cloning?
    b) What is artificial cloning?
    c) What is the difference between reproductive and therapeutic cloning?
    d) What is Canada's position on human cloning?

16. Cloning also occurs naturally.
    a) Give an example of natural clones in plants.
    b) Give an example of natural clones in animals.

17. Why do breeders use artificial insemination rather than natural reproduction methods to increase the size of their herds?

 AGRO-FOOD APPLICATIONS (pp. 249–253)

18. GMOs are a controversial subject.
    a) Give three examples to illustrate the benefits of GMOs.
    b) Identify three concerns associated with the use of GMOs.

19. Name three traits that have been added to plants to improve crop yield.

20. Why do farmers prefer growing herbicide-resistant genetically modified plants?

21. Name three genetically modified crops that are grown in significant quantities in Québec.

22. Why is it easier to genetically modify a plant rather than an animal? Give two reasons.

23. Pasteurization is a treatment process applied to some foods.
    a) What is the purpose of pasteurization?
    b) How is pasteurization carried out?
    c) Why do we pasteurize some types of food and not others?

 MEDICAL APPLICATIONS (pp. 253–263)

24. Vaccines strengthen immunity against several infectious agents. What is immunity?

25. Study the following illustrations and name the type of vaccine shown in each case.

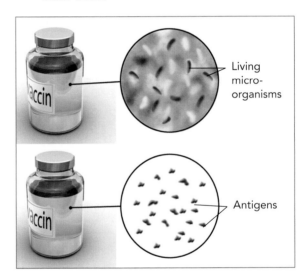

26. According to Québec's regular vaccination schedule, all children must get an MMR vaccine.
    a) Against what diseases does this vaccine develop protection?
    b) How many doses should a child receive and at what age(s)?

27. What is assisted reproduction?

28. Illustrated below are four techniques used to treat infertility. Name them.

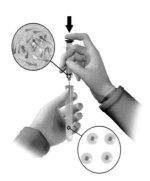

1

2

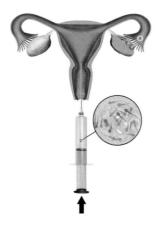

3

4

29. The human organism is made up of two types of cells: specialized cells and stem cells.

a) Describe each type.

b) Why is the culturing of stem cells so controversial?

CONCEPT MAPS

HOW TO BUILD A CONCEPT MAP

Prepare your own summary of chapter 8 by building a concept map using the following terms:

- Applications
- Assisted reproduction
- Biotechnology
- Cell cultures
- Cloning
- Food transformation
- GMO
- Genetic transformation
- Modern biotechnologies
- Pasteurization
- Processes
- Selective breeding
- Tissue and organ engineering
- Traditional biotechnologies
- Vaccine manufacturing

ANTIBIOTICS

Most people have taken antibiotics at one time or another. An antibiotic is a substance that can kill bacteria or prevent bacteria from multiplying.

8.39 TWO TYPES OF ANTIBIOTIC ACTION

Action	Description
Bactericidal	Antibiotic that kills bacteria.
Bacteriostatic	Antibiotic that prevents bacteria from multiplying. The immune system gets rid of the remaining bacteria.

In nature, microorganisms naturally produce various types of antibiotics. Thus we can obtain different kinds of antibiotics by culturing the cells of these microorganisms.

Many people mistakenly believe that antibiotics can cure all diseases. Some diseases, including chicken pox and flu, are caused by viruses, not bacteria. Antibiotics cannot fight viruses. Doctors must always check whether a patient is suffering from a bacterial or a viral infection before prescribing an antibiotic. The cause of an illness can be identified by culturing the cells of a sample taken from the patient.

Unfortunately, bacteria occasionally mutate and develop a resistance to one or more antibiotics. This is why doctors sometimes prescribe more than one type of antibiotic to treat an infection. The emergence of bacterial strains that are resistant to antibiotics has compelled scientists to look for new antibiotics.

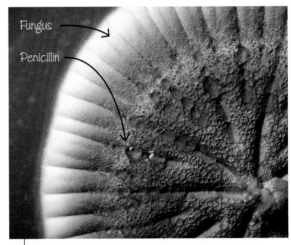

Fungus

Penicillin

8.40 The *Penicillium notatum* is a fungus that can be grown to produce large quantities of penicillin. Some people, however, are allergic to this antibiotic.

1. The West Nile virus is transmitted to humans by infected mosquitoes. The virus causes a high fever and can result in death. Is treatment by antibiotics effective against the virus? Explain your answer.

2. What questions must pharmacists ask their patients before giving them a penicillin-based antibiotic?

MÉLANIE DEMERS

When a person suffers from cancer, some cancerous cells may detach from the main tumour and form new tumours in other parts of the body. The new tumours are called *metastases*. Mélanie Demers and her team have used the tools of biotechnology to discover that the galectin-7 protein is responsible for the progression of metastatic tumours.

Demers and her colleagues used cell cultures of cancerous tumours and analyzed the quantity of galectin-7 produced by the cancerous cells. They found that the rate of cancerous tumour formation increased at the same pace as the cultured cancerous cells that produced galectin-7.

This promising discovery suggests that it may be possible to detect cancer by measuring the presence of galectin-7 in a patient. It may also lead to the development of drugs that would prevent cancer cells from producing galectin-7, thus delaying the formation of metastatic tumours.

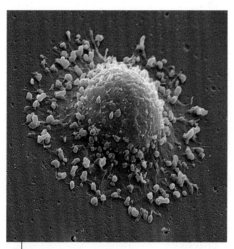

8.41 This photo shows a cancerous cell found in lung cancer.

NAME
Mélanie Demers

JOB
Researcher at the Institut Armand-Frappier

AREA WHERE SHE WORKS
Laval

EDUCATION
Bachelor's degree in biology and a Master's degree in immunology and virology

PROUDEST ACHIEVEMENT
Conducted lab research that is leading to a better understanding of cancer progression

8.42 OCCUPATIONS CONNECTED TO DEMERS' WORK

Occupation	Education required	Length of study	Main tasks
Nurse or nursing assistant	DEP in health assistance and nursing care	1800 hours	• Assist people with various health needs
Laboratory technologist	DCS in laboratory procedures	3 years	• Conduct lab experiments, compile data and transmit experimental results
Pathologist	Medical degree specializing in anatomical pathology	9 years and more	• Study human tissue to identify and analyze diseases

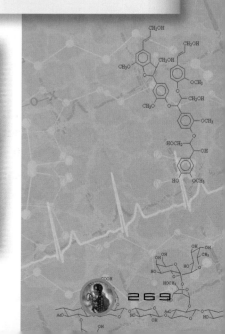

THE EARTH

AND SPACE

HUMAN LIFE EMERGED AND EVOLVED IN THE ONLY
PLACE KNOWN TO HARBOUR LIFE: PLANET EARTH.
Although our planet seems immense to us, it is only a tiny
speck in the immensity of the universe.

The history of Earth began more than four billion years ago. It includes
the story of the emergence of countless species, including our own,
but also that of the extinction of many others. To fully understand
how unique our world is, we must look at it within the context
of the vast Universe, study its geological history and
explore the conditions that have made it possible
for the development of life as we know it.

CONTENTS

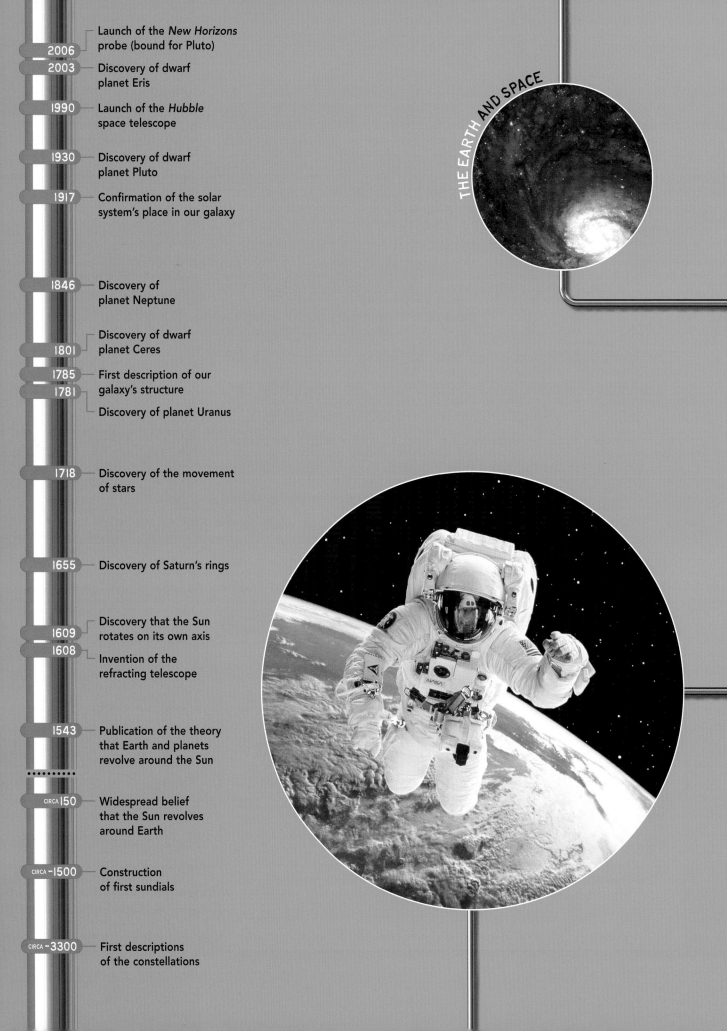

2006 — Launch of the *New Horizons* probe (bound for Pluto)

2003 — Discovery of dwarf planet Eris

1990 — Launch of the *Hubble* space telescope

1930 — Discovery of dwarf planet Pluto

1917 — Confirmation of the solar system's place in our galaxy

1846 — Discovery of planet Neptune

1801 — Discovery of dwarf planet Ceres

1785 — First description of our galaxy's structure

1781 — Discovery of planet Uranus

1718 — Discovery of the movement of stars

1655 — Discovery of Saturn's rings

1609 — Discovery that the Sun rotates on its own axis

1608 — Invention of the refracting telescope

1543 — Publication of the theory that Earth and planets revolve around the Sun

CIRCA 150 — Widespread belief that the Sun revolves around Earth

CIRCA -1500 — Construction of first sundials

CIRCA -3300 — First descriptions of the constellations

THE HUMAN ORGANISM

AND THE DIMENSIONS OF SPACE

9

A trip to the Sun, located a mere 150 million km away, at a speed of 100 km/h, would take more than 170 years. This distance may seem enormous, but it is quite insignificant on the scale of the Universe. The kilometre as a unit of measurement is too small to convey the distances between celestial bodies. Despite a 12 756-km diameter, our planet is only a tiny dot in the heavens. Since we inhabit this dot, it has significant importance. In this chapter, we will situate ourselves in the surrounding immensity by evaluating the distances that separate us from the nearest celestial bodies and studying the tools that are used to observe and understand the bright lights in the sky.

1 OBSERVATIONS OF THE SKY

Since the dawn of time, our fascination with the stars has compelled us to scrutinize the celestial horizon. At first we studied it with the naked eye. In time, the development of increasingly precise astronomical instruments and the exploration of space fostered exciting discoveries and a better understanding of the Universe.

1.1 INSTRUMENTS OF OBSERVATION

The eye was the first and, for a long time, the only instrument used in astronomy. Technologically advanced instruments were developed to assist our senses, ranging from the optical telescope, which offers a detailed view of faraway celestial bodies, to the radio telescope, which captures radio waves emitted by stars.

VISUAL OBSERVATIONS

Until the 17th century, humans relied solely on phenomena they could see with their own eyes to help them situate our planet in the Universe. They observed a variety of celestial phenomena such as:

- the alternation between day and night
- the movement of the stars in the sky
- the changes in seasons
- the phases of the Moon

The most obvious astronomical phenomenon is the alternation between day and night. It has made it possible for humans to develop their notions of *day* and *night*, and invent the clock, the first time-measuring instrument.

> **CYCLE ONE**
> - Aurora Borealis
> - Comets
> - Cycles of day and night
> - Eclipses
> - Universal gravitation
> - Meteoroid impacts
> - Phases of the moon
> - Seasons

Astronomy comes from the Greek word *astron*, meaning "star."

A LIVING SUNDIAL
The largest sundial in North America was built in 2002 in Sainte-Angèle-de-Laval, Québec. We can read the time there by standing on its centre line.

9.1 The alternation between day and night is caused by the rotation of planet Earth on its axis.

9.2 Movement of the Sun's shadow on the sundial measures time.

When we study the night sky it seems that almost all celestial bodies are revolving around one point. In the Northern Hemisphere, that point is located near the Northern Star.

9.3 A time-elapsed photograph taken over several hours of the night sky reveals that the stars seem to revolve around a point near the Northern Star.

9.4 The Earth rotates on a tilted axis pointing toward the Northern Star, giving the impression that the sky revolves around a point near this star.

This observation led to the discovery of five planets (Mercury, Venus, Mars, Jupiter and Saturn) and two other celestial bodies (the Moon and the Sun). Astronomers soon realized that these seven celestial bodies were different because they did not follow the same trajectory as the stars.

Planet comes from the Greek word *planêtês*, meaning "errant body."

The changing seasons are another visible astronomical phenomenon that led many early civilizations to define the notion of a *year* and to perfect their own calendar, a necessary tool for farmers. Observations of the lunar phases led to the notion of the *month*.

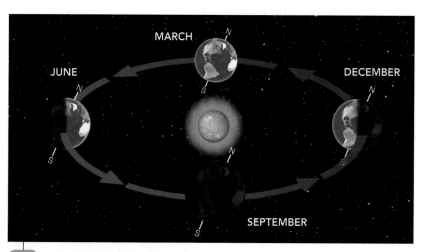

9.5 The changing seasons are attributed to Earth's rotation around the Sun and the inclination of Earth's axis of rotation.

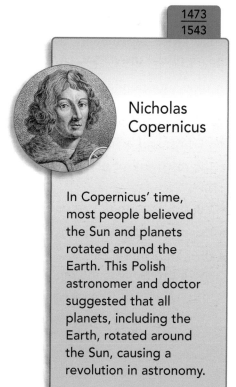

1473
1543

Nicholas Copernicus

In Copernicus' time, most people believed the Sun and planets rotated around the Earth. This Polish astronomer and doctor suggested that all planets, including the Earth, rotated around the Sun, causing a revolution in astronomy.

9.6 An aurora polaris

Other astronomical phenomena visible to the naked eye include comets passing near the Earth, solar and lunar eclipses, auroras, shooting stars and falling meteorites.

OBSERVATION USING TECHNOLOGICAL INSTRUMENTS

Since the 17th century, scientists have developed many instruments to locate and observe celestial objects more accurately.

Reflector and refractor telescopes are among the oldest instruments used to observe the sky. They helped to convince most astronomers that the Earth revolved around the Sun and not vice versa. These instruments also helped Isaac Newton develop his theory of the **UNIVERSAL LAW OF GRAVITATION**.

In time, astronomical instruments were diversified and perfected. Today, we build observatories, send satellites—such as the *Hubble* space telescope—into orbit, and launch space probes to explore the Universe. These technologically advanced tools have led to:

- the discovery of new planets (first inside, then outside the solar system)
- the observation of galaxies and nebulas (clouds of cosmic dust)
- the calculation of the speed of light
- the validation of various aspects of the theory on the origin of the Universe (e.g. the big bang theory)

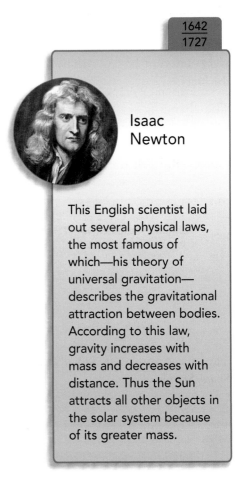

1642
1727

Isaac Newton

This English scientist laid out several physical laws, the most famous of which—his theory of universal gravitation—describes the gravitational attraction between bodies. According to this law, gravity increases with mass and decreases with distance. Thus the Sun attracts all other objects in the solar system because of its greater mass.

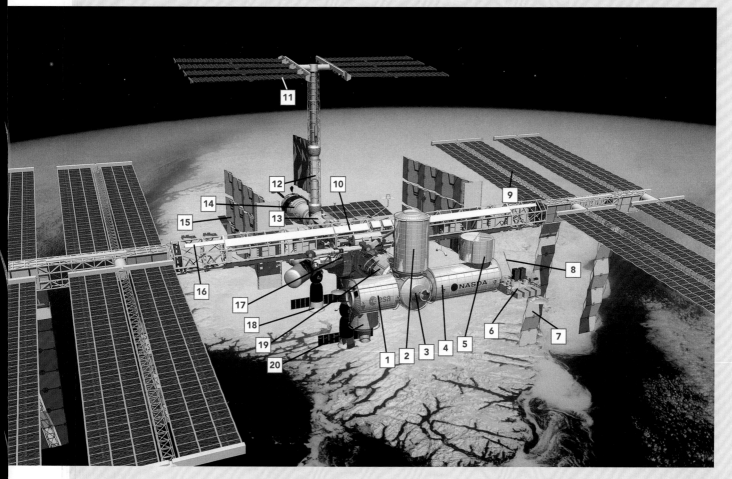

1. European science lab *Columbus*
2. Centrifuge accommodation module (cancelled)
3. Node 2
4. Japanese experiment module (JEM)
5. Experiment logistics module of the JEM
6. Japanese experiment lab (exposed facility)
7. Thermal control panels
8. JEM remote manipulator system
9. Solar panels
10. Truss structure
11. Solar panels of Russian segment
12. European robotic arm
13. *Zarya* control module
14. *Zvesda* service module
15. Thermal control panels
16. Brazilian *Express* pallet
17. U.S. habitation module (cancelled)
18. *Soyuz* vessel
19. U.S. laboratory *Destiny*
20. Node 3

9.7 Diagram of the International Space Station, as it was originally intended to look. Construction of the centrifuge accommodation module (No. 2) and the U.S. habitation module (No. 17) have since been cancelled.

Since the mid-20th century, many countries have established space programs dedicated to understanding the solar system and the Universe as a whole. These programs have led to the sending of people and spacecrafts into space, and the construction of space stations such as *Salyut 1* to *7*, *Skylab*, *Mir* and the *International Space Station*.

Figures 9.8 to 9.18 (pages 278 and 279) illustrate steps in the human exploration of space.

HUMAN TRACES IN SPACE

Q: What human-made object is currently farthest from Earth?

A: The *Voyager 1* spacecraft. It is located more than 15 billion km from the Sun.

9.8 Soviet Space Agency, October 4, 1957: *Sputnik 1* is the first satellite to be launched into orbit around Earth.

LUNA 1

9.9 Soviet space agency, January 2, 1959: *Luna 1* is launched to the Moon, becoming the first probe to fly by a celestial body other than Earth.

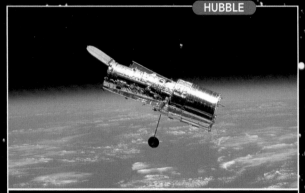

HUBBLE

9.14 NASA, April 24 1990: *Hubble*, the first space telescope, is placed in orbit around Earth, where the atmosphere will not hinder observations.

MIR

9.13 Soviet, then Russian, space agency, from 1986 to 2001: Designed for permanent habitation, the space station *Mir* is used by many astronauts as a space lab.

SOHO

9.15 NASA and European Space Agency (ESA), December 2, 1995: The Solar and Heliospheric Observatory (SOHO) is launched to study the Sun.

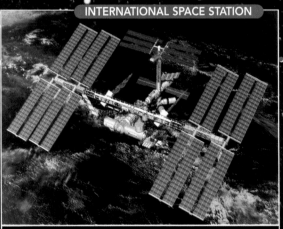

INTERNATIONAL SPACE STATION

9.16 Group of countries, November 20, 1998: The first segment of the International Space Station (ISS) is sent into orbit. The station is scheduled to be fully assembled by 2010.

VOSTOK 1

9.10 Soviet space agency, April 12, 1961: Yuri Gagarin becomes the first man in space.

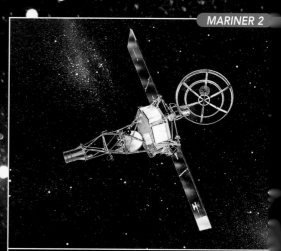

MARINER 2

9.11 National Aeronautics and Space Administration (NASA), December 14, 1962: *Mariner 2* flies by Venus and is the first probe to fly by a planet other than Earth.

APOLLO 11

9.12 NASA, July 20, 1969: Neil Armstrong and Edwin Aldrin become the first humans to walk on the Moon.

MESSENGER

9.18 NASA, August 3, 2004: *Messenger* is launched and is scheduled to enter into orbit around Mercury in March 2011, following a flyby of Venus.

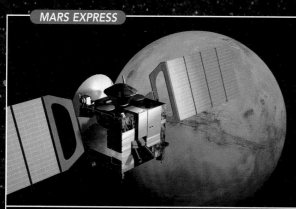

MARS EXPRESS

9.17 ESA, January 18, 2004: The probe *Mars Express* detects water in the form of ice on the surface of Mars.

Instrument	Description
Refracting telescope	Lens-equipped optical instrument that collects and amplifies light
Reflector telescope	Mirror-equipped optical instrument that collects and amplifies light
Binoculars	Instrument outfitted with two refracting telescopes to observe three-dimensional objects
Radio telescope	Instrument that collects and amplifies radio waves emitted by celestial bodies
Radar	Instrument that measures the distance between the Earth and celestial bodies, among other distances
Observatory	Building that provides the best possible conditions to observe the Universe with specialized instruments
Satellite	An object placed in orbit around a celestial body that is designed to collect and transmit data about it or other celestial bodies
Space probe	An unmanned spacecraft that is launched into space to explore celestial bodies
Space rocket	An unmanned or manned spacecraft that is launched into space, with only one salvageable section
Space shuttle	A salvageable manned spacecraft launched into space that is capable of returning to Earth
Space station	A facility placed in orbit around the Earth (or other celestial body) that is designed for habitation and to carry out various missions

A reflecting telescope

The radio telescope from Parkes Observatory (Australia)

The Mont-Mégantic Observatory in Québec

The probe *Galileo* (U.S.)

The shuttle *Atlantis* (U.S.)

A refracting telescope

A pair of binoculars

The satellite *Radarsat 2* (Canada) is equipped with a radar.

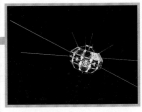

The satellite *Alouette 1* (Canada)

Delta II rocket (U.S.)

Skylab station (U.S.)

1.2 MEASUREMENTS IN ASTRONOMY

On Earth, the kilometre is used to measure distance. The city of Québec, for example, is located about 250 km from Montréal. In astronomy, however, distances are astronomical. They often number more than millions of kilometres. For example, Venus, the planet closest to Earth, is located over 43 000 000 km away. Astronomers, therefore, use units of measurement that are better adapted to the dimensions of the Universe. Such units are the astronomical unit and the light year.

THE ASTRONOMICAL UNIT

The astronomical unit (AU) is a unit of measurement equal to the mean distance between Earth and the Sun. The distance separating the two celestial bodies varies because Earth's trajectory around the Sun forms an ellipse, that is, a slightly elongated circle. In the mid-20th century, the use of radar in astronomy led to more precise measurements: officially, the astronomical unit is equal to 149 597 870.691 km.

9.20 Earth is located at 1 AU from the Sun.

▶ The ASTRONOMICAL UNIT (AU) is a unit of measurement equal to about 150 million kilometres, the average distance between Earth and the Sun.

  CONNECTIONS MATHEMATICS

Calculations with big numbers

The word *astronomical* is commonly used to describe something huge, such as very big numbers. Scientists use scientific notation to simplify the manipulation of very large or very small numbers.

e.g. 43 000 000 written as 4.3×10^7 in scientific notation

For the addition or subtraction of two numbers written in scientific notation, both must be of the same order of magnitude, that is, base 10 to the same power. If the exponents differ, one of them must be converted to the other before adding or subtracting the two decimal numbers.

e.g. $(1.2879 \times 10^4) + (3.4089 \times 10^1) = (1.2879 \times 10^4) + (0.003\ 408\ 9 \times 10^4)$
$= (1.2879 + 0.003\ 408\ 9) \times 10^4$
$= 1.291\ 308\ 9 \times 10^4$

To multiply two numbers written in scientific notation, first multiply the decimal numbers, then add the exponents.

e.g. $(1.045 \times 10^7) \times (6.7789 \times 10^4) = (1.045 \times 6.7789) \times (10^{7+4})$
$= 7.083\ 950\ 5 \times 10^{11}$

To divide two numbers written in scientific notation, first divide the larger decimal number by the smaller decimal number, then subtract the smaller exponent from the larger exponent.

e.g.: $(9.2928 \times 10^7) \div (3.63 \times 10^3) = (9.2928 \div 3.63) \times (10^{7-3})$
$= 2.56 \times 10^4$

We often confuse the words *exact* and *precise*. An exact value is the actual value of a measure or data: two plus two is exactly four. A precise value depends on the accuracy of the instrument used and always carries a margin of error. For example, radar measures the value of an astronomical unit with a margin of error of plus or minus six metres, which is insignificant compared to 150 million kilometres. To obtain a value as close as possible to the exact value, future generations of scientists will have to improve the accuracy of our radars, which they will most likely do.

The astronomical unit is the best unit of measurement to express distances within the solar system.

THE LIGHT YEAR

Many objects in the Universe are located so far away that even the astronomical unit isn't always helpful. In these cases, another unit of measurement can be used in astronomy, one that is based on the speed of light.

In space, light can travel 299 792 km in one second. In one year, it can travel approximately 9 500 billion km.

$$299\ 792\ \frac{km}{sec} \times 60\ \frac{sec}{min} \times 60\ \frac{min}{hr} \times 24\ \frac{hr}{day} \times 365.26\ days$$
$$= 9\ 460\ 530\ 000\ 000\ km$$

The resulting distance corresponds to a unit of measure called the *light year*. Its symbol is *ly*.

> ► A LIGHT YEAR (ly) is a unit of measurement equal to the distance light travels in one year, which is about 9 500 billion kilometres.

The light year is the best measurement to express distance between stars.

1644
1710

Ole Christansen Römer

This Danish astronomer was the first person to estimate the distance light travels in one second. His calculations led to the conclusion that light has a maximum speed and does not spread instantaneously.

9.21 CHARACTERISTICS OF THE ASTRONOMICAL UNIT AND THE LIGHT YEAR

Unit of measurement	Symbol	Equivalence in kilometres	Application
Astronomical unit	AU	150 million	Distances within the solar system
Light year	ly	9 500 billion	Distances between stars

In the next section, the astronomical unit and the light year will help us determine Earth's place in the vastness of the Universe.

2 THE EARTH IN THE UNIVERSE

Here are a few astronomical terms to learn before we travel to the ends of the Universe (Figure 9.22).

CYCLE ONE
└ Solar system

9.22 Common terms used in astronomy

CELESTIAL BODY

All natural objects in the Universe
Synonym: celestial object

Celestial bodies visible in the night sky

STAR

Celestial body with a brilliance that comes from the energy it produces

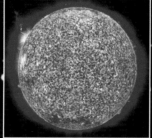

Our star: the Sun

PLANET

Celestial body of spherical shape that orbits a star and does not shine brightly. It only shares its orbit with its own natural satellites, not other celestial bodies.

Our planet: Earth

DWARF PLANET

Celestial body of spherical shape that orbits a star and does not shine on its own. It shares its orbit with celestial bodies other than its own natural satellites.

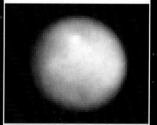

A dwarf planet: Ceres

SMALL SOLAR SYSTEM BODY

Any celestial body in orbit around the Sun that is neither a planet nor a dwarf planet, e.g. asteroids and comets

An asteroid belt includes a multitude of small solar system bodies.

SATELLITE

Celestial body in orbit around another celestial body that is not a star

A satellite (of Jupiter): Io

ASTEROID

Celestial body of irregular shape, in orbit around the Sun

An asteroid: Ida

COMET

Celestial body covered in ice that releases gas and ice debris as it passes the Sun. The debris forms a tail that is lit up by the Sun.

A comet: Hale-Bopp

2.1 EARTH AND THE MOON

The Moon is Earth's only natural satellite. It is located an average of 384 000 km away. Moving at a speed of 100 km per hour, it would take 160 days to travel the distance between our planet and this satellite.

Earth
12 756 km

The Moon
3 476 km

384 000 km

9.23 The distance between Earth and its moon is equal to 30 times the diameter of Earth. The Moon's diameter is three times smaller than Earth's. (This illustration was drawn to scale.)

9.24 DATA ON THE MOON

Surface type	Surface temperature by day	Surface temperature by night	Diameter	Atmosphere
Rocky	127°C	– 173°C	3 476 km	No atmosphere

Although our natural satellite does not emit any light, it shines brightly in the sky. This is due to light from the Sun reflecting on its surface like a mirror.

The Moon always presents the same face to Earth. This is because it takes as much time for the Moon to orbit Earth as it does to complete one rotation on its own axis, that is, 27.32 days (Figure 9.25).

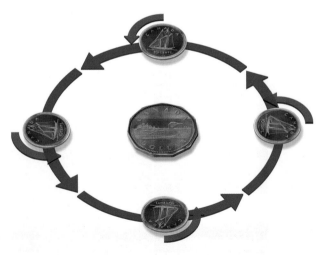

9.25 The Loonie represents Earth and the dime represents the Moon. This illustration shows how both the rotation and orbit of the Moon are synchronous, explaining why only one side of the Moon is ever visible to us.

9.26 The near side of the Moon

2.2 EARTH IN THE SOLAR SYSTEM

The solar system is composed of a star, eight planets (Mercury, Venus, Earth, Mars, Jupiter, Saturn, Uranus and Neptune), dwarf planets (currently three: Ceres, Pluto and Eris), and many satellites, asteroids and comets. The entire solar system revolves around the Sun, its only star.

> ▶ Our SOLAR SYSTEM is made up of the Sun and all the celestial bodies travelling in its orbit

THE SUN

The Sun is the main source of light and heat in the solar system. Its energy comes from nuclear reactions at its core. Light emitted by the star takes eight minutes to reach Earth.

EXOTIC WORLDS

Rain on Venus contains sulphuric acid, and on Jupiter, it contains ammonia. Titan, a moon of Saturn, contains oceans of methane. Volcanoes on Io, a moon of Jupiter, spit sulphur, while Europa, another moon of Jupiter, spits water.

9.27 DATA ON THE SUN

Average surface temperature	Average core temperature	Diameter
6 000°C	15 000 000°C	1 390 000 km

THE PLANETS AND DWARF PLANETS

There are eight planets and three dwarf planets in the solar system. In the near future, several celestial bodies will be promoted to dwarf planet status. Figure 9.29 (pages 286 and 287) illustrates the location of the planets and dwarf planets, while Table 9.30 lists their characteristics (pages 286 and 287).

THE ASTEROID BELT

Most asteroids in our solar system and the dwarf planet Ceres, discovered in 1801, are part of an asteroid belt located between the planets Mars and Jupiter. If we were to group Ceres and all the asteroids together, the diameter of the group would be two times smaller than that of the Moon. To date, a probe has never collided with an asteroid from the belt. The probability that such an event would occur is quite low, since the average distance between two asteroids is many times greater than the distance between Earth and the Moon.

9.28 Ceres is in the foreground with the Sun in the background. Between the two lie a myriad of small celestial bodies, forming an asteroid belt.

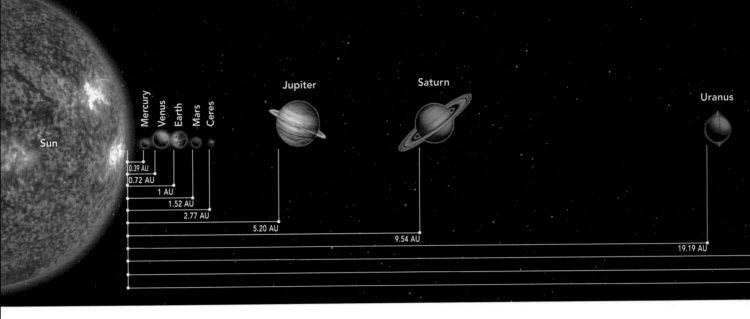

9.30 DATA ON PLANETS AND DWARF PLANETS

Name	Characteristics	Surface type	Average surface temperature
Mercury	Very hot during the day, because of its close proximity to the Sun. Nights are really cold because there is no atmosphere to retain heat.	Rock	167°C (between −180°C and 450°C)
Venus	The third brightest body in the sky, after the Sun and Moon. Its atmosphere is mainly carbon dioxide, a greenhouse gas, which causes temperatures to remain extremely high.	Rock	477°C
Earth	Oceans make our planet look blue in places; continents make it brown and green in parts; and clouds and snow give it its white areas.	Rock and liquid water	20°C
Mars	Its red colour can be seen with the naked eye, and is caused by an abundance of ferrous oxide, that is, rust. In addition, it has lots of water in the form of ice.	Rock	−40°C
Ceres (Dwarf planet)	A third of the asteroid belt could be contained inside this dwarf planet.	Rock	−100°C
Jupiter	The largest planet in the solar system. Its mass is 2½ times larger than all the other planets combined and its diameter is 11 times that of Earth.	Gas	−110°C
Saturn	The second biggest planet in the solar system. Its magnificent rings make it stand out; they are visible even with a less than powerful telescope.	Gas	−180°C
Uranus	Not visible to the naked eye. It was discovered in 1781, using a refracting telescope.	Gas	−221°C
Neptune	It was discovered in 1846, and is sometimes called *the other blue planet*. The methane gas in its atmosphere gives it a blue colour.	Gas	−230°C
Pluto (Dwarf planet)	This dwarf is smaller than Earth's moon, and was discovered in 1930. It was considered a planet until 2006.	Ice	−238°C
Eris (Dwarf planet)	Its elliptical orbit varies between 37.77 AU and 97.56 AU. It was discovered in 2003.	Ice	−243°C

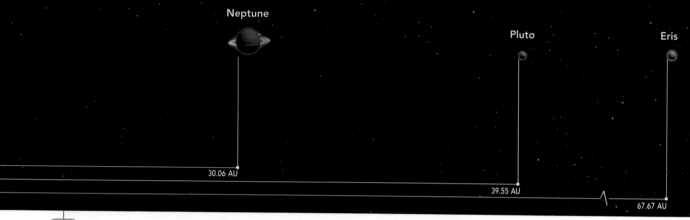

Neptune

Pluto

Eris

30.06 AU

39.55 AU

67.67 AU

9.29 Average distance between the planets and dwarf planets and the Sun (illustration not to scale)

Diameter at equator	Duration of orbit around Sun	Duration of rotation	Number of natural satellites	Major known atmospheric constituents
4878 km	88 days	58.7 days	0	Hydrogen and helium (very thin atmosphere)
12 104 km	224.7 days	243 days	0	Carbon dioxide and nitrogen
12 756 km	365.26 days	23 h 56 min 04 s	1 (the Moon)	Nitrogen and oxygen
6 794 km	1.88 year	24 h 37 min 23 s	2 (Phobos and Deimos)	Carbon dioxide, nitrogen and argon
940 km	4.6 years	9 h 4 min 28 s	0	Unknown
142 800 km	11.86 years	9 h 55 min 30 s	63 (including Io, Europa, Ganymede and Callisto)	Hydrogen, helium and methane
120 000 km	29.46 years	10 h 39 min 25 s	33 (including Titan)	Hydrogen, helium and methane
51 120 km	84.04 years	17 h 12 min	27	Hydrogen, helium and methane
49 528 km	164.8 years	16 h 6 min	13 (including Triton)	Hydrogen, helium and methane
2 290 km	247.7 years	6.39 days	3 (including Charon)	Unknown
Approximately 2 400 km	Approximately 557 years	Unknown	1 (Dysnomia)	Unknown

Pluto loses its planet status

Following a heated weeklong debate, astronomers gathered in Prague for the International Astronomical Union convention, from August 14 to 25, 2006, have adopted a new definition of the word *planet* that excludes Pluto. According to this definition, a planet is a spherical celestial body orbiting a star; in this case, the Sun. Another criterion requires that a planet's orbit be exempt from any cosmic debris. Pluto fails to meet this last criterion since its gravitational force is too weak to create the necessary vacuum around it.

Pluto's status has been contested for many years. It is much smaller than was thought

Pluto and its biggest moon, Charon

upon its discovery in 1930 by American Clyde Tombaugh. Also, most planets are made up of rock (like Earth) or gas (like Jupiter); Pluto is primarily made up of ice.

Adapted from Pauline Gravel, "Le système solaire perd une planète," *Le Devoir*, August 25, 2006, p. A1. *[Traduction]*

THE KUIPER BELT

Our solar system includes more than a sun, eight planets, three dwarf planets and an asteroid belt. Beyond Neptune's orbit lies a second comet and asteroid belt called the *Kuiper belt*. Discovered in 1992, its exact location is still unknown but is thought to extend between 40 AU to more than 120 AU from the Sun. Dwarf planets Pluto and Eris are part of the Kuiper belt.

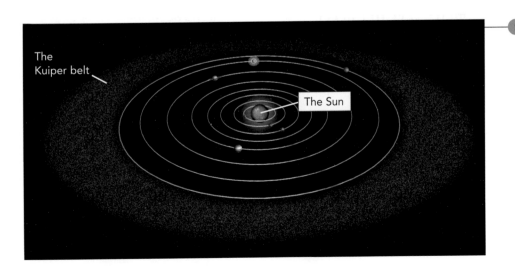

The Kuiper belt

The Sun

9.31 The Kuiper belt has a width of approximately 80 AU.

  CHAPTER 9

Much farther away in our solar system, at between 40 000 AU to 150 000 AU from the Sun, lies an enormous collection of asteroids and comets called the *Oort cloud*. Sometimes, the orbit of an asteroid from the Oort cloud deviates toward the Sun. The ice on the asteroid's surface partially melts and becomes a comet. It was in calculating the orbit of several comets passing near the Sun that astronomers were able to deduce the existence of the Oort cloud. Celestial objects forming the cloud are too small and faraway to be observed directly. The location of the Oort cloud corresponds to the farthest limits of our solar system.

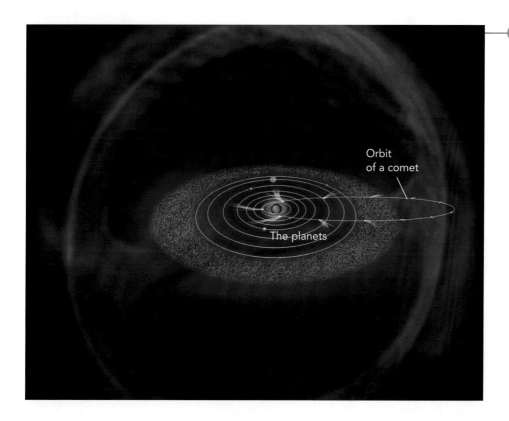

Orbit
of a comet

The planets

9.32 The spherical shape of the Oort cloud gives it the appearance of a bubble.

2.3 THE SOLAR SYSTEM IN ITS GALAXY: THE MILKY WAY

Astronomers now know that our sun is only a star among millions of other stars. There are smaller, larger, hotter, colder, older or younger stars. Scientists are discovering more and more celestial bodies, called exoplanets, that orbit stars, leading to the hypothesis that solar systems similar to ours could also exist in the Universe.

> *Exoplanet* is formed with the prefix *exo* meaning "outer."

The star closest to our solar system is called *Proxima Centauri*, and is located 4.22 ly away from our planet. It is 275 000 times farther from Earth than is the Sun.

LIGHTS BLOCKING OUT THE STARS

Many people are opposed to night skiing on Mount Orford (Estrie region). One reason is because they wish to limit the light pollution that affects the Mont-Mégantic Observatory, the only facility in North America where we can observe the outer reaches of our galaxy.

Large clusters of stars are called *galaxies*. All galaxies contain cosmic dust and celestial bodies similar to planets and asteroids. All matter in a galaxy orbits its centre. The Sun and our entire solar system take some 220 million years to complete an orbit of the centre of our galaxy.

▶ **A GALAXY is a massive cluster of stars and matter that orbits its centre.**

Our solar system is part of the galaxy called the *Milky Way*, so named because of its resemblance to a milky band crossing the sky. All stars visible to the naked eye are part of this galaxy. Although we are only able to identify 6 000 stars, there are actually more than 200 billion in the Milky Way.

> *Galaxy* comes from the Greek word *gala*, meaning "milk."

▶ **The MILKY WAY is the galaxy we inhabit.**

The diameter of the Milky Way is 100 000 ly. Our Sun and solar system are situated 26 000 ly from its centre, or nucleus.

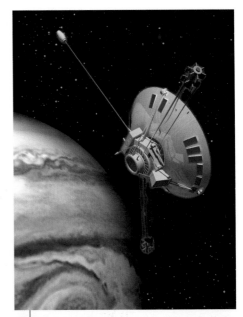

9.33 After having explored Jupiter, the probe *Pioneer 10* is currently headed toward Aldebaran, a star closer to our solar system, located at a distance of 65 ly. At its current speed of 43 000 km/h, *Pioneer 10* should reach the star in about two million years!

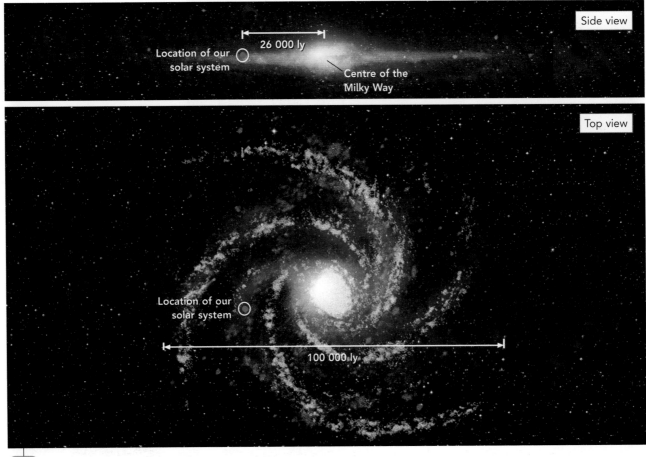

Side view

Location of our solar system

26 000 ly

Centre of the Milky Way

Top view

Location of our solar system

100 000 ly

9.34 The Milky Way looks like a disc.

2.4 THE MILKY WAY IN THE UNIVERSE

Observations indicate that the Milky Way is among millions of galaxies dotting the Universe. The number of stars in a galaxy varies from a few million to hundreds of billions.

SPIRAL GALAXY   **ELLIPTICAL GALAXY**   **IRREGULAR GALAXY**

9.35 The three types of galaxies

Galaxies are classified into three types according to their shape: spiral, elliptical and irregular. The Milky Way is a spiral galaxy.

The galaxy closest to the Milky Way is called *Canis Major*, located 25 000 ly from our solar system. Canis Major is a smaller galaxy found directly below the Milky Way. Its and whose irregular shape suggests that it is being pulled apart by our galaxy's gravitational force.

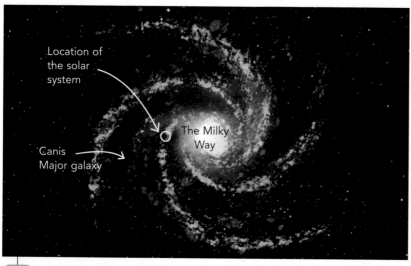

9.36 The Milky Way (in blue) and its closest neighbour, Canis Major (in red), discovered in November 2003

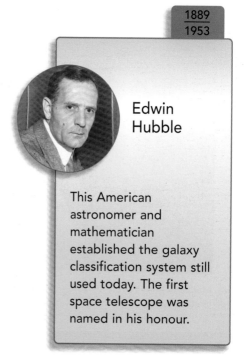

1889
1953

Edwin Hubble

This American astronomer and mathematician established the galaxy classification system still used today. The first space telescope was named in his honour.

THE DIMENSIONS OF SPACE   291

The Andromeda galaxy is 2.5 million light years away. The Milky Way and Andromeda are the two largest galaxies in a cluster of 30 galaxies, referred to by scientists as the *Local Group*. Similar clusters are found all over the Universe.

The Universe can be observed up to a distance of 15 billion ly, a tiny fraction of the Universe as a whole.

According to current knowledge, the Universe contains an infinite number of celestial bodies and galaxies. Questions about whether there are other solar systems similar to ours, and whether other celestial bodies could sustain life, remain unanswered. Research continues, however, because the existence of extraterrestrial life interests not only astronomers, but all of humanity.

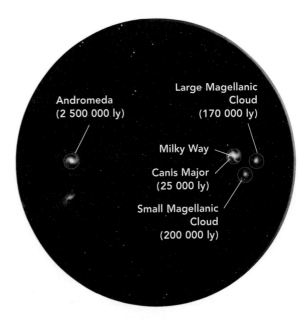

Andromeda (2 500 000 ly)

Large Magellanic Cloud (170 000 ly)

Milky Way

Canis Major (25 000 ly)

Small Magellanic Cloud (200 000 ly)

9.37 The Local Group includes the Milky Way and other neighbouring galaxies.

In search of extraterrestrial life

Margaret Turnbull in front of the Arecibo radio telescope in Puerto Rico

People combing the skies in search of extraterrestrial life will now know in which directions to point their instruments. During a conference of the American Association for the Advancement of Science, Margaret Turnbull presented a shortlist of ten stars most likely to harbour life.

The astronomer from the Carnegie Institution of Washington (U.S.) selected stars according to their physicochemical characteristics. First of all, stars must be at least three billion years old, enough time for a planet and life to form, and have an abundance of heavy metals, especially iron.

Of the ten candidates, half could be heard through radio telescope, while others located closer to Earth may one day be directly observed by space telescope. ∎

Adapted from Yaroslav Pigenet,
"À saisir : espace parfait pour vie extraterrestre,"
20minutes.fr website, February 21, 2006. *[Translation]*

CHECKUP

1 OBSERVATIONS **OF THE SKY**
(pp. 274–282)

1. Certain astronomical phenomena can be seen with the naked eye, while others must be observed with instruments. Which of the following phenomena can be observed with the naked eye?
   - A lunar eclipse
   - The Great Red Spot of Jupiter
   - A meteor crashing on Mars
   - The movement of the stars in the sky
   - Saturn's rings
   - Day and night on Earth

2. Name three instruments used to observe the night sky.

3. Which five planets were discovered through visual observation?

4. Which two planets were discovered thanks to either the refracting telescope or the reflecting telescope?

5. Define the terms *astronomical unit* and *light year*.

6. What is the speed of light (km/s)?

7. The kilometre, the astronomical unit and the light year are three units of measurement used to calculate distances. Which would be used to calculate each of the following?
   a) The distance between Jupiter and Mercury
   b) The distance between the Sun and the star Rigel
   c) The distance between Earth and the Moon
   d) The distance between Gaspé and Rouyn-Noranda

e) The distance between the Milky Way and Andromeda

8. On April 3, 2024, Earth and Jupiter will be, respectively, 1.0 AU and 5.0 AU from the Sun.
   a) How much farther will Jupiter be from the Sun than Earth?
   b) Is this data sufficient to calculate the distance between Earth and Jupiter on that date? Use a diagram to explain your answer.
   c) On that date, how many kilometres will separate Jupiter from the Sun?

9. In 1987, an explosion of the SN1987A star was observed. It was located 170 000 ly away from our planet.

Star SN1987A

   a) How long ago did this explosion occur? Explain your answer.
   b) How many kilometres separated Earth and SN1987 when it exploded? Include your calculations.

10. The Small Magellanic Cloud is a neighbouring galaxy. It is located 200 000 ly away. Convert this distance to kilometres.

2 THE EARTH IN THE UNIVERSE
(pp. 283–292)

11. The Sun is a heat and light source for Earth and the entire solar system. Is the Sun a star? Explain your answer.

12. For a long time, humans thought all celestial bodies revolved around Earth. We now know that is not the case. There is only one celestial body orbiting Earth.
    a) What is it called?
    b) What is its average distance from Earth?

13. How much time elapses between two full moons.

14. What phenomenon is at the source of the Sun's energy?

15. How many times is the Sun's diameter greater than Earth's?

16. Which planets in our solar system do not possess any known natural satellites?

17. "My Very Eager Mother Just Served Us Noodles" is a sentence used to remember the names and order of the planets. The first letter of each word corresponds to the first letter of each planet.
    a) Identify the planets corresponding to the first letter of each word in the sentence.
    b) Indicate the average distance of each planet from the Sun.
    c) Identify the three dwarf planets and indicate their average distance from the Sun.

18. A planet in our solar system is located at 4 500 000 000 km from the Sun.
    a) What is the distance in astronomical units?
    b) Identify the planet.

19. Planets with a rocky surface, such as Earth, are also called *terrestrial planets*.
    a) Which planets in our solar system are terrestrial planets?
    b) Which dwarf planet also has a rocky surface?
    c) What is the surface composition of the other two dwarf planets?

20. It is not likely that spacecraft would be able to land on a planet whose orbit is beyond that of Mars. To explore such planets, spacecraft must do flybys.
    a) Which planets have an orbit beyond that of Mars?
    b) Why are spacecraft not able to land on such planets?

21. Answer the following questions.
    a) Why is the average surface temperature of Venus so high?

b) Why does Mars look red?

c) Why does Neptune look blue?

22. What is the difference between a comet and an asteroid?

23. The Milky Way is the name of our galaxy.

    a) What is a galaxy?

    b) How far away are we from the centre of our galaxy?

    c) Approximately how many stars are in the Milky Way?

    d) What is our closest neighbouring galaxy?

    e) How far away is it from our galaxy?

24. The Andromeda galaxy is pictured below.

    a) Is it an elliptical, spiral or irregular galaxy?

    b) Is the Milky Way the same type of galaxy as Andromeda? If not, what type is it?

25. True or false?

    a) The Sun is located at the centre of the solar system.

    b) The solar system is located at the centre of the Milky Way.

    c) The Milky Way is at the centre of the Universe.

CONCEPT MAPS

HOW TO BUILD
A CONCEPT MAP

Prepare your own summary of Chapter 9 by building a concept map using the following terms:

- Astronomical unit
- Earth
- Galaxies
- Light year
- Milky Way
- Moon
- Planets
- Satellites
- Solar system
- Stars
- Sun
- Universe

SPACE ADAPTATION SYNDROME (SAS)

Astronauts in a spaceship or space station orbiting Earth experience the effects of zero gravity, that of weightlessness. This is the main cause of *space adaptation syndrome* or *space sickness*, a syndrome that often afflicts astronauts. It is defined as the sum of all symptoms felt during a space voyage.

First the astronaut feels disoriented and off balance, which in turn causes nausea, vertigo and hallucinations. Space sickness usually lasts about three days, until the body becomes accustomed to zero gravity.

The absence of gravity has a visible effect on the astronauts. The longer the time in space, the greater the physiological effects will be, as illustrated in Figure 9.38.

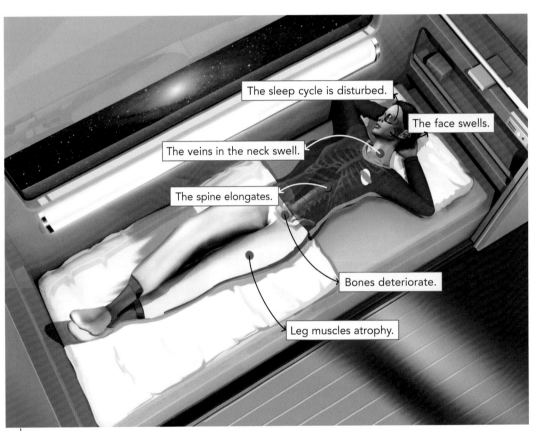

9.38 Physiological effects of space adaptation syndrome on an astronaut

1. Imagine you are offered a trip into space. Would you accept? In a table, indicate the advantages and disadvantages of a space voyage.

2. What are the similarities and differences between seasickness and space sickness. List them in a table.

JULIE PAYETTE

Julie Payette went through extensive training to prepare for her space mission. From May 26 to June 6, 1999, she was part of the crew aboard the space shuttle *Discovery* on its 26th mission, making her the first Canadian to set foot on the International Space Station. During the mission, she repaired the station's solar batteries, was in charge of the transfer, storage and installation of four tonnes of equipment, operated the Canadarm and built a file with photos of the station's exterior and of less photographed parts of planet Earth.

9.39 Julie Payette working in the space shuttle

NAME

Julie Payette

OCCUPATION

Astronaut with NASA and Chief Astronaut with the Canadian Space Agency

PLACE OF EMPLOYMENT

All over the world, including Canada and Europe

EDUCATION

Master's degree in computer science, commercial pilot licence, deep-sea diving certification, and astronaut training at NASA

PROUDEST ACHIEVEMENT

Participated in the first manual docking of the space shuttle *Discovery* at the International Space Station

9.40 OCCUPATIONS CONNECTED TO PAYETTE'S WORK

Occupation	Education required	Length of study	Main tasks
Aircraft accessories mechanic	DEP in aircraft mechanical assembly	1035 hours	• Repair, install and maintain mechanical and hydraulic systems
Aircraft pilot	DCS in aviation training	3 years	• Pilot aircraft • Apply aviation rules
Astrophysicist	Bachelor's degree in physics with a specialization	3 or more years	• Conduct scientific research on physical and astronomical phenomena

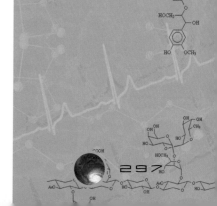

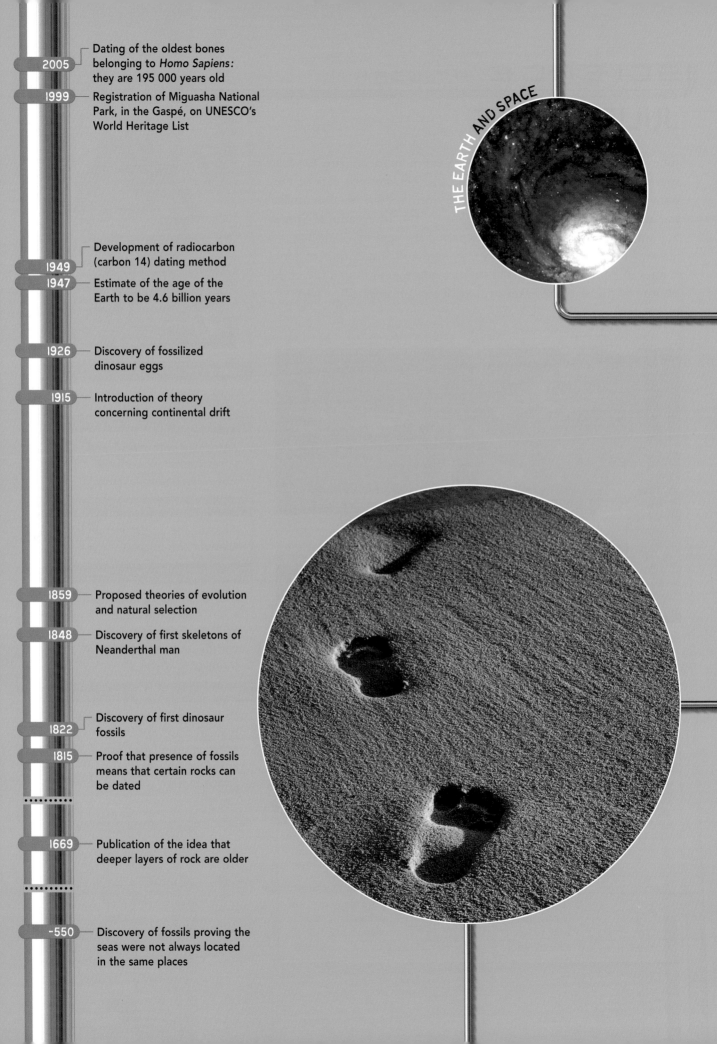

2005 — Dating of the oldest bones belonging to *Homo Sapiens*: they are 195 000 years old

1999 — Registration of Miguasha National Park, in the Gaspé, on UNESCO's World Heritage List

1949 — Development of radiocarbon (carbon 14) dating method

1947 — Estimate of the age of the Earth to be 4.6 billion years

1926 — Discovery of fossilized dinosaur eggs

1915 — Introduction of theory concerning continental drift

1859 — Proposed theories of evolution and natural selection

1848 — Discovery of first skeletons of Neanderthal man

1822 — Discovery of first dinosaur fossils

1815 — Proof that presence of fossils means that certain rocks can be dated

1669 — Publication of the idea that deeper layers of rock are older

-550 — Discovery of fossils proving the seas were not always located in the same places

THE HUMAN ORGANISM

AND THE ORIGIN
OF LIFE

The history of life on Earth is a very long one indeed, dating back billions of years. Even so, our own species, *Homo Sapiens*, has only been around for about 195 000 years—a very small number on a geological time scale. This means none of our closest ancestors ran alongside the dinosaurs, the animals that dominated our planet for millions of years before disappearing. This chapter, which describes the major stages in the history of life on Earth, takes a look at the conditions that made it possible for life to emerge on this planet, how life evolved and how we can know with any certainty that other now-extinct species existed millions of years ago.

1 THE ORIGIN OF LIFE

Earth is the only place where life is currently known to exist. Since its formation, our planet has undergone numerous changes that made it possible for life to emerge and diversify into all the forms that exist today. One billion years separate the formation of Earth and the birth of life.

1.1 THE FORMATION OF EARTH

About 4.6 billion years ago, our solar system was created from a cloud of gas and dust. The Sun formed at the centre of that cloud, making up 98 percent of the solar system's mass. The other planets and celestial bodies of the solar system formed around the Sun.

Earth is therefore a part of the matter that orbited around the Sun and condensed to form our planet. Earth slowly cooled down over time, which led to the formation of its core, mantle and crust. Figure 10.1 illustrates the changes of Earth's structure since its formation.

THE EARTH

4.6 BILLION YEARS AGO

Small particles of rock, dust and gas slowly come together under the effects of their own gravity, in a process called *accretion*. After millions of years, planet Earth takes shape.

4.2 BILLION YEARS AGO

The pressure at Earth's core is so intense that rocks melt and mix together. Gases escape. The planet's surface cools and forms a crust of solid rock.

3.5 BILLION YEARS AGO

The oceans and atmosphere develop. The atmosphere is made up of volcanic gases that trigger rains, filling the oceans. Rocky surfaces not submerged under water create the first continents. It is at this point that life is thought to have emerged.

10.1 The formation of Earth and its present structure

Countless celestial bodies (asteroids, meteors, comets) bombarded Earth during its first few million years of existence. One of the impacts may have produced the Moon. It is believed that a large celestial body collided with Earth with such force that it broke off a piece of the planet. The debris from the impact condensed and orbited around Earth, gradually forming the Moon.

10.2 The impact of a massive celestial body hitting Earth could have led to the creation of the Moon.

Most scientists agree the intensive meteorite bombardments ended 3.9 billion years ago, making it possible for life to emerge. For that to occur, hospitable conditions had to exist on Earth.

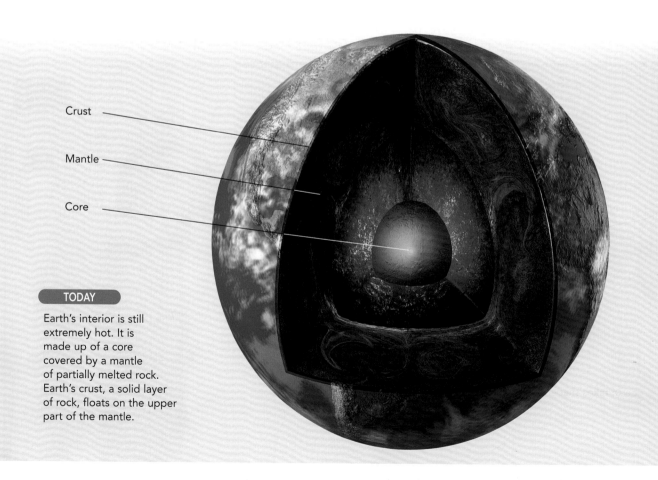

Crust

Mantle

Core

TODAY

Earth's interior is still extremely hot. It is made up of a core covered by a mantle of partially melted rock. Earth's crust, a solid layer of rock, floats on the upper part of the mantle.

1.2 FAVOURABLE CONDITIONS FOR THE EMERGENCE OF LIFE

The world's oldest rocks have been discovered in northern Québec. They date back about 3.8 billion years. Although some of their chemical properties suggest that life could have existed that long ago, the first evidence of life—that is, the oldest **FOSSILS** of living organisms—only dates back 3.5 billion years. This means that life probably emerged between 3.5 and 3.8 billion years ago. Let's take a look at how this happened.

First, we must keep in mind that all living organisms are made up of water and complex molecules, such as proteins, sugars, fat and hormones. Thus, the first molecules on Earth had to be simple molecules, such as carbon dioxide (CO_2) and nitrogen gas (N_2). For life to appear:

- Simple molecules had to reorganize themselves through chemical reactions into complex molecules.

- These complex molecules had to have bonded to form cells that were able to replicate into other similar cells.

A great deal of energy is required for simple molecules to synthesize into complex molecules in nature, and the resulting molecules are unstable and can easily break down. For life to take hold, therefore, certain conditions had to be met, *conditions essential for the emergence of life on Earth.*

> The **CONDITIONS ESSENTIAL FOR THE EMERGENCE OF LIFE ON EARTH** are those conditions that made it possible for the synthesis of the first organic molecules and their development into living cells.

The conditions that are necessary for the emergence of life are:
- the presence of essential chemical elements
- the presence of an energy source
- the presence of liquid water
- a very long period of time

Figure 10.3 illustrates how these conditions made it possible for the first living cells to develop.

Thus, about 3.5 billion years ago, the necessary conditions existed on Earth. The atmosphere, oceans and continents began to take shape, volcanoes ejected gases containing elements essential to life and there was an abundance of liquid water. Now, let's take a look at this situation in more detail.

CYCLE ONE
- Atmosphere
- Element
- Molecule

1930

Stanley Miller

In 1953, this American scientist, along with his professor, Harold Urey, demonstrated that it is possible to achieve synthesis of complex organic molecules from simple molecules in a lab setting. Afterward, many researchers conducted similar experiments with success.

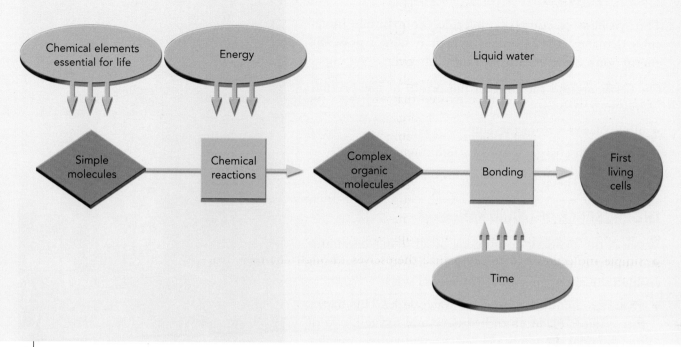

10.3 A system that would have favoured the emergence of life

THE PRESENCE OF ESSENTIAL CHEMICAL ELEMENTS

Complex organic molecules are mainly made up of four elements:

- carbon (C)
- oxygen (O)
- hydrogen (H)
- nitrogen (N)

Other elements, such as sulphur (S), can also be found in these organic molecules.

Scientists have good reason to believe the atmosphere of Earth in its early stages was mostly composed of water vapour (H_2O), carbon dioxide (CO_2) and nitrogen gas (N_2), as well as low amounts of methane (CH_4), ammonia (NH_3) and sulphur dioxide (SO_2). These substances could have provided the elements needed to form the first complex organic molecules.

10.4 According to several theories, substances ejected into the atmosphere by volcanoes contained the elements (C, N, O, H, S, and so on) essential for the synthesis of complex organic molecules.

THE PRESENCE OF AN ENERGY SOURCE

The synthesis of complex molecules from simple molecules demands lots of energy, which is why a powerful energy source was essential for life to begin.

On Earth, around the time of the origin of life, possible energy sources were:

- ultraviolet rays from the Sun
- electrical discharges caused by lightning
- heat released from volcanic eruptions and hot springs

THE PRESENCE OF LIQUID WATER

Water is the primary constituent of all living organisms and thus it is absolutely necessary for life to begin. Water enabled the emergence of life in several ways:

- First, the chemical formula of water, H_2O. This means that water is made up of hydrogen and oxygen, two of the essential elements needed to synthesize complex organic molecules.

- Next, life probably first appeared in water. It is believed that complex molecules existed in water in a kind of *primitive broth*. Molecules were able to bond there and eventually form living cells.

- Finally, water may have also protected the first living organisms from the harsh climatic conditions found on dry land.

10.5 Hot springs are underwater chimneys that spit out extremely hot water containing dissolved gases and metals.

10.6 It is very likely that life began in water.

A VERY LONG PERIOD OF TIME

The organizing of complex molecules into living cells was on the whole a fairly random occurrence. The probability of obtaining the right mix was very low to start with. Scientists have estimated that the probability of obtaining the right mix of complex molecules to form cells was less than 1 in 1 000 000 000 at the start, which is why an extremely long period of time was necessary for life to emerge:

• The more time passed, the greater the number of molecular bonds formed, and the greater the probability of producing living cells.

Once all the conditions necessary for the emergence of life were met, the first unicellular organisms, probably cyanobacteria as shown in Figure 10.7, began to appear. From then on, over the course of millions of years, life grew ever more complex and diverse.

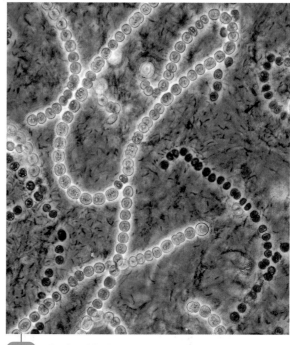

10.7 The first life forms must have looked like these cyanobacteria, which are able to make their own food because of the rays of the Sun (photosynthesis).

2 HISTORY OF LIFE ON EARTH

Once life appeared, about 3.5 to 3.8 billion years ago, it underwent many modifications that led to the formation of new species, as well as the extinction of some of them.

2.1 LAWS OF EVOLUTION

Life diversified over time through a very slow process referred to as *evolution*. Evolution brings about changes that create new species.

> ▶ EVOLUTION is a very slow process that brings about changes in living organisms.

Evolution occurs randomly and selectively:

• First, **GENES** randomly mutate, causing changes at the level of the individual.

• Then, these changes are screened by *natural selection*. If they offer advantages to the individual, helping it survive, the changes are transmitted from one generation to the next. If not, these changes disappear.

▶ **NATURAL SELECTION** is a process that occurs naturally within a species. It results in the reproduction of organisms with traits that allow them to survive better in their environment.

Since the dawn of life, evolution has led to the emergence of millions of species of bacteria, protists, fungi, plants and animals. Figure 10.10 (pages 308 and 309) depicts groups of living organisms that exist because of evolution. An estimated 99 percent of species that have appeared in groups of living organisms at one time or another have disappeared. Figure 10.9 illustrates one of these examples.

The history of the early eons of life features numerous critical events, including:

- When life began, Earth's atmosphere contained very little oxygen. The first living organisms (bacteria) produced oxygen through photosynthesis. At first it was diluted in water. After millions of years, it began to accumulate in the atmosphere, and living organisms were able to develop traits allowing them to breathe oxygen in air.

- Life multiplied in the water at the start. Little by little, living organisms developed traits that allowed them to inhabit dry land. For example, the transformation of fins into limbs and the development of lungs led to the appearance of the first amphibians, animals that can live in water and on dry land. Plants adapted to land life by developing roots.

> *Amphibian* comes from the Greek words *amphi*, meaning "both, or double," and *bioun*, meaning "who lives."

- Living organisms have had to adapt to numerous climate changes since their appearance on Earth. Some, for example, had to adapt to Earth's ice ages. An ice age is a period during which the climate is cold, and large parts of the continents are covered in ice.

Scientists have organized the evolution of life into time periods, using the geological time scale studied in Section 2.2.

Sixth finger

10.8 The giant panda has developed a sixth finger through natural selection. It allows the panda to better grasp bamboo twigs, its primary food source.

The first fish to climb on land

A defining moment in the evolution of life on Earth occurred at the end of the Devonian period: some fish, as their fins were replaced by limbs, managed to climb out of water and move about on dry land.

Researchers have uncovered an important piece of the puzzle of how fish first ventured outside water, with their discovery of a 375-million-year old fossil from the fish species, *Tiktaalik roseæ*, in Nunavut territory in northern Canada.

The operculum, a large bone that covers the gills of bony fish, is absent in this species. This means that the animal likely used its lungs more often than its gills to breathe. Also the fins of *Tiktaalik roseæ* exhibit a crude outline of fingers.

On the right lies the fossilized *Tiktaalik roseæ* discovered in Nunavut. A reconstruction of what the animal would have looked like poses on the left.

The animal lived in an equatorial climate (at one time Nunavut was located at the equator), in a muddy and swampy environment.

Adapted from Christiane Galus, "Découverte du poisson qui, le premier, a marché sur terre," *Le Monde*, April 7, 2006. [Translation]

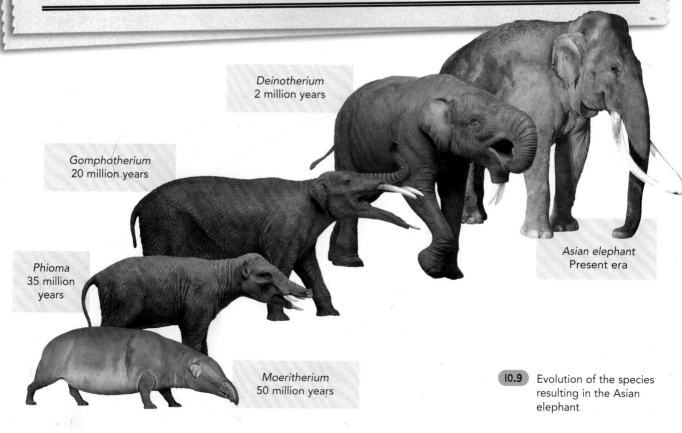

Deinotherium
2 million years

Gomphotherium
20 million years

Phioma
35 million years

Moeritherium
50 million years

Asian elephant
Present era

10.9 Evolution of the species resulting in the Asian elephant

FLOWERING PLANTS

Plants with seeds enclosed in a fruit

CONIFERS

Plants with seeds not enclosed in a fruit

FERNS

Plants with a vascular system that transports fluids without flowers or seeds

MOSSES

Plants without a vascular system to transport fluids

ALGAE

Plants found mostly in an aquatic habitat

PLANTS

Multicellular organisms using photosynthesis to nourish themselves

FUNGI

Organisms incapable of movement, that nourish themselves through absorption

PROTISTS

Unicellular organisms with a cell nucleus

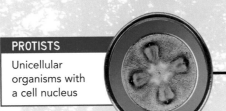

BACTERIA

Unicellular organisms without a cell nucleus

LIVING ORGANISMS

PRIMATES

Mammals (including monkeys and humans) endowed with hands that can grasp objects, mainly living in trees

MAMMALS

Vertebrates whose females are endowed with mammary glands to feed their young

BIRDS

Vertebrates covered with feathers, each equipped with a beak, two wings and two legs

DINOSAURS (EXTINCT)

Reptiles that lived in the Triassic, Jurassic and Cretaceous periods

INSECTS

Invertebrates with three pairs of legs, one or two pairs of wings and a pair of antennae

REPTILES

Vertebrates covered with scales, whose eggs develop outside water

AMPHIBIANS

Vertebrates, endowed with four legs, that live in water and on land

VARIOUS INVERTEBRATES

Invertebrates with a soft body, sometimes enclosed in a shell

FISH

Aquatic vertebrates covered with scales and equipped with fins

VERTEBRATES
Presence of a vertebral column

INVERTEBRATES
Absence of a vertebral column

ANIMALS
Living organisms capable of movement, able to nourish themselves on other organisms or their remains

The history of life is defined by the succession and renewal of species and groups of living organisms. Presented here are some groups of living organisms and their general characteristics.

2.2 GEOLOGICAL TIME SCALE

The geological time scale begins 4.6 billion years ago, with the formation of Earth, and extends to the present time.

> ▶ The GEOLOGICAL TIME SCALE is a tool that represents the main divisions in the history of Earth, based on the major events that have occurred in the history of life.

Geology is from the Greek words *gê*, meaning "earth," and *logia*, meaning "speech, words."

The geological time scale is divided into four eras:

- Precambrian, began 4.6 billion years ago
- Paleozoic, began 543 million years ago
- Mesozoic, began 245 million years ago
- Cenozoic, began 65 million years ago

The three most recent geological eras are subdivided into periods. Each era and period corresponds to a major episode in the evolution of the environment and life.

Descriptions of the geological eras and a simplified geological time scale are included on pages 312 and 313.

2.3 EXTINCTIONS

Since life formed on Earth, climatic and chemical conditions have often changed, at times quite abruptly, thus transforming the environment. The temperature of the oceans, for example, has varied over the years as has composition of the atmosphere.

When a species is unable to adapt to changes in its habitat, it disappears from the planet. This is what is called the extinction of a species.

> ▶ The EXTINCTION OF A SPECIES is the disappearance of all individuals belonging to that species. It is caused by the inability of the individuals to adapt to change(s) in their environment.

Throughout history there have been five mass extinctions of species, also called *extinction events,* which involved the disappearance of numerous species in a relatively short time. The five periods that ended with extinction events are identified with an asterisk on the geological time scale on page 312. In the following pages, we will take an in-depth look at events that occurred during the Permian and Cretaceous periods whose causes are well known.

1890
1965

Arthur Holmes

Scientists established the first geological time scales in the 18th century. In the 1930s, the work of British geologist Arthur Holmes led to the development of a scale with more precise geological time dating. He is considered to be the father of the geological time scale.

THE PERMIAN MASS EXTINCTION

The Permian extinction event occurred about 245 million years ago, marking the transition from the Paleozoic to the Mesozoic era. More than 90 percent of marine life and 70 percent of land-dwelling species became extinct during this time period. It represents the most devastating extinction to ever take place on Earth.

During the Permian, continental drift caused major rifts in the Earth's crust. This led to the most intense volcanic eruptions of the last 500 million years, especially in the region where Siberia is located. Volcanoes are thought to have ejected such enormous amounts of carbon dioxide into the atmosphere that they triggered a global warming of Earth's climates and the disappearance of a large number of species unable to adapt.

CYCLE ONE
└ Tectonic plate

10.11 Massive volcanic eruptions caused by continental drift led to the extinction event at the end of the Paleozoic era.

Even though the volcanic eruption hypothesis is widely accepted by scientists, the recent discovery of a crater at the bottom of the Antarctic Ocean could also explain this extinction event. According to geological data, there is evidence of a crater buried beneath 1.6 km of ice dating back 250 million years and coinciding with the end of the Permian. The catastrophic effect of an impact from a meteor 50 km in diameter could explain the mass extinction of species inhabiting Earth at the time.

MORE EXTINCTIONS TO COME?

In 2006, 18 animal species were classified as endangered or vulnerable in Québec, including the golden eagle, the caribou, the wood turtle and the beluga. Another 107 species, sub-species or populations were considered to be at risk of being included on the list.

Era	Period	Start of the period (in millions of years before present time)	Major events in the history of life
Cenozoic	Quaternary	1.8	Period in which we live at present Appearance of first human beings Ice ages (the last one ended 10 000 years ago)
Cenozoic	Tertiary	65	Appearance of chimpanzee and human ancestors Appearance of first primates Multiplication of flowering plant species Multiplication of mammal and bird species
Mesozoic	Cretaceous*	144	Appearance of first flowering plants
Mesozoic	Jurassic	206	Appearance of first birds Multiplication of dinosaur species
Mesozoic	Triassic*	245	Appearance of first dinosaurs and mammals Multiplication of conifer species
Paleozoic	Permian*	290	Multiplication of reptile species Multiplication of insect species
Paleozoic	Carboniferous	363	Multiplication of amphibian species Appearance of first reptiles Appearance of first conifers Presence of vast humid forests
Paleozoic	Devonian*	409	Appearance of first amphibians and insects Multiplication of fish species
Paleozoic	Silurian	439	Multiplication of terrestrial plant species
Paleozoic	Ordovician*	510	Colonization of dry land by animals Colonization of dry land by plant life Appearance of first marine vertebrates (fish) Presence of numerous marine algae species
Paleozoic	Cambrian	543	Multiplication of aquatic invertebrate species Appearance of invertebrates with hard shells
Precambrian		4600	Appearance of first animals: soft-bodied invertebrates Appearance of first protists Beginning of oxygen accumulation in the atmosphere Appearance of first bacteria First signs of life Beginning of the formation of Earth

* Period ending with a mass extinction of species

CENOZOIC

The Cenozoic, our present era, has lasted 65 million years. It is during this era that most of the species of birds, mammals and flowering plants we know today appeared. Our species arrived very late in this era, about 200 000 years ago.

Common scene in the early Cenozoic Era 10.13

MESOZOIC

The Mesozoic is also referred to as the *Age of the Dinosaurs*, because reptiles dominated the world during this era. The Mesozoic spans about 180 million years and ended 65 million years ago with the mass extinction of the dinosaurs.

Common scene in the Mesozoic Era 10.14

PALEOZOIC

The Paleozoic spanned about 300 million years. It began with the appearance of many species of invertebrates with hard shells and concluded with the mass extinction of about 90% of marine species and 70% of terrestrial species.

Common scene in the Paleozoic Era 10.15

PRECAMBRIAN

The Precambrian includes 88% of the planet's history, spanning over 4 billion years. Earth and life itself formed during this era. Fossils from this time are rarely recovered because most living organisms had soft bodies.

Common scene in the Precambrian Era 10.16

RELATIVE DURATION OF ERAS

1.5%

4%

6.5%

88%

MASS EXTINCTION OF THE CRETACEOUS

The extinction event of the Cretaceous Period occurred some 65 million years ago. Not as significant as the Permian mass extinction, it nevertheless caused the disappearance of about 50 percent of marine species and many plants and animals, including the dinosaurs.

The generally accepted, and most spectacular hypothesis explaining this extinction is that a huge impact from an asteroid measuring 10 km in diameter caused it. The impact released an enormous amount of dust into the atmosphere. The dust would have blocked out the Sun, causing the climate to cool and resulting in a severe reduction of photosynthesis by plants—a fatal consequence for many species.

10.17 Dinosaurs, whose name means *Terrible Lizard*, suffered a mass extinction during the Cretaceous Period.

CONNECTIONS HISTORY

The grandfathers of the bison

Although Native North American people have a long acquaintance with dinosaur fossils, which they refer to as the *grandfathers of the bison*, it was only in 1874 that a scientist, geologist George Mercer Dawson, discovered dinosaur fossils in Canada. The notion of *dinosaur*, established in 1843, was still relatively new.

At the time, Canadian geologists were actually searching for bituminous coal deposits, instead of dinosaurs. Bituminous coal was essential to the construction of the Canada-wide railway system, which had begun to be laid in 1871.

In 1884, one of Dawson's assistants, Joseph Burr Tyrell, uncovered a dinosaur skull in Red Deer Valley, now in the province of Alberta. The dinosaur was named *Albertosaurus*. Subsequent excavations in that region led to the uncovering of more than 300 dinosaur skeletons.

In 1910, when American scientists started excavations in Canada, searching for dinosaurs, Canadian authorities realized the importance of their heritage and decided to protect it, launching a kind of scientific dinosaur hunt.

The discovery of dinosaur bones in Red Deer, Alberta, in 1915

Despite the harsh conditions that have often prevailed on Earth, some species have always managed to survive. Our own species was able to emerge because of the evolution of some of these species.

2.4 THE ORIGINS OF OUR SPECIES

We often hear that our species descends from the monkeys. It would be more accurate to say monkeys are our *cousins*. In fact, humans and all species of monkey have a common ancestor and are part of the same group: the order of Primates.

What first distinguished humans from monkeys was the ability to move around on two feet, referred to as *bipedalism*. An animal is considered to be a biped if it is capable of movement on two feet. Our species is therefore bipedal. Although chimpanzees and certain other apes are able to move on two feet, they are not considered to be bipedal since they seldom use this type of locomotion.

The human lineage separated from the great apes several million years ago.

10.18 The chimpanzee is not a biped because it rarely, and only awkwardly, walks on two feet.

10.19 Evolution of humans and living species of great apes. This illustration shows that chimpanzees are our closest cousins.

Due to a lack of fossil evidence, the evolution of the human species is not well understood by scientists. Figure 10.20 (next page) presents a timeline with the three main genera: *Australopithecus*, *Paranthropus* and *Homo*. Of the species grouped within these three genera, only the species *Homo sapiens* has survived.

PARANTHROPUS

Paranthropus is also called
Australopithecus robustus. Members of
this genus were bigger and taller than
the *Australopithecus*. With robust skulls
and teeth, certain species of
Paranthropus lived at the same time as
some species of the genus *Homo*.

Example of species

Paranthropus robustus

AUSTRALOPITHECUS

Australopithecus were humans of
short stature, with a smaller skull
than our own. Scientists believe
they walked on ground by day and
sought shelter in trees by night.
Evolution of the species within the
genus *Australopithecus* led to the
Paranthropus and *Homo* genera.

Example of species

Australopithecus afarensis

1.0

2.4

2.5

2.7

4.4

**(millions
of years ago)**

HOMO

The genus *Homo* groups our species,
Homo sapiens, and those closest to
us. All species of the *Homo* genus
were almost exclusively bipedal,
while species from other genera
used other types of locomotion
as well.

Two other species of the genus
Homo lived concurrently with our own:

- *Homo neanderthalensis* or
  Neanderthal man, shared the
  territories of Europe, Asia and
  Africa with our species and
  disappeared some 30 000
  years ago.
- *Homo floresiensis* lived on the
  Indonesian island of Flores. This
  species became extinct 12 000
  years ago following a volcanic
  eruption.

Examples of species

*Homo
neanderthalensis*   *Homo
floresiensis*

Homo sapiens

10.20 The human lineage

SPECIES *HOMO SAPIENS*

Our species, *Homo sapiens*, is the only surviving member of the human lineage. It appeared about 195 000 years ago.

Human traits that have appeared through evolution and that help distinguish our species from other animal species include:

- Bipedalism freed up our hands, allowing them to be put to various uses, such as making clothes and tools.

- Our hair is finer than that of other mammals, and covers less. Partial nudity was advantageous for humans because of the need to keep cool during the day in the scorching heat of the African savanna. Plus, the human body contains more sweat glands than that of any other species.

- Our brain is large and complex, making it possible for us to have superior mental capabilities compared to other animals. This brain enabled us to become very inventive, to meet a multitude of wants and needs and to communicate using complex languages.

Scientists are still uncertain about the reason behind the major development of our brain. Some believe this evolution occurred to improve our socialization skills, help us find more ingenious ways of gathering food and protect us from predators.

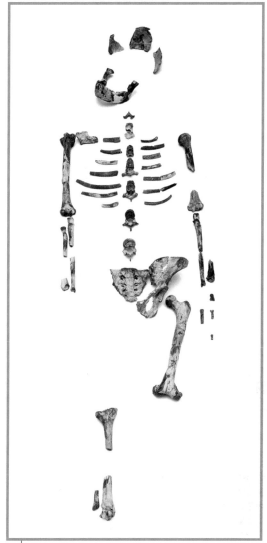

10.21 In 1974, the skeleton of a female member of the *Australopithecus afarensis* species was discovered in Ethiopia and was named Lucy.

10.22 These primate skulls are placed in chronological order. On the far left, we can see the skull of a type of lemur that lived 50 million years ago. The two skulls on the far right belong to members of the *Homo sapiens* species, one dates back 92 000 years and the other 22 000 years.

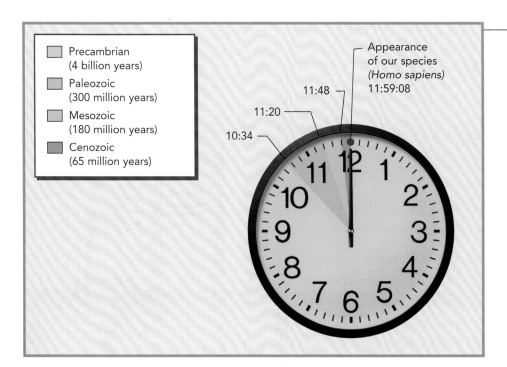

Precambrian
(4 billion years)

Paleozoic
(300 million years)

Mesozoic
(180 million years)

Cenozoic
(65 million years)

10:34

11:20

11:48

Appearance
of our species
(*Homo sapiens*)
11:59:08

10.23 If Earth had formed 12 hours ago, our species *Homo sapiens* would have appeared 2 seconds ago.

All things considered, our species emerged quite late in the history of the Earth. Over time, because of intellectual capacity, *homo sapiens* has become the dominant species of the planet, with members numbering in the billions.

The discovery of "Lucy's daughter"

An almost complete skeleton of a child from the *Australopithecus afarensis* species was discovered in 2000 in Dikika, Ethiopia. The skeleton is 3.3 million years old. Already, in 1974, an adult skeleton had been discovered and named Lucy. This time, the bones were those of a three-year-old girl named Selam.

Australopithecus afarensis had both human and simian (monkey-like) characteristics. Although this hominid had a small brain, it could stand upright and walk.

Researchers do not know whether Selam was able to climb trees like a monkey. Her slow growth rate suggests she was closer to the human species. Human beings develop at a slower rate than monkeys, in order to allow time for the development of their higher functions.

Adapted from "Découverte de 'la fille de Lucy'," *BBC Afrique* website. *[Translation]*

The skull of Selam, a young *Australopithecus* who lived 3.3 million years ago

3 FOSSILS

CYCLE ONE
- Erosion
- Types of rocks

To establish the history of life on Earth, scientists refer to the remains of living organisms that inhabited our planet in the past. These remains, called *fossils,* are like documents that help reconstruct the history of life. Experts in the study and research of fossils are called *paleontologists.*

Fossil comes from the Latin word *fossilis,* meaning "dug out of the earth."

10.24 Paleontologists are experts in the study of fossils.

Usually when an organism dies, its remains decompose quickly. But sometimes, they become preserved inside Earth's crust, that is, they become fossilized.

Not only can the long-preserved remains of an organism become fossilized, but so too can other traces, such as footprints. Scientists have discovered fossilized dinosaur footprints, for example, which were preserved when the soil hardened.

> ▶ A FOSSIL is any remains or trace of an organism that has been preserved for a very long period of time in Earth's crust.

10.25 Embedded in a rock is a fossil of a trilobite, an organism that lived in the seas over 225 million years ago.

More often, fossils are discovered in sedimentary rocks formed under-water by the accumulation of solid particles (sand, silt, clay) called *sediments*. Over time, the sediments compress and harden to form sedimentary rocks.

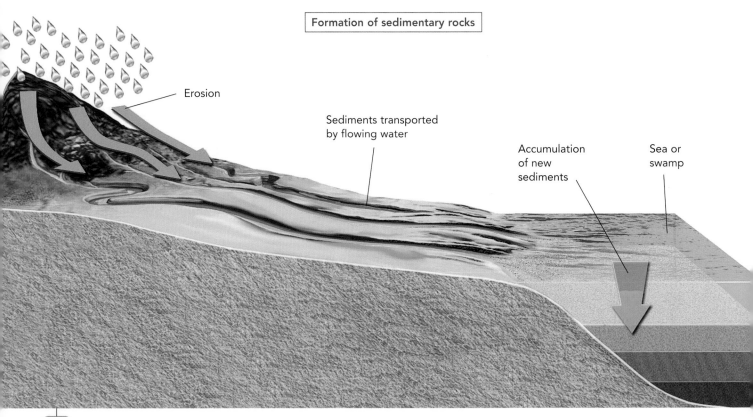

| Formation of sedimentary rocks |

Erosion

Sediments transported by flowing water

Accumulation of new sediments

Sea or swamp

10.26 Sedimentary rocks are formed by the compression and hardening of sediments.

3.1 TYPES OF FOSSILS

There are four types of fossils, defined according to the way they are formed. Certain fossils are of mixed types, meaning that one part of the fossil is formed one way, and the other another way. The four fossil types are:

- petrified fossils
- cast fossils
- body fossils
- trace fossils

Let's examine each of these fossil types in detail.

FOSSILS FROM GASPÉ

Percé Rock in the Gaspé Peninsula is not only a tourist attraction, but it also has important geological value. It contains many fossil species dating from the Devonian period, such as trilobites.

PETRIFIED FOSSILS

Petrified fossils are the remains of organisms that harden during fossilization, becoming as hard as rock. In general, when an organism dies, the soft tissue quickly decomposes. The hard tissue that makes up bones, teeth, shells or tree trunks, for example, is most likely to become petrified fossils. Figure 10.27 outlines the formation of this fossil type.

①

②

③

④

The organism dies. Its soft tissue decomposes or is eaten by other organisms. The hard tissue, in its entirety or in part, is deposited underwater, at the bottom, where there are sediments.

This stage lasts a very long time. Hard tissue is buried under layers of sediment. Little by little, minerals replace the organism's hard tissue and preserve its shape.

With the movement of Earth's crust, the layer of rock in which the remains have been mineralized can move back up to the surface.

Once near the surface, erosion of the rocks that covered the fossil can cause it to emerge or be uncovered by researchers during a dig.

10.27 The formation of a petrified fossil

Remains of organisms that petrify in this way usually conserve their original form. Figures 10.28 and 10.29 show examples of petrified fossils.

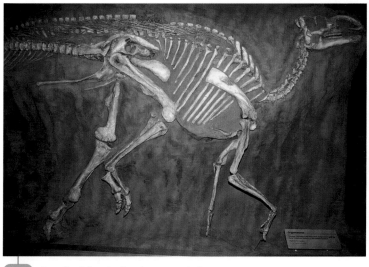

10.28 Petrified fossil of a dinosaur skeleton

10.29 Fossilized dinosaur eggs

CAST OR MOULD FOSSILS

A great number of fossils discovered in sedimentary rocks are not actually the remains of organisms. Sedimentary rocks took the shape of the organism's remains, which later decomposed. The resulting impression in the rock could be empty *(mould fossil)* or filled in with minerals *(cast fossil)*. Figure 10.30 illustrates an example of a partial mould fossil.

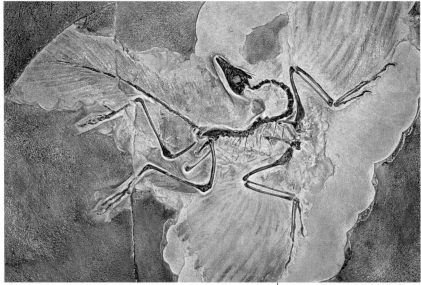

BODY FOSSILS

Certain fossils form when organisms become trapped in matter that prevents the formation of microorganisms, which could make it decompose. The entire body, including soft tissue, is fossilized. For example, mammoths, bison and prehistoric humans frozen in ice became fossilized in their original condition. In a similar context, a great number of insects and small animals became trapped in a substance called *amber*. Amber is the solidified result of resin produced by certain prehistoric plants.

10.30 An archaeopteryx, the first known bird. The outline of the feathers is a mould fossil, while the bones are petrified.

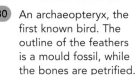

10.31 This insect was trapped in resin that turned into amber.

10.32 In 2002, a mammoth was discovered in the Siberian ice where it had been preserved for 20 000 years.

TRACE FOSSILS

Trace fossils are traces left in soft soil by an organism that lived a long time ago and that have fossilized over the years. Figure 10.33 shows the fossilized traces made by a dinosaur.

10.33 Dinosaur trace fossils

3.2 FOSSIL DATING

Fossil dating is carried out using various methods. Let's take a look at some of them.

STRATIGRAPHIC LAYERS AND RELATIVE DATING

As we have already seen, most fossils are preserved in sedimentary rock that forms through the accumulation of sediments under water.

If we examine a cross-section of sedimentary rock, we can see how the rock formed in strata, or layers, with more recent sediments layering on top of older sediments. These *stratigraphic layers* form according to one of the following principles:

- The Law of Original Continuity: All sedimentary rock contained in a single stratigraphic layer formed in the same time period.

- The Law of Superposition: The deeper a stratigraphic layer is in the ground, the older it is.

> ▶ A STRATIGRAPHIC LAYER is a stratum of sedimentary rock that formed in the same time period as the rock.

CANADIAN SITES TEEM WITH FOSSILS

Miguasha National Park, in the Gaspé Peninsula, is registered on UNESCO's World Heritage List because of the quality of Devonian fossils found there. Alberta's Dinosaur Provincial Park is also on the list because of its wealth of dinosaur fossils, as is the Burgess Shale (found in Yoho National Park in the Canadian Rockies) because of its abundance of soft-bodied marine life fossils.

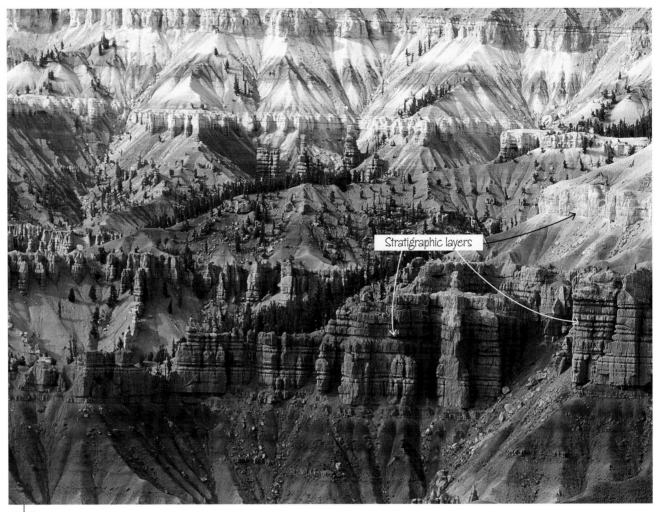

10.34 The walls of this canyon display many stratigraphic layers.

As fossils form simultaneously as the stratigraphic layers, the laws of continuity and superposition also apply to them:

- Fossils found in the same stratigraphic layer were formed during the same period.
- Older fossils are buried in deeper stratigraphic layers than more recent fossils.

Comparing the location of two fossils in stratigraphic layers is called *relative dating*. Relative dating does not identify the actual age of fossils; it only indicates whether one fossil is older or younger than the other.

▶ RELATIVE DATING is a method that helps establish the order in which the fossils formed, without identifying their absolute age.

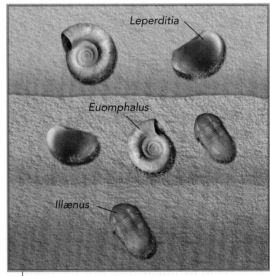

10.35 The location of these fossils in the stratigraphic layers is evidence that *Illænus* appeared first. It also indicates that *Illænus* lived during the same time period as *Euomphalus* and *Leperditia*, but that it disappeared before them.

ABSOLUTE DATING

Scientists used the relative dating method for fossils and rocks for a long time, due to a lack of more advanced technology. Absolute dating methods were only developed in the mid-20th century. These methods provide the age of fossils or rocks from stratigraphic layers. Even though the term *absolute* is used, there is always a margin of error present when determining the age of fossils or rocks.

> ▶ ABSOLUTE DATING is a method used to determine the age of fossils in years.

The difference between relative and absolute dating can be explained using the example of trees. We can look at the size of a tree and, by using relative dating, tell whether it is older or younger than another tree; a smaller tree is younger than a bigger tree. To tell the exact age of a tree, however, we can use the absolute dating method of counting annual growth rings, as shown in Figure 10.36.

The first absolute dating methods of fossils and rocks involved the **RADIOACTIVE** properties of certain elements. By measuring the level of radioactive elements present in a fossil or rock, scientists were able to determine its age.

Carbon-14 dating is an example of an absolute dating method that uses an element's radioactive properties. In its lifetime, an organism absorbs a small amount of carbon-14, a radioactive type of carbon. After the organism dies, the carbon-14 present in the remains slowly disintegrates, at a regular rate, into non-radioactive carbon. By measuring the proportion of carbon-14 contained in the fossil, scientists can pinpoint the approximate age of the fossil.

Carbon-14 dating is used on very *young* fossils, that is, under the age of 60 000. For older fossils, other radioactive elements such as uranium are used.

➕ Although absolute dating methods are the most often used, other methods have been developed as well, such as the study of amino acid structure. When an organism dies, the structure of its amino acids changes at a constant rate. The age of a fossil can be determined by comparing these modified amino acids to amino acids that still retain their original structure.

Growth rings

10.36 By counting the growth rings in a tree trunk, the absolute age of a tree can be determined. This tree was 11 years old when it was cut down.

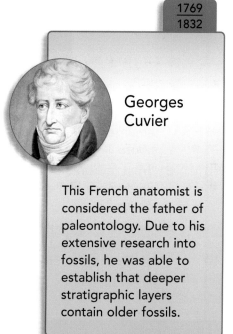

1769
1832

Georges Cuvier

This French anatomist is considered the father of paleontology. Due to his extensive research into fossils, he was able to establish that deeper stratigraphic layers contain older fossils.

CHECKUP

1 THE ORIGIN OF LIFE (pp. 300–305)

1. Earth took millions of years to form.
   a) Where did the matter that formed our planet come from?
   b) How long ago did Earth form?
   c) How did the Moon form?

2. Look at the photos below.

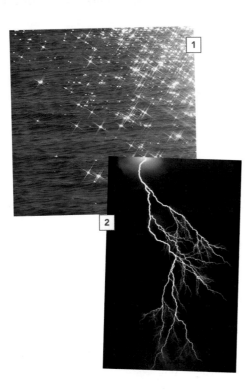

   a) What favourable condition for the emergence of life is illustrated in photo 1?
   b) What favourable condition for the emergence of life is illustrated in photo 2?
   c) What are the other two favourable conditions essential for the emergence of life and that are not illustrated in these photos?

3. a) Complex organic molecules are mainly made up of which chemical elements?
   b) Where do scientists believe these organic molecules were when they first organized into living cells?
   c) Why did it take so long for the first cells to form?
   d) When did life first appear on Earth?
   e) Which were the first forms of life to appear on Earth?

2 THE HISTORY OF LIFE ON EARTH (pp. 305–318)

4. A great number of species have appeared since the beginning of life on Earth.
   a) Name the very slow process that brings about modifications in living beings.
   b) Name the natural process that gradually results in the reproduction of living organisms better adapted to their environment.

5. Which of the four geological eras is described in each of the following examples?
   a) era in which we live at present
   b) era when many dinosaur species lived, as well as when they all became extinct
   c) the longest geological era of the four
   d) era during which most species of mammals appeared
   e) era which ended with the biggest extinction event ever

6. Here are a few important events in the history of life:
   - appearance of amphibians and insects
   - appearance of our species
   - appearance of dinosaurs
   - first evidence of life
   - appearance of vertebrates
   - extinction of about 90 percent of all marine species
   - appearance of soft-bodied invertebrates
   - appearance of fish
   - extinction of dinosaurs

   Reproduce a table like the one below.

   a) In the first column, write the events in chronological order.

   b) In the second column, write the geological era in which each event occurred.

   c) In the third column, write the geological period in which each event occurred.

   Do not indicate anything for events that occurred during the Precambrian.

Event	Era	Period

7. Below is a photo of the fossil of a species of fish that lived 380 million years ago in an area that is now the Gaspé Peninsula.

   In which era and period on the geological time scale did this fish live?

8. *Jurassic Park*, the first film of a science fiction trilogy about dinosaurs, was released in theatres in 1993. Why was this an appropriate title for a film about dinosaurs?

9. Apes and humans are animals from the order of Primates.

   a) Which ape is our closest cousin?

   b) What characteristic do paleontologists rely on to distinguish humans and apes in evolution?

10. The human lineage contains many species, all of which are extinct except our own.

    a) What are the three main genera of the human lineage?

    b) What is the scientific name of our species?

    c) What are the names of the two human species that once lived at the same time as us?

11. Our species has undergone many adaptations since its appearance. Explain one advantage for each of the following adaptations.

    a) bipedalism

    b) our brain, which is highly developed compared to that of other species

    c) our hair, which is finer than that of other mammals

    d) our many sweat glands

12. Explain why it is difficult for scientists to establish exactly how the human species evolved.

3 FOSSILS (pp. 319–325)

13. In what type of rock are fossils most often discovered?

14. Look at the photos below.

a) Identify the type of fossil illustrated in each one.

b) Briefly describe how each fossil was formed.

Write your answers in a table like the one below.

Fossil	Type	Formation

15. a) What type of fossil is not included in the photos in question 14?

b) Provide two examples of this type of fossil, and how each was formed.

16. True or false? Explain your answers.

a) Geologists specialize in the study and research of fossils.

b) A tree trunk can become fossilized.

c) Many fossils are found in Québec, mainly in magmatic rock.

d) All the organisms that die will one day become fossils.

e) On a fossil, parts of an organism can be petrified and others moulded.

f) Relative dating is more accurate than absolute dating.

g) A fossil that formed 25 million years ago contains more carbon-14 than one that formed 60 million years ago.

17. In your own words, explain the Laws of Continuity and Superposition of stratigraphic layers.

18. What type of dating is referred to in each of the following examples?

a) One tree is older than another because it is bigger.

b) A tree is 12 years old because it has 12 growth rings.

19. a) On what properties of certain elements is carbon-14 dating based?

b) How can the age of a fossil be determined using this method of absolute dating?

20. Carefully study the illustration below. It includes three stratigraphic layers and the fossils they contain.

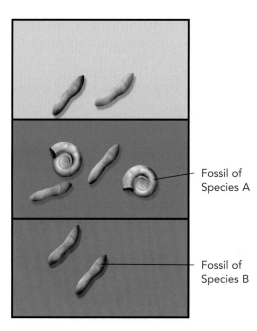

Fossil of Species A

Fossil of Species B

a) What colour is the oldest stratigraphic layer? Explain your answer using the principle on which it is based.

b) What species first appeared? Explain your answer.

c) What species disappeared last? Explain your answer.

d) Did Species B exist at the same time as Species A? Explain your answer.

e) What type of dating helps determine the age of a stratigraphic layer according to its location with regard to other layers?

f) If fossils of Species A and Species B are estimated to be over 60 000 years old, what radioactive element could be used to determine the age of the two fossils?

CONCEPT MAPS

HOW TO BUILD A CONCEPT MAP

Prepare your own summary of Chapter 10 by building a concept map using the following terms:

- Cenozoic
- Favourable conditions for the emergence of life
- Fossils
- Geological time
- History of life
- Living species
- Mass extinctions
- Mesozoic
- Paleozoic
- Precambrian
- Stratigraphic layers

EPIDEMICS: DISEASES THAT THREATEN HUMAN POPULATIONS

If the number of people suffering from a specific illness, in a given area and for a certain period of time, rapidly increases, the illness is referred to as an *epidemic*. Almost every winter, for example, the population in this province is stricken by a flu epidemic.

In general, an epidemic occurs when people come into contact with a disease to which they have no immunity. Infected people then spread the new disease to new locations during their everyday travels.

In the beginning of the history of humanity, people lived in groups isolated from one another. As exchanges between groups were infrequent, so too were epidemics. Epidemics have come about due to the creation of cities and roads, because the transmission of disease between populations became easier.

When an epidemic strikes most of the population of one or more continents, it is called a *pandemic*. Some of the deadliest pandemics include:

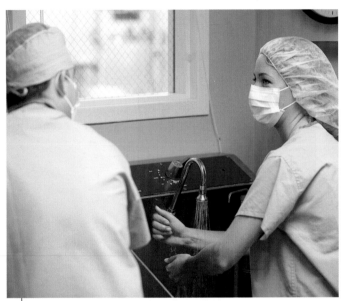

10.37 Medical personnel must wash their hands frequently to limit the spread of disease.

- the Black Plague, also known as the Black Death, which killed over 20 million people in Europe between 1346 and 1350

- the Spanish flu, which killed close to 40 million people across Asia, Europe and America between 1918 and 1920

- AIDS, which has killed 25 million people throughout the world to date (since its appearance in 1981)

1. What is the difference between an epidemic and a pandemic?

2. What methods must be used to limit the spread of an epidemic?

SCIENCE AT WORK

SYLVAIN DESBIENS

Paleontologist Sylvain Desbiens is a true fossil enthusiast. His job at Miguasha National Park consists of coordinating team members as they search for fossils and adequately conserve them. His work mainly focuses on the Devonian Period in Québec and the search for new fossiliferous sites. During the Devonian, a geological period sometimes referred to as *The Age of Fish*, the southern part of Québec and the Gaspé Peninsula were located near the equator and were partly submerged underwater. Miguasha National Park is world renowned for the abundance and quality of fish and plant fossils from that period.

10.38 This fresco, located in the Museum of Natural History in Miguasha National Park, depicts the Miguasha environment during the Devonian.

NAME
Sylvain Desbiens

JOB
Responsible for conservation and research at Miguasha National Park

AREA OF EMPLOYMENT
Miguasha, in the Gaspé

EDUCATION
Bachelor's degree in geology Master's degree and Doctorate in paleontology

PROUDEST ACHIEVEMENT
Participated in the discovery of important sites for research in the field of paleontology

10.39 OTHER OCCUPATIONS CONNECTED TO DESBIENS' WORK

Occupation	Required training	Length of study	Main Tasks
Tourist officer	DEP in the protection and management of wildlife territories	1320 hours	• Patrol sites • Provide information to visitors
Museum technician	DCS in museum techniques	3 years	• Work in the preservation of museum pieces • Carry out the layout of exhibit spaces
Geologist	Bachelor's degree in geology	3 or more years	• Analysis of the soil and the rocks it contains

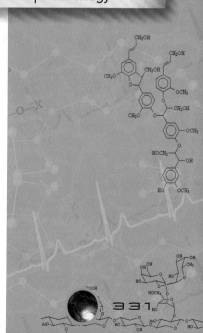

THE TECHNOLOGICAL

WORLD

THE HUMAN ORGANISM DEPENDS ON TECHNOLOGY.
Without the countless developments in technology, our lives would be completely different. We use technology every single day: when we get dressed, when we turn on an electric lamp, and when we take public transit.

Technology involves the processes that help us to design, build and maintain objects and systems that answer our needs and wants. In order to understand how people use technology to create objects and systems, we need to examine how they are represented, the materials that are used to make them and the functions of their various parts and mechanisms.

CONTENTS

THE TECHNOLOGICAL WORLD

2009 — Planned inauguration of the highest tower in the world, located in Dubai, United Arab Emirates

1976 — Completion of the construction of the CN Tower in Toronto

1963 — Development of the first software for technical design

1938 — Invention of the ball-point pen

1917 — Completion of the construction of the Québec Bridge, the longest cantilever bridge in the world

1896 — Opening of the first school of architecture at a Canadian university (McGill University in Montréal)

1850 — First North American manufacturing of drawing instruments

1564 — Invention of the lead pencil

1040 — Invention in China of the first printing press

CIRCA -30 — Drafting of the first known treatise on architecture

CIRCA -2000 — First invention of an alphabet

CIRCA -3000 — First appearance of hieroglyphics

CIRCA -80 000 — The oldest known geometric figures

THE HUMAN ORGANISM

AND THE DEVELOPMENT OF TECHNOLOGY

"A picture is worth a thousand words." This well-known phrase applies particularly well to technology. It is thanks to images, and more specifically to technical drawings, that there have been so many technological advancements in the history of humanity. Without technical drawings, constructions such as the Roman aqueducts, the Eiffel Tower and the Confederation Bridge, between Prince Edward Island and New Brunswick, would not have been possible.

Technical drawings represent a language shared by all those who work in the field of technology, regardless of their particular specialty. In this chapter, we'll get to know this language and discover how designers represent the objects that they want to create. And just like engineers and architects, we'll learn how to "read" the information in a technical drawing.

1 COMMUNICATING WITH SYMBOLS

Humans have highly developed communication skills. We can express our thoughts through gestures, speech and drawings. When we use drawings, we are using graphics to communicate.

> *Graphic* comes from the Greek word *graphikos*, which refers to the act of writing.

The need to describe a situation, an object, a person or an idea with drawings goes back to the oldest periods of human history. There are drawings dating from prehistoric times on the walls of caves, such as the Cave of Lascaux in France.

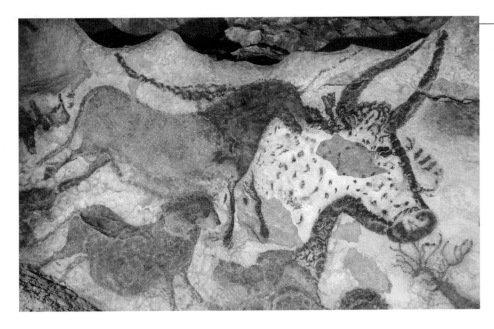

II.I The pictures that grace the walls of the Cave of Lascaux, in France, are believed to have been drawn almost 20 000 years ago.

The birth of symbolic thinking

It has long been believed that the first forms of symbolic expression, that is, the representation of an object or an idea with the use of symbols, occurred in Europe sometime between 35 000 and 40 000 years ago. A discovery by archaeologist Christopher S. Henshilwood and his team of researchers has now invalidated that theory.

On a shore in South Africa, in the cave of Blombos, these archaeologists found two blocks of red ochre, each a few centimetres long, engraved and dated 77 000 years before the Common Era. The engravings that are formed by rows of parallel lines are almost identical on the two pieces, leading archaeologists to believe that the markings are a symbolic code.

The findings of the research suggest the presence of symbolic thinking on the African continent nearly 80 000 years ago.

Adapted from Jean-François Dortier, "Quand est apparue la pensée symbolique," *Sciences humaines* 126 (April 2002), pp. 32-35. *[Translation]*

This block of red ochre was engraved by our ancestors about 80 000 years ago.

Writing is another form of graphic communication. The letters of the alphabet are small drawings that have been given precise meanings. Technical drawing is a form of graphic communication specific to the field of technology. The most common types of technical drawings are engenineering drawings and diagrams.

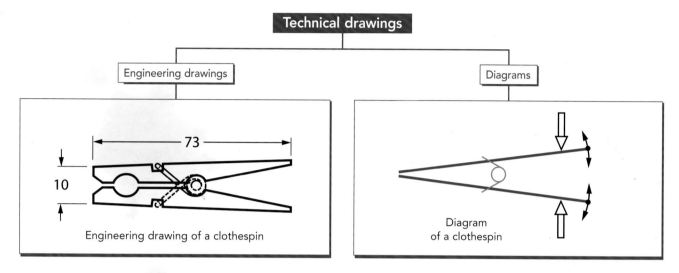

Technical drawings are necessary in the field of technology because they make it possible to design the objects and systems that we want or need.

▶ **TECHNOLOGY is a set of techniques used by humans to design, build and maintain objects and systems that we want or need.**

In this chapter, we'll begin by presenting the tools needed to make technical drawings. Next, we'll examine projections and their use in the development of engineering drawings. In the last section, we'll take a close look at diagrams.

11.2 The two most common types of technical drawings used in technology. The unit of measurement us in the drawings above is the millimetre.

2 LINES AND GEOMETRY IN TECHNICAL DRAWINGS

Technical drawings contain the precise pieces of information required to construct an object or a system. They make it possible for the designer to communicate to the manufacturer the exact shapes of the objects to be made.

▶ **TECHNICAL DRAWINGS are used in technology to communicate information about an object or a system.**

In order to make a technical drawing, designers must respect conventions. By doing so, everyone else working on the same project is able to understand and interpret the meaning of the drawing. Among the conventions in use are basic lines and geometric lines.

2.1 BASIC LINES

All drawings are made of lines. In drafting, there are different kinds of basic lines. International conventions have given precise definitions to the appearance and meaning of these lines.

> ▶ **BASIC LINES** used in drafting are lines whose appearance and meaning are determined by international agreements.

There are three line widths used to draw a basic line: thick lines, medium lines and fine lines. Figure 11.3 (below) and Table 11.4 (facing page) describe the most common types of basic lines used in technical drawing.

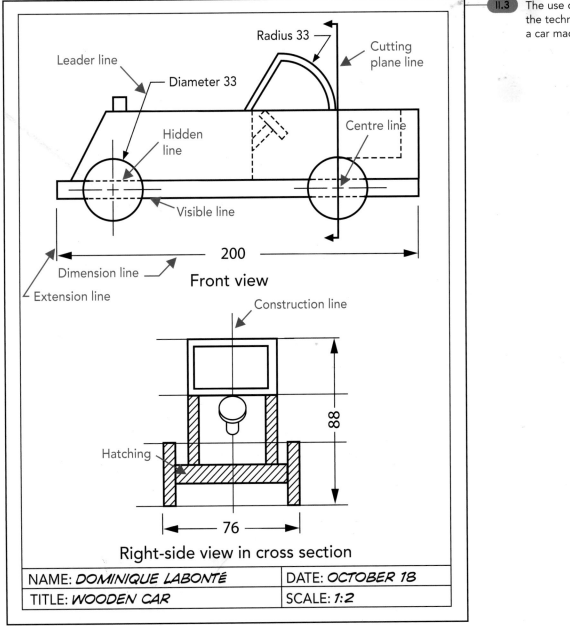

11.3 The use of basic lines in the technical drawing of a car made of wood

Radius 33

Cutting plane line

Leader line

Diameter 33

Hidden line

Centre line

Visible line

200

Dimension line

Front view

Extension line

Construction line

88

Hatching

76

Right-side view in cross section

| NAME: *DOMINIQUE LABONTÉ* | DATE: *OCTOBER 18* |
| TITLE: *WOODEN CAR* | SCALE: *1:2* |

Name	Characteristics	Purpose	Example
Visible line	• Thick • Continuous	• Indicates the visible outlines (or contours) of an object	———————————
Hidden line	• Medium • Broken line	• Indicates the outlines (or contours) that are not visible in the current view	– – – – – – – – – –
Construction line	• Fine • Continuous	• Used in preliminary sketches; after final drawing is completed, it is either darkened or erased	———————————
Centre line	• Fine • Has a small dash in the centre	• Indicates the centre of a circle or other symmetrical feature • Also used to indicate the placement of a section	——— – ———
Cutting plane line	• Thick • Continuous • Indicates the matching sectional view; includes arrowheads at each end	• Indicates the placement of an imaginary cut	↑———————↑
Dimension line	• Fine • Continuous • Includes arrowheads at each end	• Indicates the length of an object or a part of an object; always placed between extension lines at each end	←——— 2.75 ———→
Extension line	• Fine • Continuous	• Indicates a surface as it would appear in cross section	| |
Hatching	• Fine • Slanted • Equally spaced	• Indicates the surface where an imaginary cut has produced a sectional view	/////////////
Leader line	• Fine • Continuous • Has an arrowhead at one end • Generally has an angle of 30°, 45° or 60°	• Ties a dimension to a particular feature	↙

2.2 GEOMETRIC LINES

It is only necessary to know a few rules of geometry in order to draw most of the basic forms, or *geometric lines*, in drafting. By combining different geometric lines and using the basic lines effectively, surprisingly complex drawings are possible.

> ▶ GEOMETRIC LINES are figures that are composed according to the rules of geometry, the art of drafting lines and curves with a ruler and a compass.

The use of geometric rules and tools allows draftspeople to be able to draw:

- horizontal straight lines that are perfectly parallel to each other
- vertical straight lines that are perfectly parallel to each other and perfectly perpendicular to the horizontal lines
- oblique lines
- circles and ELLIPSES with defined radii

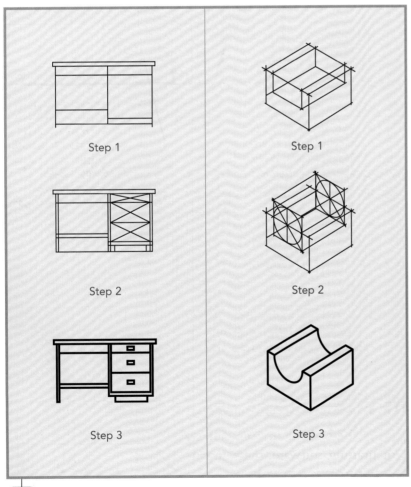

Step 1   Step 1

Step 2   Step 2

Step 3   Step 3

11.5 These drawings were made with geometric lines.

Circa –90
Circa –20

Marcus Vitruvius Pollio (also called Vitruve)

This Roman architect served under Julius Caesar. He is the author of the only known architectural treatise dating back to antiquity. Vitruve emphasized the importance of a good understanding of geometry for describing architectural works.

A RIBBON WITHOUT END

The Moebius strip is a surface with just one side and one boundary. Its symbol is also used to denote recycling.

HOW TO DRAW A GEOMETRIC LINE

2.3 THREE WAYS OF PRODUCING TECHNICAL DRAWINGS

Technical drawings can be done in three different ways:

● Freehand. This sort of drawing is referred to as a *sketch*.

● With the use of drafting tools. For this, the term *manual drafting instruments* is used.

● With the use of drafting software on a computer. This one is called *computer-aided drawing*, or *CAD*.

HOW TO MAKE
COMPUTER-AIDED
DRAWINGS (CAD)

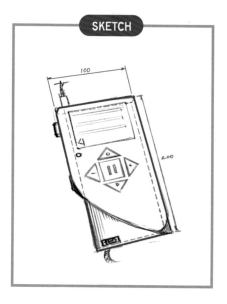

SKETCH

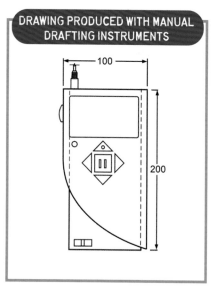

DRAWING PRODUCED WITH MANUAL DRAFTING INSTRUMENTS

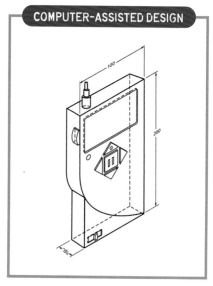

COMPUTER-ASSISTED DESIGN

II.6 The three ways of making a technical drawing. When they are done well, designs produced with manual instruments and computer-assisted designs look practically identical.

SKETCH

A sketch is generally used to make a quick illustration of an object. This is why it usually contains just the essential characteristics. It is made freehand, with only a pencil, eraser and a ruler when necessary. Even when making a sketch, however, the conventions of drafting must be respected, and basic lines and geometric lines used properly.

▶ **A SKETCH is a freehand drawing that respects, as much as possible, the conventions of drafting.**

Generally speaking, the first drawings for a new object are sketches. Next, when the designers agree on what they want to make, new drawings are drafted that are more complete and precise using manual drafting instruments or computer software.

DRAWING WITH DRAFTING INSTRUMENTS

Most of the conventions for drafting were established for manual drafting instruments. Prior to the development of drafting software, these instruments were the best way to create very precise technical drawings.

Today, computers have almost entirely replaced the use of manual drafting instruments. It is, however, by learning to use drafting instruments that we can best understand the rules and conventions that govern drafting. What's more, manual instruments cost less than computers, and they can produce drawings that are equally precise.

There are many different types of drafting instruments. Some of the most common are shown in Figure 11.7.

COMPUTER-ASSISTED DESIGN

The software used to make technical drawings is commonly referred to as *CAD*. Since its appearance in the 1960s, drafting software has come a long way. It can take many hours to learn how to use CAD software. Once the software has been mastered, however, it is often simpler and quicker to make a CAD drawing than a drawing with manual instruments.

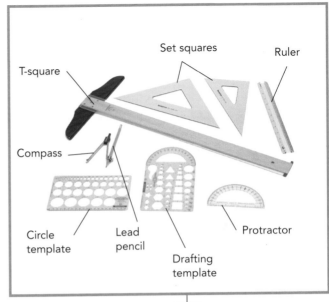

11.7 Various manual drafting instruments

Designing spaces on a computer screen

Manual drafting instruments, which were for many years the preferred tools for architects and interior designers, have been taken over by computers equipped with powerful design software.

When design work was completed by hand, it took an entire day to make the technical drawings and another day for colours, shading, materials, and so on. These days, one whole house project might not even take an entire day. The drawings can then be sent by e-mail to a client on the other side of the world.

The use of software has many other advantages as well. With computers, it is easy to present the building from different angles, see the same view under day or night lighting, and project shadows. To make corrections, architects no longer need to erase or start their drawings over. The work can be redone with a few clicks of a mouse.

Adapted from Stéphanie Martin, "Sculpter l'espace à l'écran d'un ordinateur," *Le Soleil*, March 11, 2006, p. E3. *[Translation]*

Interior design created with design software

3 PROJECTIONS AND THEIR USE IN TECHNICAL DRAWINGS

1452
1519

Leonardo da Vinci

The oldest known work referring to projection was written by this Italian artist and scientist. The work is his *Treatise on Painting*. Da Vinci used the principles that he set out in this treatise to produce engineering drawings for his numerous inventions and ideas.

When we want to represent an object in a technical drawing, one major obstacle comes to mind: how can we correctly illustrate a three-dimensional object on a sheet of two-dimensional paper? To solve this problem, different kinds of projections have been developed.

> ▶ A PROJECTION is a representation of a three-dimensional object in two dimensions.

There are many ways to project an object onto a flat surface, such as a sheet of paper. In this section, we will present three of them: a multiview projection, an isometric projection and an oblique projection. Then we'll explore how the various projections are used in drafting.

But first, it will help if we review some of the terminology that relates to this area of study, as shown in table 11.8.

11.8 TERMINOLOGY RELATING TO THE DESCRIPTION OF A SPACE OCCUPIED BY AN OBJECT

Concept	Explanation	Example
Dimension	An object generally occupies three dimensions in space: length, height and depth (or width).	Height, Length, Depth
Measurement	The measurements of an object correspond to the numbers associated with a unit of measurement (for example, a millimetre).	10 ← Measurement, 10, 10
Side	A side is a flat surface; it has two dimensions (for example, a square).	Side →
Edge	An edge is a line; it only has one dimension. It indicates the limits of a side or the shared border between two sides.	Edge →
Vertex	A vertex is a point; it has no dimensions at all. It indicates the point where two or more edges meet.	Vertex →

HOW TO USE PROJECTIONS IN DRAFTING

Projections differ in the following two aspects:

- the position of the object with respect to a sheet of paper
- the angle between the visual rays and a sheet of paper.

11.9 COMMON TYPES OF PROJECTIONS

Projection	Position of the object with respect to the paper		Angle between the visual rays and the paper	Result
A multiview projection	One side of the object is parallel to the paper.	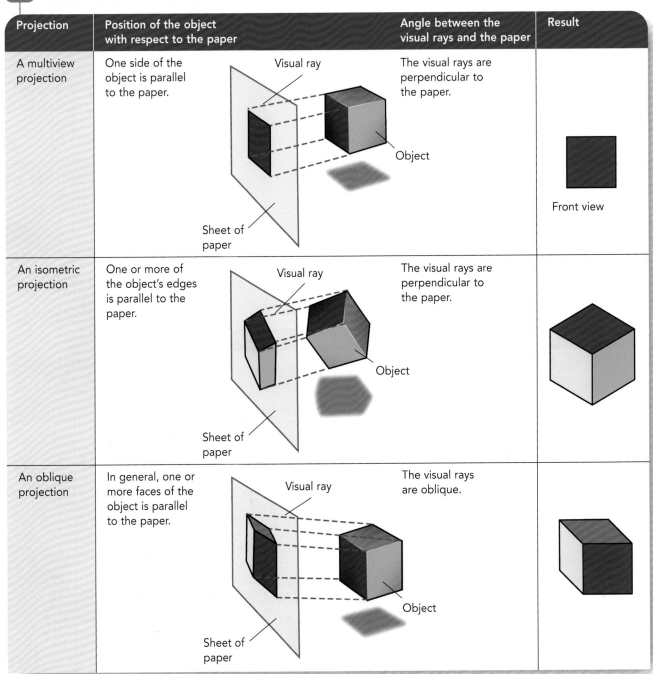	The visual rays are perpendicular to the paper.	Front view
An isometric projection	One or more of the object's edges is parallel to the paper.		The visual rays are perpendicular to the paper.	
An oblique projection	In general, one or more faces of the object is parallel to the paper.		The visual rays are oblique.	

Table 11.9 shows us that in multiview and isometric projections the visual rays are perpendicular to the paper. This is why they are called *orthogonal* projections.

Orthogonal comes from the Latin word *orthogonus*, meaning "at right angle."

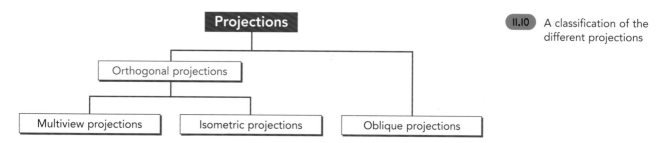

▶ An ORTHOGONAL PROJECTION is a projection in which all of the visual rays from the object are perpendicular to the surface of a sheet of paper.

Projections

Orthogonal projections

Multiview projections   Isometric projections   Oblique projections

11.10 A classification of the different projections

3.1 MULTIVIEW PROJECTIONS

All objects, whatever they are, can be viewed from six different angles: front view, rear view, left-side view, right-side view, top view and bottom view. Together, these six views give us a global idea about the shape of an object.

Figure 11.11 shows the six views of an object. In drafting, we generally choose the front view as the view that best describes the object. It is often the one that contains the most detail.

To represent each of the six views graphically, first imagine the object inside the middle of a transparent cube. Each of the sides of the cube is a flat surface on which we can project an image of the object, as if taking a picture. Each view of the object becomes a two-dimensional projection on the sides of this imaginary transparent cube.

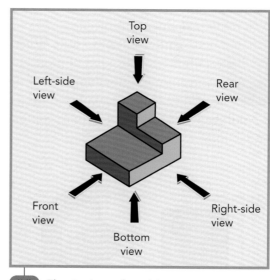

11.11 The six views of an object

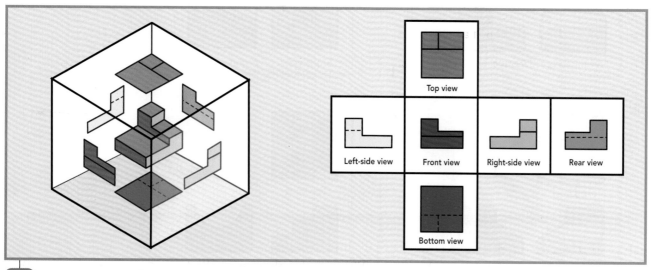

11.12 Each of the six views is a two-dimensional projection of the object on the interior sides of an imaginary transparent cube. The hidden lines are represented by dotted lines.

It is often not necessary to present all six views of an object. In general, the front, top and right-side views are sufficient to accurately portray an object. In Québec and throughout the rest of North America, these three views are conventionally placed in an L-shape as in Figure 11.13. This configuration allows us to make a rapid comparison of the dimensions for the different views.

▶ A MULTIVIEW PROJECTION, also known as an orthographic projection, is a two-dimensional representation of the different views of an object.

In a multiview, or orthographic, projection, one of the sides of the object is parallel to the sheet of paper. In other words, the length and the width of the object are parallel to the length and the width of the paper. As well, the drawing of the object is placed in such a way that the visual rays run perpendicular to the paper (Table 11.9, on page 344).

As a result, a multiview projection allows us to represent all of the measurements, either as is or to scale. What is more, all of the angles are exact. This is why this kind of projection is often used in drafting. A certain amount of training, not to mention a good imagination, is needed to visualize an object using only this representation. A multiview projection is often combined with an isometric projection.

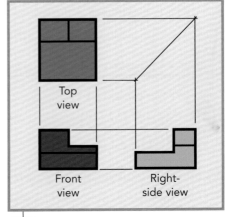

11.13 The usual L-shaped positioning of the top, front and right-side views in drafting

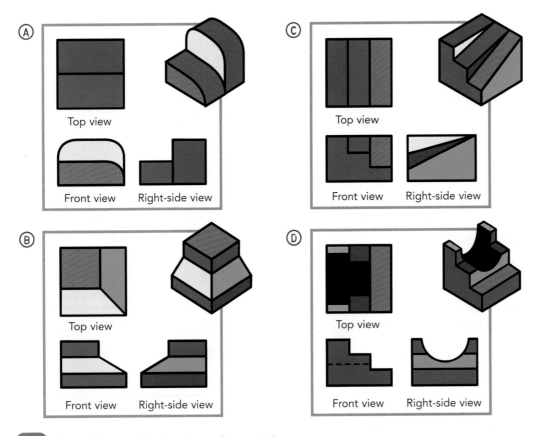

11.14 Some objects and their orthographic projections

3.2 ISOMETRIC PROJECTIONS

Instead of using many two-dimensional views to represent an object, as in multiview projections, including the three dimensions of an object in one single drawing can be useful. To do this, we use perspective in the representation. Isometric projections are a form of perspective drawing.

> ▶ A PERSPECTIVE DRAWING represents the three dimensions of an object in the same view.

In an │isometric│ projection, the principal edges of the projected object are arranged on three axes, where the angles each measure 120°. They are called *isometric axes*.

Isometric comes from the Greek words *isos*, meaning "equal," and *metrikos*, meaning "measure."

> ▶ An ISOMETRIC PROJECTION is a perspective drawing of an object where the principal edges are arranged on three isometric axes.

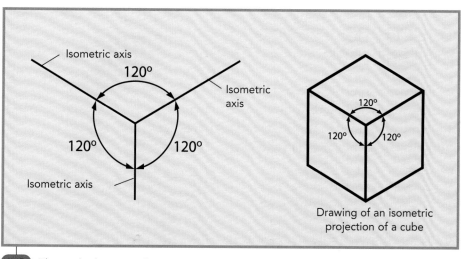

11.15 The angles between the isometric axes are all 120°. Together, they look like the letter Y.

As a result of this arrangement, no surface of the projected object is parallel to the paper. The object has one or more edges facing forward and it is positioned so that the visual rays are perpendicular to the paper (Table 11.9, page 344).

Thus, the measurements of all of the edges parallel to the isometric axes are exact or to scale while the angles are not.(Figure 11.16)

11.16

In an isometric projection, the measurements of the edges that are parallel to the isometric axes are exact or to scale. The angles, however, are altered.

3.3 OBLIQUE PROJECTIONS

Like isometric projections, oblique projections show the object in three dimensions. Thus, they too are perspective drawings.

However, where an object drawn in an isometric projection is angled toward the sheet of paper, drawings in oblique projection generally show one side parallel to the paper. The viewer, therefore, must imagine that the object is placed so that the visual rays meet the paper at an oblique angle (Table 11.9, page 344).

> ▶ An OBLIQUE PROJECTION is a perspective drawing in which one of the object's sides is parallel to the sheet of paper, but its depth is represented by parallel straight lines drawn at an oblique angle.

Oblique projections produce a drawing with precise measurements for two of the dimensions: height and length. The measurement and angle of the third dimension (depth) do not conform to the original object. They tend to be smaller.

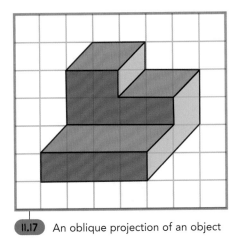

11.17 An oblique projection of an object

3.4 THE USE OF PROJECTIONS IN ENGINEERING DRAWINGS

TECH 5

Drawings produced by designers meet very specific needs. The choice of a particular projection depends on these needs and on the object to be drawn. Most often, one or more projections are combined in the engineering drawings for a project. The most commonly used ones are the following:

- general drawings
- exploded view drawings
- detail drawings

Let's take a closer look at these three types of engineering drawings, their uses and the projections that best serve their needs.

GENERAL DRAWINGS

Among the engineering drawings needed to represent an object, we generally need to have one that contains a description of its general appearance—its overall shape, its parts and their arrangement. This is called a *general drawing*. The most commonly used projections for general drawings are multiview and isometric projections.

> ▶ A GENERAL DRAWING is an engineering drawing that shows the overall design of an object.

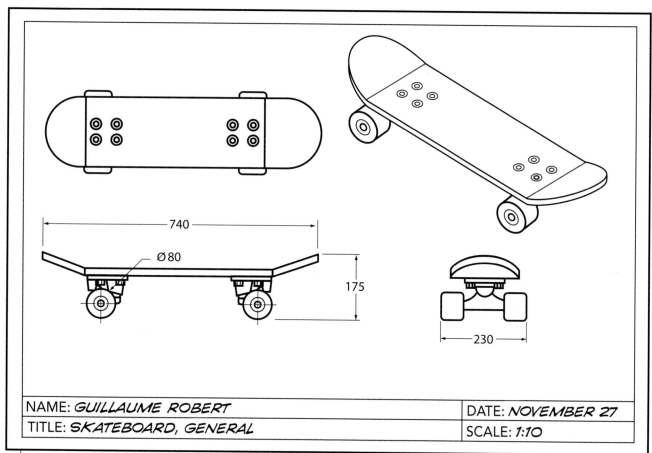

NAME: *GUILLAUME ROBERT* DATE: *NOVEMBER 27*
TITLE: *SKATEBOARD, GENERAL* SCALE: *1:10*

11.18 A general drawing of a skateboard

AN EXPLODED VIEW DRAWING

When an object is made up of many different parts, the drawing can be "exploded." In this case, the object is drawn in perspective and each part, or feature, is separate from the other. The most commonly used projection for this type of drawing is the isometric projection.

> ▶ An **EXPLODED VIEW DRAWING** is an engineering drawing that shows the different parts, or features, of the object separately.

This type of drawing is also often accompanied by the nomenclature of each part, that is, the names for each part. Thus, in addition to the drawing itself, there is also the name of each part, the quantity, and the materials needed for its construction, called a *bill of materials*.

11.19

An exploded view drawing of a skateboard

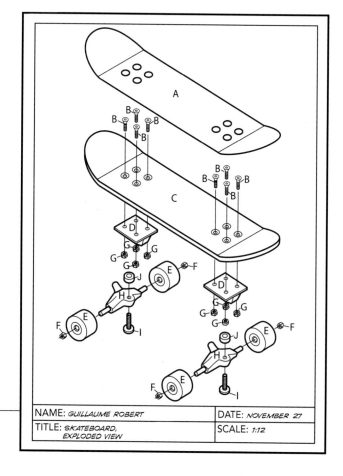

NAME: *GUILLAUME ROBERT* DATE: *NOVEMBER 27*
TITLE: *SKATEBOARD, EXPLODED VIEW* SCALE: *1:12*

A DETAIL DRAWING

Even if it is practical to have a general, overall view of an object, it is often indispensable to produce drawings that provide the details necessary for the construction of various features (size, position and diameter of its holes, and so on). Such a drawing is called a *detail drawing*.

Detail drawings are produced using one or more views of a part of an object. Therefore, a multiview projection is usually used to produce a detail drawing.

▶ **A DETAIL DRAWING** is an engineering drawing that specifies all the details necessary to make a particular part of an object.

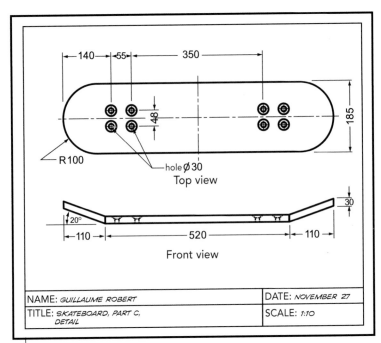

11.20 A detail drawing of part C of the skateboard

Technology in service of sports

Technology plays a large part in the world of sports. Take, for example, the many models of skis, racquets and bicycles, not to mention the accessories, such as helmets, goggles and clothing. Each object is designed to meet the needs of a particular sporting activity and to produce the best possible performance, safety and comfort.

Sports shoes are an example of how high-technology products must be chosen with care. They must be appropriate for the activity in question.

If you are playing a team sport in a gym, wearing a shoe designed for running, even if the shoe is of excellent quality, may cause you to sprain an ankle. The design of a running shoe is not made for the rapid lateral movement typical of sports, such as squash, badminton and volleyball. A running shoe, with its raised and cushioned heel, is designed instead to absorb the types of impacts that come with running.

Some of the more common specialized sports shoes include hiking shoes, which are waterproof and have soles with thick treads; shoes for aerobic dancing, which are light, stable and very flexible in the toe; and golf shoes, which have cleats on the soles.

Each type of sports shoe is designed to meet the precise needs of its sport.

Table 11.21 summarizes the use of projection for the different types of engineering drawings.

11.21 THE MOST COMMON PROJECTIONS USED IN ENGINEERING DRAWINGS

Type of drawing	Description	Projections
General	A drawing that shows the overall appearance of an object.	• Multiview • Isometric
Exploded view	A drawing that illustrates the different parts of an object, separately. May include a bill of materials.	• Isometric
Detail	A drawing that contains all the necessary elements to construct an object.	• Multiview

4. WHAT'S IN AN ENGINEERING DRAWING?

Now that we know about the different kinds of engineering drawings that are generally used in drafting, let's take a closer look at the information they can contain. First, we'll see how measurements are indicated, with concepts of scale, dimension and tolerance. Next, we'll examine how the details inside an object can be shown using cross sections and sections.

HOW TO MAKE
SCALE DRAWINGS

4.1 SCALE

Often it is not practical to draw an object using its real measurements. Many objects are either too small or too large to be correctly represented on a sheet of paper. Most of the time, we make a reduced or an enlarged representation. This is called *drawing to scale*.

When we reduce all the measurements of an object by the same factor, it's called a *scale reduction*. Not surprisingly, when we increase all the measurements by the same factor, it's called a *scale increase*. An object represented with its real measurements, is full-size.

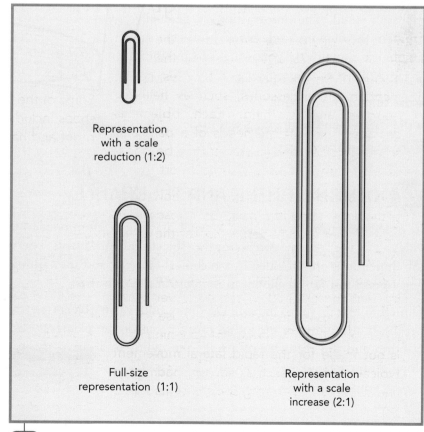

Representation with a scale reduction (1:2)

Full-size representation (1:1)

Representation with a scale increase (2:1)

11.22 Here are three scaled representations of a paperclip.

▶ In an engineering drawing, SCALE is the relationship between the measurements of an object on a sheet of paper and the real measurements of the object.

To determine the value of a scale, we need to know the factor of magnification. Table 11.23 shows how we indicate scale, with some examples.

11.23 DIFFERENT SCALES

Scale	Example	Ratio
Scale reduction	The measurements of a house are 50 times smaller in the drawing than in real life. The factor for the scale reduction, on the right in the ratio column, is *50*.	1:50
Full-size	The measurements of a stapler are the same in the drawing as in real life.	1:1
Scale increase	The measurements of the gear cogs in a watch are 10 times larger in the drawing than in real life. The factor for the scale increase on the left in the ratio column, is *10*.	10:1

Since the factor of magnification is always on the left in the ratio of scale, and the factor of reduction is always on the right, it is easy to tell quickly what the scale is when looking at a drawing.

In a technical drawing it is essential to indicate the scale used. The information is generally found in the drawing's title block. Normally, the title block contains the following information:

- the name of the draftsperson
- the title of the drawing
- the date when the drawing was made
- the scale that was used

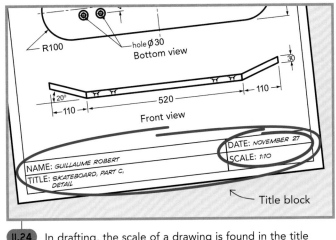

11.24 In drafting, the scale of a drawing is found in the title block.

4.2 DIMENSIONING AND TOLERANCE

In order to construct an object, a detail drawing is often needed that provides all of the information about the object's measurements. The values of the dimensions are included in a technical drawing and they should always correspond to the real-life measurements of the object.

Dimensioning serves to indicate the dimensions of an object (length, height, depth). It also indicates the location of various design elements, such as the position and the diameter of a hole, the radius of a curve, the value of a slope, and so on.

The dimensions are typically placed outside the drawing of an object, but sometimes they are placed inside, if the result is clearer

> ▶ DIMENSIONING refers to the process of indicating the real dimensions of an object as well as the position of various elements of the object.

To label a part with its dimensions, we use dimension lines and extension lines, as well as other symbols such as:

- Ø, which indicates the diameter of a hole or of a circle
- R, which indicates the radius of a circle or of a curve
- ⟍, which indicates the degrees of an angle

Measurements are generally noted in millimetres. Sometimes, however, particularly in construction drawings, the measurements may still be noted in feet and inches (the imperial measurement system).

In addition to the measurements provided by dimensioning, the drawings sometimes indicate the limits of the acceptable difference between the measurements in the drawing and the real measurements. This value is called *tolerance*.

> ▶ TOLERANCE refers to the maximum variation of a specified dimension between a measurement on a drawing and the real-life measurement.

Tolerance is generally only indicated when this specification is important for the proper functioning of the object. When it appears on a drawing, it is placed beside the dimension line that applies to the particular part or measurement. When a certain tolerance value applies to the entire drawing, it is found in the title block.

For example, in the case of a drawing for the construction of a birdhouse for swallows, the diameter of the hole for the swallows is important. If the hole is too small, a swallow would get trapped inside; a hole too big would allow larger birds inside. Figure 11.26 shows an example of how tolerance can be indicated.

In industry, the less tolerance, the more expensive an object is to build. There is a greater risk that if a part doesn't fit, it may have to be rebuilt or thrown away. As a result, production costs increase.

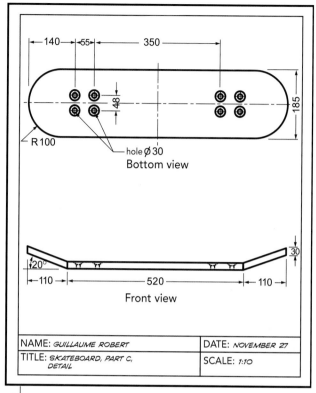

11.25 Dimension lines and extension lines are the two basic lines used to dimension a drawing.

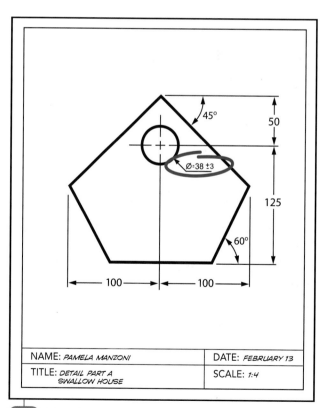

11.26 The tolerance of the diameter of the hole is listed on the drawing. It indicates that the diameter of the hole must be between 35 mm and 41 mm.

HOW TO CREATE A CROSS-SECTIONAL VIEW AND A SECTION.

In engineering drawings produced for the construction of an object, the visible details are represented by continuous lines, while the hidden details are represented by broken lines (Table 11.4). Some objects, however, have so many hidden details that when drawn they would be superimposed one on top of the other. Their representation by broken lines would render the drawing incomprehensible. In such cases, a cross section may be used to reveal the details inside.

> ● A CROSS SECTION reveals the interior of an object, exposing its hidden details to view.

Anyone who has peered inside a toaster can see features that are invisible from the outside. A cross section makes it possible for the designer to draw these details (Figure 11.27).

The first step to obtaining a cross section is to choose which dimension (length, height or width) the imaginary cut line will pass through to produce the desired cross-sectional view. In a multiview projection, a cross-sectional view is represented with the help of a cutting plane line (Figure 11.28).

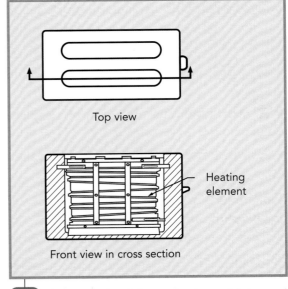

11.27 A cross-sectional view makes it possible to see the inside of a toaster slot.

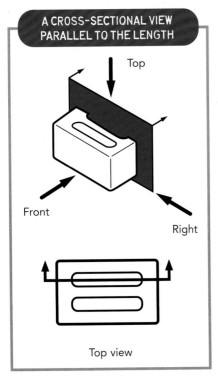

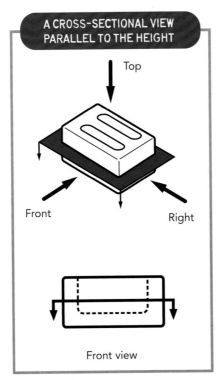

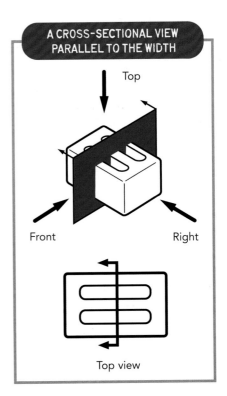

11.28 Three examples of cross-sectional views: upper, using an isometric projection; lower, using a multiview projection.

The next step is to draw the cross-sectional view that is located on the side indicated by the arrowheads of the cutting plane line. In this type of view, the broken hidden lines are generally left out. In addition, the surface that has been "cut" by the cutting plane line is hatched.

In order to best represent an object, designers may also provide drawings of sections of the object. A section reveals a surface located in a cross-sectional view. In a multiview projection, using sections makes it possible to show, for example, the shape of the outer surface of different parts.

> A SECTION represents a surface located in a cross-sectional view.

In an engineering drawing, a cross-sectional view that represents a section is indicated by an axis line. The sections are drawn with the help of visible lines and hatching. The sections can be found in two places on the drawing:

- inside the object (called an *aligned sectional view*)
- outside the object (called an *offset sectional view*), if producing an aligned sectional view makes the drawing less clear.

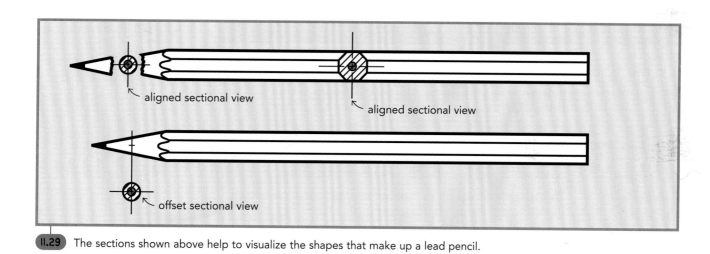

11.29 The sections shown above help to visualize the shapes that make up a lead pencil.

5 DIAGRAMS

Just like engineering drawings, diagrams are a form of language used in technical drawing. They are simplified drawings that make it possible to provide information about the way objects work, or about the way to construct objects or systems.

Diagram comes from the Greek words *dia*, meaning "through," and *graphein*, meaning "write."

> A DIAGRAM is a simplified representation of an object, a part of an object or a system.

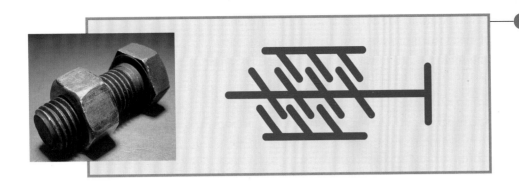

11.30 A diagram of a bolt and a nut. In a diagram, the representation of an object is as simple as possible.

5.1 RULES AND SYMBOLS IN DIAGRAMS

TECH
9 and 10

HOW TO DRAW
A DIAGRAM WITH SYMBOLS

Even though diagrams are simplified representations of objects, they must still follow certain guidelines in order to be understood by all. Table 11.31 contains some of these guidelines.

11.31 COMMON RULES TO FOLLOW WHEN DRAWING A DIAGRAM

Element	Rule
Lines	The lines must be clean and clear. They may be drawn freehand or with drafting software.
Colour	Colour may be added to the diagram. Different colours are used to represent different parts that touch one another. This makes the diagram easier to understand.
Representation	The object is generally drawn in two dimensions. Different perspectives may be used, details enlarged or sections displayed to best show the object or provide information.
Proportions of parts	The measurements of the parts do not need to be exact or to scale, but all proportions must be respected.
Dimensions	Dimensioning is not required, but if dimensions are shown, they must follow the same rules as they do for engineering drawings.

In order to simplify diagrams, designers have agreed on the use of certain symbols. There are various elements of a diagram that can be represented by symbols, such as:

- the different forces and limitations that affect the object
- the movements of parts
- various parts
- certain types of guides
- the components of an electrical circuit

Table 11.32 on the next page provides an overview of the symbols that can be used when producing a diagram.

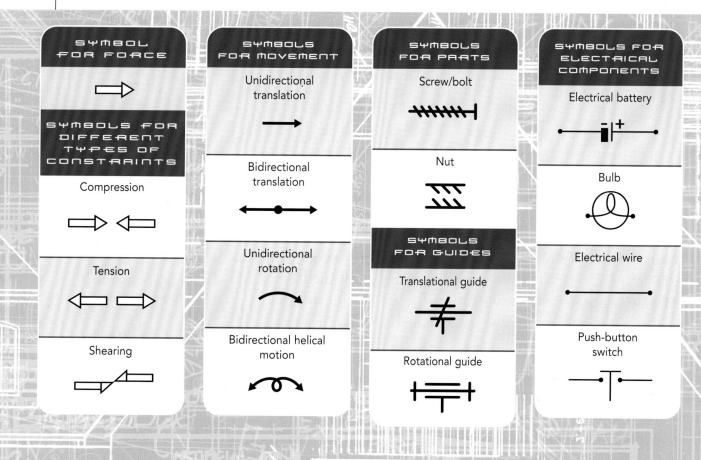

The diagram of a C-clamp in Figure 11.33 is an example of a diagram that respects the rules and guidelines for creating diagrams. It is cleanly done, the pieces that are in contact are different colours and the proportion of the parts has been respected. We only need one view to represent this object.

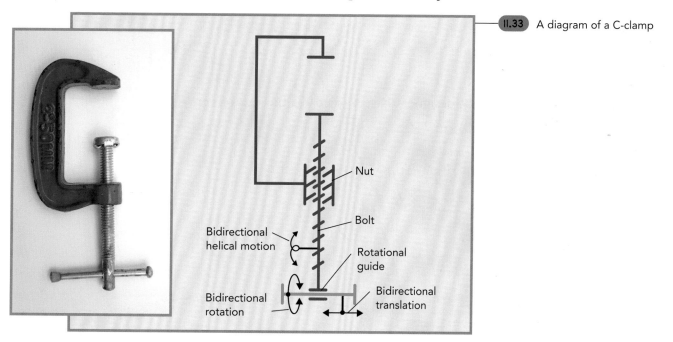

11.33 A diagram of a C-clamp

5.2 COMMON TYPES OF DIAGRAMS

There are many types of diagrams, and their use depends on what kind of information is being communicated. The most common types are design plans, technical diagrams and circuit diagrams.

DESIGN PLANS

A design plan seeks to explain the way an object works, that is, the movements that the parts can make and the forces needed to make them move. Figure 11.34 shows two design plans. These diagrams usually contain the following information:

- a simplified representation of the parts using, wherever possible, the appropriate symbols
- the names of the illustrated parts
- the symbols for the types of motion and the forces involved in the function of the object
- any other useful information about the functioning of the object

> ▶ A DESIGN PLAN is a simplified drawing that represents one or more aspects of the functioning of an object.

Elizabeth Muriel Gregory MacGill

This Canadian engineer was the first woman to obtain her degree in aeronautical engineering. This achievement led her to participate in the design of the first airplane made entirely of metal in Canada. She also contributed to the development and study of many diagrams and engineering drawings.

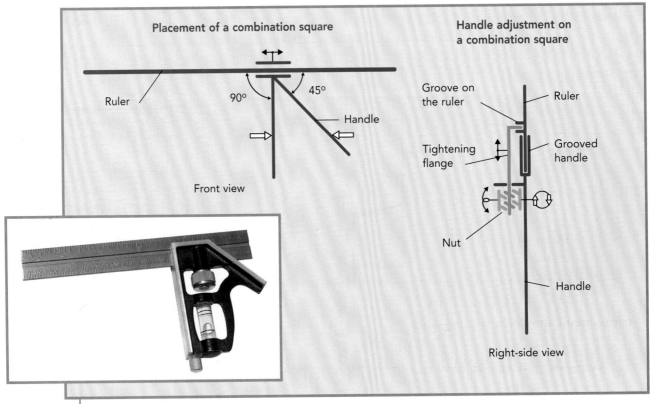

11.34 These diagrams illustrate two important aspects of the functioning of a combination square.

TECHNICAL DIAGRAMS

A technical diagram can contain the construction solutions that ensure the proper functioning of an object. This type of diagram includes information about the shapes and nature of the materials to be used, the way the parts are assembled and the precautions that are needed to ensure that the object works properly. In general, a technical diagram contains the following information:

- the shapes to consider when constructing the parts
- the names and quantities of the parts that are illustrated
- the materials to be used
- the elements to use for the linking components, if there are any (Chapter 12, page 385)
- the types of guides, if there are any
- any other information that would be useful to know when manufacturing the object

> ▶ A TECHNICAL DIAGRAM is a simplified diagram that contains information about the construction solutions for manufacturing an object or a system.

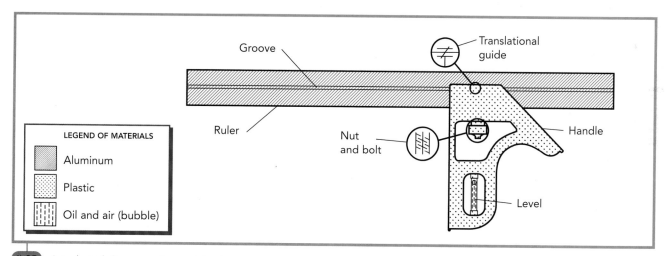

II.35 A technical diagram of a combination square

CIRCUIT DIAGRAM

In technology, we often use circuit diagrams as a simplified representation of electrical circuits. In these diagrams, we find the following information:

- a symbol representing each part of the electrical circuit
- any other useful information that helps to explain how the electrical circuit should be put together

> ▶ A CIRCUIT DIAGRAM is a simplified drawing using symbols that shows how to connect the various parts (bulb, wire, battery, switch, etc.) of an electrical circuit.

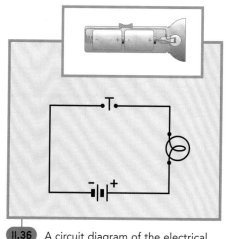

II.36 A circuit diagram of the electrical circuit in a flashlight

1 COMMUNICATING WITH SYMBOLS
(pp. 336–337)

1. What are the two types of drawings most commonly used in technology?

2. What is technology?

2 LINES AND GEOMETRY IN TECHNICAL DRAWINGS (pp. 337–342)

3. Below is a cross-sectional view of a deodorant stick.

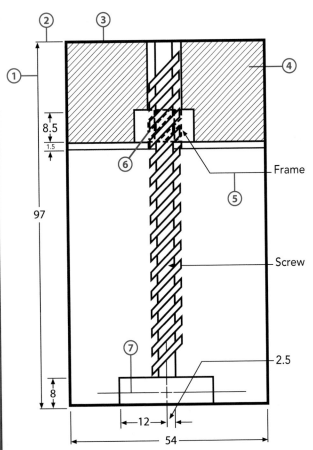

a) For each number in the diagram, give the name of the corresponding basic line.

b) Give the function of these basic lines in the diagram.

c) Two of the basic lines discussed in Chapter 11 are not in this diagram. Name them and describe their function.

4. Geometric lines can be made using manual drafting instruments.

a) What are the main instruments for drafting?

b) Three types of straight lines can be made with geometric lines. What are they?

c) Name two drafting instruments that are used to draw circles.

5. Look at these two representations of a stop sign. Which one is a sketch? Explain your answer.

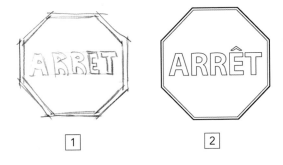

3 PROJECTIONS AND THEIR USE IN TECHNICAL DRAWINGS (pp. 343–351)

6. Projections are different ways to draw an object on a two-dimensional surface.

a) Name two projections in which the visual rays are perpendicular to the sheet of paper.

b) What name is given to these two projections?

7. An object can be drawn from six different angles.

   a) What are these six views?

   b) Which views are conventionally used when using a multiview projection to draw an object?

8. Look at these three drawings of the same object.

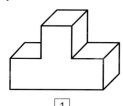

1

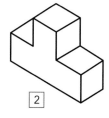

2

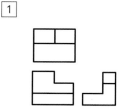

3

   a) Which projection was used for each illustration?

   b) Which ones are perspective drawings?

9. Match the isometric projections on the left with their multiview projections on the right.

A

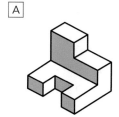

1

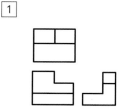

B

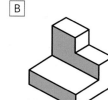

2

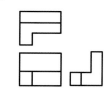

C

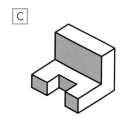

3

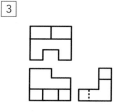

D

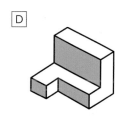

4

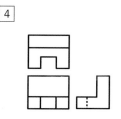

4
WHAT'S IN AN ENGINEERING DRAWING ? (pp. 351–355)

10. Jonathan is building a model car. He is reducing all of the measurements 40 times.

    a) What scale is he using?

    b) How would you indicate that scale?

    c) The car he has chosen measures four metres in length. What will the length of the finished model be? Give your answer in millimetres.

11. The following diagram is a reproduction of a soccer field with a scale of 1:2000. The world cup soccer finals are played on fields with the same dimensions. Calculate the width and the length of the soccer fields, using its representation to scale.

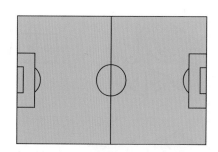

12. Look at the diagram below.

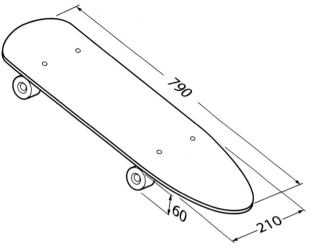

a) What is the length of the skateboard?

b) What is its width?

c) What is the diameter of each wheel?

13. What is the name of the maximum possible difference between a measurement as specified on a diagram and the real-life measurement?

14. Where possible, match the objects on the left to their corresponding cross-sectional views on the right.

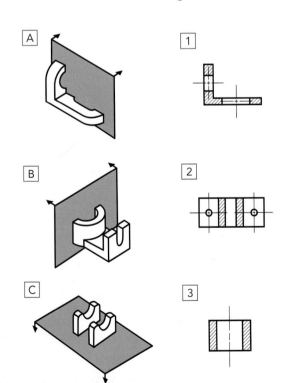

15. Look at the diagram of a wrench below.

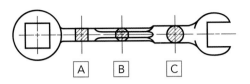

a) Which section shows that the handle of the wrench has an octagonal shape?

b) What is the shape of the handle indicated in section C?

c) Are the sections in the diagram aligned or offset? Explain your answer.

5 DIAGRAMS (pp. 355–359)

16. Look at the following design plan and technical diagram of a kitchen scale.

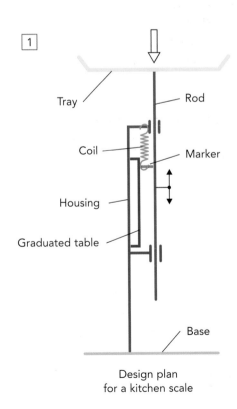

Design plan
for a kitchen scale

2

Tray

Rod

Coil

Marker

Graduated table

Housing

Plastic
Steel

Base

**Technical diagram
of a kitchen scale**

a) On which part of the scale is force exerted?

b) In total, how many screws were used to make this scale?

c) What kind of movement can the rod make?

d) Once the force has been removed, what allows the rod to return to its initial position?

CONCEPT
MAPS

HOW TO BUILD
A CONCEPT MAP

Prepare your own summary of Chapter 11 by building a concept map based on the following terms and phrases:

- Basic lines
- Circuit diagram
- Computer-assisted design (CAD)
- Cross section
- Design produced with manual drafting instruments
- Detail drawing
- Diagrams
- Dimensioning
- Design plan
- Drafting
- Electric diagram
- Engineering drawing
- Exploded view drawing
- General drawing
- Geometric lines
- Isometric projection
- Multiview projection
- Oblique projection
- Orthographic projection
- Rules
- Scale
- Section
- Sketch
- Symbols
- Technical diagram
- Technical drawing
- Tolerance

SCOLIOSIS, LORDOSIS AND KYPHOSIS

Seen from the side, our spinal column has four curves that give it an S-shape. Normally, these curves provide us support and keep the spinal column flexible and supple.

There are, however, a number of abnormal curvatures of the spine. Some are present from birth, others come about after an illness. Poor posture when seated or when lifting objects can also cause abnormal curvature. To describe these curvatures, we often use the terms scoliosis, lordosis and kyphosis. Table 11.38 describes these terms.

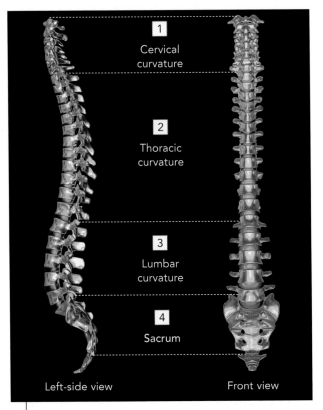

11.37 The four normal curvatures of the spinal column

11.38 ABNORMAL CURVATURES OF THE SPINAL COLUMN

Name	Explanation
Scoliosis	Lateral (to the side) curvature of the spinal column
Lordosis	Excessive inward curvature of the spinal column. Curvatures 1 and 3 in Figure 11.37 are inward. Pregnant women often suffer from temporary lordosis.
Kyphosis	Excessive outward curvature ("bowing") of the spinal column. Curvatures 2 and 4 in Figure 11.37 are outward. People who work seated often have a rounded posture, which can lead to kyphosis.

1. Many people adopt a rounded posture when they are sitting down. Ergonomic chairs have been designed to correct this problem. The backs of these chairs have the same curvature as a normal spinal column. Make a sketch of an isometric projection of such a chair back.

2. To lift a heavy load, it is better to bend your legs and keep your back straight. This way, you protect your spinal column while lifting. Make a diagram representing a person lifting a heavy object the correct way. Don't forget to include the movement of the back and the object.

DANIEL LANGLOIS

Thanks to Daniel Langlois, the movie industry can no longer live without computer-assisted design. In 1986, he founded a company in Montréal that specializes in the development of software for three-dimensional animation and special effects for video games and movies. His company earned international attention in 1993 when its software was used to create and animate the dinosaurs in the Hollywood film *Jurassic Park*, directed by Steven Spielberg.

In 1997, Daniel Langlois created a foundation to promote the integration of the arts, science and technology.

II.39 The dinosaurs in the film *Jurassic Park* were created with software developed by Daniel Langlois' company.

NAME	
Daniel Langlois	
JOB	
Designer and businessman	
AREA WHERE HE WORKS	
In the province of Québec, and around the world	
EDUCATION	
Bachelor's degree in design	
PROUDEST ACHIEVEMENT	
Founded a company that specializes in the development of animation software	

II.40 OCCUPATIONS CONNECTED TO LANGLOIS' WORK

Occupation	Education required	Length of study	Main tasks
Photographer	DEP in photography	1 800 hours	• Choose or compose the ideal setting for a photo • Make technical adjustments to the photos
Graphics technician	DCS in animation techniques and computer-generated imagery	3 years	• Produce computerized images and animation
Computer scientist	Bachelor's degree in computer science	4 years	• Produce software and other computer-related product development

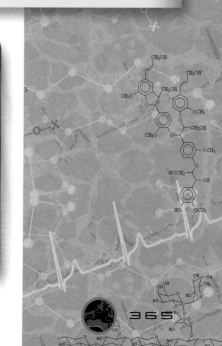

2004 End of residential use of arsenic-treated wood in Canada

1989 Invention of the first biodegradable plastics

Development of stainless steel

1913

1901 Opening of Canada's first aluminum plant in Shawinigan

1889 Invention of the bicycle derailleur

1874 Invention of the light bulb

1865 Synthesis of celluloid, the first plastic material

1859 Sinking of the first oil well

1800 Invention of the first electrical cell

1737 Opening of Canada's first foundry in Trois-Rivières

CIRCA 1400 Invention of ice skates made of iron

Invention of a clock with gears that turn at a regular rhythm

723

CIRCA 100 Invention of the horseshoe

CIRCA -1500 Earliest heat treatment of iron to improve its properties

CIRCA -3700 Invention of bronze

CIRCA -5000 Earliest extraction of lead, copper and pewter

THE TECHNOLOGICAL WORLD

THE HUMAN ORGANISM

ORGANISM

AND TECHNOLOGY IN ACTION

We use wood, plastic and metal to create a great number of objects. Our homes are partly built with wood, basements are often insulated with a plastic material and electricity runs through metal materials. It is therefore essential to understand the properties of different materials in order to design objects that are adapted to our needs.

Understanding how some objects work may seem complicated. But even in the case of complex objects such as motors and watches, it is simply a matter of understanding how to combine simple systems and applying a few basic mechanical and electrical concepts.

1 TECHNICAL OBJECTS

Technical objects are made by humans, examples of which include chairs, cars and tents. On the other hand, rocks, trees and glaciers are not technical objects, but natural objects. Technical objects are created to meet the needs and wants of human beings. They are based on technology.

CYCLE ONE
- Raw material
- Material
- Equipment

> ▶ **A TECHNICAL OBJECT** is an object conceived and manufactured by humans to meet one or more needs or wants.

12.1 Examples of technical objects

A substance is considered to be a material when it is used to make one or more parts of a technical object. All technical objects are made with either one or more materials.

Material is from the Latin word *materia*, meaning "that which a thing is composed of."

The terms *raw material*, *material* and *equipment* are often confused. Here is how to distinguish them:

- Raw material is a natural substance that must be transformed before being used to manufacture an object. For example, trees require processing prior to being used to make objects.

- Material is a substance that has been completed or transformed by humans and is then used to make an object or its parts. For example, planks of wood are used to make many different kinds of objects.

- Equipment includes all instruments used to produce an object. For example, equipment such as hammers, screwdrivers and saws can be used to shape a piece of wood.

12.2 Trees are raw material.

12.3 Planks of wood are materials.

12.4 A lathe and a wood chisel are equipment.

In Section 2 of this chapter, we'll examine in detail the characteristics of some materials that are used to make the parts of a technical object. Then, in Sections 3 and 4, we'll learn how the parts of a technical object can be assembled to fulfil various mechanical functions such as linking, guiding and the transmission or transformation of motion. In Section 5, we'll learn how parts of technical objects can also serve electrical functions. Finally, Section 6 will conclude this chapter by describing the manufacturing process of a technical object.

2 MATERIALS

There are countless different types of materials available on the market today. To select those most suitable for manufacturing a particular technical object, a knowledge of their characteristics is essential. It is necessary to know, for example, how a material reacts to external forces, makes required movements and responds to the rigours of its environment such as temperature, humidity and pressure.

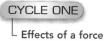

CYCLE ONE
└ Effects of a force

2.1 THE EFFECTS VARIOUS FORCES HAVE ON MATERIALS

When technical objects are in use, they are subjected to one or more external forces. These external forces push or pull the object by means of one or more of its parts.

TECH
11

MECHANICAL CONSTRAINTS

External forces, also called *mechanical constraints*, produce various effects inside a material. The five principal mechanical constraints are called *compression*, *tension*, *torsion*, *bending* and *shearing*. They are illustrated in Figure 12.5 on the following page.

Constraint comes from the Latin word *constringere*, meaning "to tighten."

▸ A MECHANICAL CONSTRAINT describes the stress produced within a material when it is subjected to external forces.

Compression

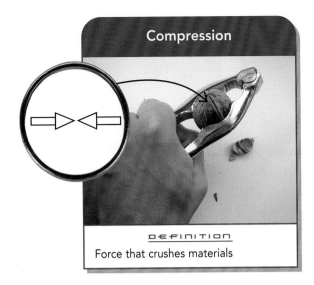

DEFINITION

Force that crushes materials

Tension

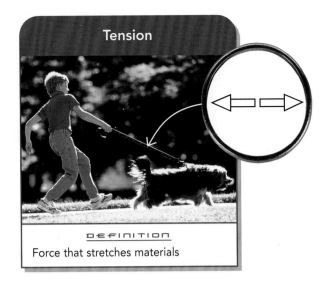

DEFINITION

Force that stretches materials

Torsion

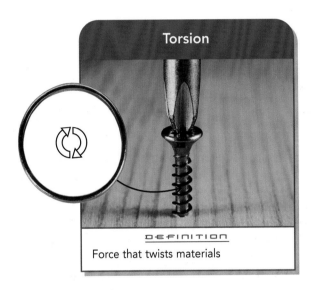

DEFINITION

Force that twists materials

Bending

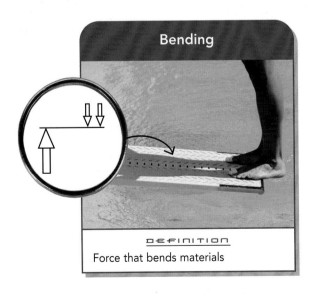

DEFINITION

Force that bends materials

Shearing

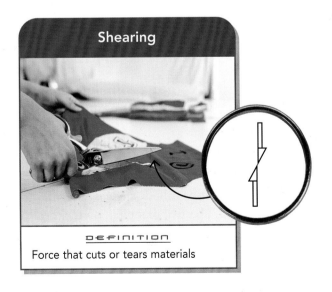

DEFINITION

Force that cuts or tears materials

12.5 Principal types of mechanical constraints

Materials can only resist mechanical constraints a certain amount before becoming deformed. The three types of deformations are called *elastic deformation*, *plastic deformation* and *fracture*. The greater the intensity of the constraint, the greater the risk of rupturing the material. Table 12.6 lists these deformations in order of the increasing intensity of the applied force.

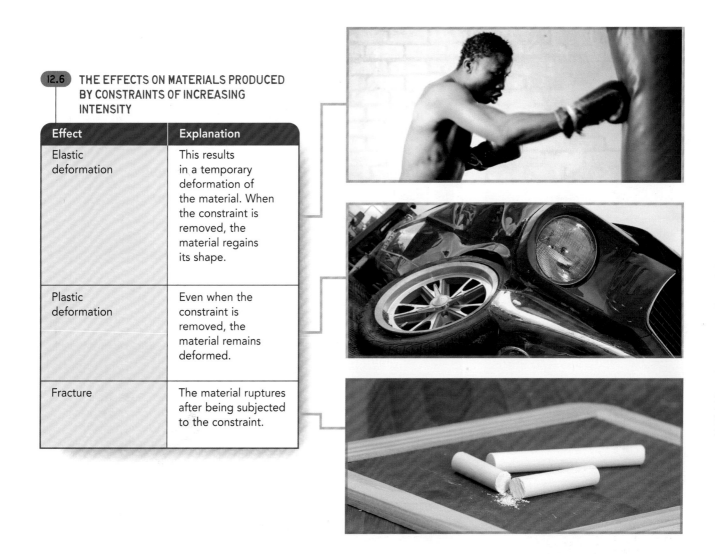

12.6 THE EFFECTS ON MATERIALS PRODUCED BY CONSTRAINTS OF INCREASING INTENSITY

Effect	Explanation
Elastic deformation	This results in a temporary deformation of the material. When the constraint is removed, the material regains its shape.
Plastic deformation	Even when the constraint is removed, the material remains deformed.
Fracture	The material ruptures after being subjected to the constraint.

MECHANICAL PROPERTIES

Different materials react differently when subjected to physical constraints. For example, chalk is more easily broken than a steel rod of the same size. A material's reaction to an applied force varies according to its mechanical properties.

> ▶ A MECHANICAL PROPERTY determines how a material will react when it is subjected to one or more mechanical constraints.

There are various types of mechanical properties including hardness, elasticity, resilience, ductility, malleability and tensile strength.

Hardness

DEFINITION

Resists penetration (reacts to locally applied pressure force by elastic deformation)

Marble is hard; it is difficult to make a hole in it.

Elasticity

DEFINITION

Regains its initial shape after being subjected to a force (reacts to force by elastic deformation)

Coils are springy.

Resilience

DEFINITION

Resists physical impacts (reacts to temporary force by elastic deformation)

The steel frame adds resilience to this construction.

Ductility

DEFINITION

Stretches without breaking (reacts to tension force by plastic deformation)

Copper can be stretched to make wires.

Malleability

DEFINITION

Flattens or bends without breaking (reacts to bending or compression by plastic deformation)

Metals are malleable enough to be made into sheets.

Tensile strength

DEFINITION

Resists tension without becoming permanently deformed (reacts to tension force by elastic deformation)

The crane's cable must have enough tensile strength to resist the tension placed on it by the wrecking ball.

12.7 Some mechanical properties of materials

There are many different categories of materials, such as:

- wood
- metal
- plastic
- stone
- ceramic
- textile
- glass
- synthetic materials

Individual characteristics help distinguish one material from another. The following sections provide detailed information on the characteristics of the first three categories.

2.2 WOOD

Wood is a material that has been used since early in the history of humanity. Today wood is used in various industries, such as the housing and tool industries.

> **WOOD** is a material that comes from cutting and processing trees.

Industries primarily use the tree trunk, specifically the *sapwood* and *heartwood*. Tree roots, branches and bark have little or no commercial value.

Bark

Sapwood

Heartwood

12.8 Materials obtained from trees mostly come from the sapwood and heartwood.

HARDWOOD AND SOFTWOOD

Wood is classified into two principal types: hardwood and softwood.

Hardwood comes from deciduous trees and is primarily used in the manufacture of furniture and flooring.

Softwood comes from coniferous trees and is primarily used in residential construction and paper manufacture.

The mechanical properties of wood are identified in Table 12.9 on the next page. These properties vary greatly from one tree species to another, and also among trees within the same species. Factors that can affect the mechanical properties of wood are as follows:

- species of tree
- growth rate of tree
- moisture content of tree
- injuries sustained by tree

MELTING INSTEAD OF GLUING

A team of French and Swiss researchers have developed an innovative furniture assembly process that does not require any glue, nails or screws. Pieces of wood are rubbed together under pressure. The heat that is produced melts the wood fibres, which then fuse to form a link as strong as glue. ▤

Mechanical property	Variation among species
Hardness	As the names suggest, hardwood is harder than softwood. Healthier trees have a higher level of hardness. Moisture content, which varies among species, and cold temperatures increase hardness. Rot affects the hardness of wood as well.
Elasticity	Wood usually has good elasticity. It can suffer many impacts without becoming permanently deformed. Defects and rot in the wood, however, will reduce its elasticity.
Resilience	When wood has adequate moisture content it is resilient and resistant to breakage. When wood is dry, it breaks easily.
Ductility	Wood has very little to no ductility. It can scarely be stretched at all.
Malleability	Heat increases the malleability of wood. A plank or piece of wood can be bent if it is heated a certain amount.
Tensile strength	Wood has excellent tensile strength so it is often used to support heavy loads. Hardwood has more tensile strength than softwood. Rot decreases the tensile strength of wood.

There are four reasons why wood is such a commonly used material in the manufacture of technical objects:

TECH
13

- Wood is easily worked.
- Wood is easy to assemble.
- Wood is a good thermal insulator.
- Wood does not conduct electricity.

Figure 12.12 on the next page demonstrates several uses for the principal hardwood and softwood species grown in Québec for manufacturing technical objects.

12.10 Wood is used extensively in residential construction.

12.11 A pulp and paper mill

Maple

Light-coloured wood, with shades ranging from cream-white to light brown

APPLICATIONS

- Furniture
- Flooring
- Trim

Yellow birch

Darker than maple, with shades ranging from white to dark brown

APPLICATIONS

- Furniture
- Flooring
- Toys
- Kitchen cabinetry

Oak

Darker than yellow birch, with shades ranging from light brown to pinkish-brown

APPLICATIONS

- Furniture
- Flooring
- Kitchen cabinetry
- Support columns

Spruce

Light-coloured wood, almost white

APPLICATIONS

- Papermaking pulp
- Building construction
- Manufacture of musical instruments
- Railway ties

Pine

Light-coloured wood, with shades ranging from white to light brown

APPLICATIONS

- Furniture
- Doors
- Papermaking pulp
- Building construction
- Railway ties

Cedar

Wood of varying colours and shades, desirable in part because of its aroma

APPLICATIONS

- Outdoor decks
- Closets
- Furniture
- Building construction

12.12 The principal species of wood used in Québec

The organic alternative

Architects and interior designers have discovered the advantages of bamboo.

If I told you that there is a building material that is up to 50 times stronger than oak, lighter than steel or concrete, flexible, aesthetically pleasing and highly rated for its green credentials, you would probably say it sounds too good to be true. But such a product does exist. It is called bamboo.

Today, architects and interior designers increasingly use this member of the grass family not only to build bridges, entire houses and public buildings, but also to create flooring, kitchen cabinets, furniture and other useful items.

In traditional housing, bamboo culms (stalks) are lashed together with vines or other natural fibres, producing a joint that weakens over time as climate and age affect the fibres. New methods, however, use mortar to fill part of the hollow stalk and bolts to join pieces together, creating stable structures. Giant bamboo, which grows at rates of more than a metre a day, reach heights of 30 m and more and diameters of up to 25 cm. Currently they are being cultivated and harvested for modern architect-designed structures.

Adapted from Paul Miles, "The Organic Alternative," *Financial Times*, Europe, January 7, 2007.

MODIFIED WOOD

Today, most trees that are cut down in our forests are no longer used to make planks or beams, but instead are used to make a material called *modified wood*. Modified woods are made up mostly of wood, but may also contain other substances such as glue, plastics or preservatives.

> ▶ **MODIFIED WOOD** is treated wood or material made with wood mixed with other substances.

Modified wood has the following advantages:

- It has stable mechanical properties (the properties of wood vary greatly, even within the same species).
- It has more resistance to inclement weather.
- It can be used to manufacture large materials. (Keep in mind that material made exclusively of wood cannot be larger than the tree that produces the wood.)
- It can be made from small trees.
- It can be made with wood chips and wood waste (such as saw dust).

12.13 Wood chips can be used to make modified wood.

Modified wood is very versatile. Table 12.14 includes some types of modified wood and and their usage.

12.14 MODIFIED WOOD AND ITS USES

Modified wood	Manufacturing process	Applications
Treated wood	Treated wood is made by heating to high temperatures or by dipping into a copper-based chemical product.	• Objects or structures in which wood is exposed to rain or snow
Laminated wood	Laminated wood is made by gluing small pieces of wood together.	• Snowshoes • Building structures • Tables
Plywood	Plywood is made by gluing together large sheets of wood so that the fibres of one sheet are at right angles to those below them.	• Work tables • Building construction (floors mainly)
Particle board	Particle board is made with wood chips and wood waste produced by wood and plywood industries. Particles are bonded with various products.	• Building construction • Trunks • Toys
Fibreboard	Fibreboard is made by first separating wood fibres, using smaller bits than those used to make other modified wood. Fibres are bonded with various products.	• Insulation • Furniture • Floating floors • Various kinds of construction

2.3 METALS AND ALLOYS

Like wood, metals are naturally occurring materials. They are extracted from ores located in mines in the Earth's crust. Ores often contain many other substances that must be separated from the desired metal. The separation techniques that are employed vary from one type of ore to the next.

CYCLE ONE

└ Element
└ Periodic table

12.15   Iron and titanium ores are excavated at the Tio mine near Havre-Saint-Pierre, in Québec.

1921
–

Ursula Franklin

Ursula Franklin, a Canadian of German descent, is an expert in metal and alloy structures. Her work has led to the development of many techniques for the analysis of metallic materials found during archaeological digs.

The development of metal separation processes and methods that use them to manufacture technical objects represent significant advances in the history of humanity. You need only think of the Bronze and Iron ages that followed the Stone Age, marking the end of prehistory, to understand the consequences of these developments.

Metal is a shiny substance that conducts electricity and heats up very well. Some metals are corrosion-resistant, while others are not. Corrosion modifies the properties of metals. It is caused by environmental factors such as the oxygen present in the air and in water.

Corrosion comes from the Latin word corrodo, meaning "to gnaw away."

> ▶ A METAL is a material extracted from an ore. Metals are usually shiny and are good conductors of electricity and heat.

All elements found on the left side of the periodic table, with the exception of hydrogen, are metals. Notice that in the periodic table on the inside back cover of this textbook, the chemical symbols for metals are written in black.

Table 12.16 features the most commonly used metals and their properties. Since metallic materials are rarely made of pure metal, the examples of objects listed in the table are only partly made with the metal described.

Metal (chemical symbol)	Characteristics	Useful properties	Applications
Iron (Fe)	• Silvery • Soft • Can rust if exposed to oxygen • Most commonly used metal	• Ductility • Malleability	• Automobiles • Building structures • Utensils • Cables • Nails
Copper (Cu)	• Red-brown • One of the best conductors of electricity	• Ductility • Malleability • Excellent electrical conductivity	• Electrical wires • Musical instruments • One-cent coins
Aluminum (Al)	• White • Soft • Very abundant in nature • Most commonly used metal after iron	• Malleability • Lightness (weight) • Corrosion resistance • Very good electrical conductivity	• Pleasure boat • Aluminum foil • Cans • Electrical products
Zinc (Zn)	• White, slightly bluish	• Ductility • Malleability • Corrosion resistance	• Electrical wires • Gutters • Surface coatings
Magnesium (Mg)	• Silvery white • Can burn on contact with air	• Lightness • Flammable	• Fireworks and Bengal lights • Cans
Nickel (Ni)	• Grey	• Hardness • Malleability • Corrosion resistance	• Heating elements • Coins
Chrome (Cr)	• White, slightly bluish	• Extreme hardness • Corrosion resistance	• Surface coatings
Tin (Sn)	• Silvery white	• Ductility • Malleability • Lowest melting point	• Welding • Utensils

An alloy is produced when a metal is mixed with other substances, metallic or not. The materials that are produced possess the properties of the various substances they contain. Alloys make it possible to select or create customized materials that have properties that can be adapted to meet specific needs. For this reason, metal alloys are more often used than pure metals.

> An ALLOY is the result of mixing a metal with one or more metallic or non-metallic substances.

There are two types of alloys: ferrous alloys and non–ferrous alloys.

> A FERROUS ALLOY is an alloy whose main constituent is iron.

> A NON-FERROUS ALLOY is an alloy whose main constituent is a metal other than iron.

	Alloy	Composition and description	Useful properties	Applications
Ferrous Alloys	Steel	• Mix of iron and carbon (less than 1.5% carbon) • Nickel, chrome and zinc are often added	• Hardness • Resilience • Malleability • Tensile strength	• Construction tools • Building structures • Automobile industry
	Cast-iron	• Mix of iron and carbon (over 2% carbon)	• Hardness	• Cookware • Wood stoves • Engine blocks
Non-ferrous alloys	Brass	• Mix of copper and zinc • Can take on various colours according to metal content (white, grey, pink or golden)	• Ductility • Malleability • Corrosion resistance • Excellent electrical conductivity	• Decoration • Automobile industry • Electrical components
	Bronze	• Mix of copper and tin • Colour varies from yellow to red to brown.	• Hardness • Malleability • High density • Corrosion and wear resistance	• Art objects • Olympic medals • Boat propellers
	Aluminum alloy	• There are many aluminum alloys to which a small amount of one or more other substances has been added (e.g. copper, manganese, silicon, zinc, magnesium, etc.).	• Malleability • Low density • Corrosion resistance • Lightness (weight)	• Car parts • Airplane parts • Electronic parts

The strength of metal with the flexibility of plastic

The properties of shape-memory alloys, discovered in 1932 by a Swede, still fascinate scientists today. These are truly exceptional materials. Forty times more flexible than ordinary metals, they can deform quite easily, a feature called *superelasticity*, and then regain their original shape, referred to as *shape memory*.

Shape-memory alloys have many applications. They are used most notably to make earpieces for glasses or cellphone antennae, as well as various medical implants.

Adapted from Gaëtan Tremblay, "Les alliages à mémoire de forme : la souplesse du plastique, la force du métal," *Le Technologue*, Ordre des technologues professionnels du Québec, January-February 2004.
[Translation]

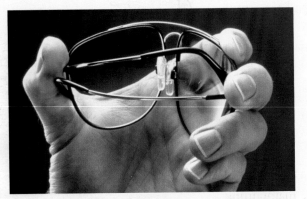

Glasses frames in shape-memory alloy easily regain their shape after being deformed.

2.4 PLASTICS

Wood, metal and alloys have long been used by humans. Since the 1970s, a new type of material called *plastics* has taken the lead in the manufacturing of technical objects.

Plastics are made of molecules called polymers. Polymers are made up of chains of multiple identical units called *monomers*. The plastic polypropylene, as shown in Figure 12.18, is made up of propylene monomers. Polypropylene is commonly used to manufacture margarine and yogurt containers.

CYCLE ONE
- Plant and animal cells
- Molecules

Polymer comes from the Greek words *polus*, meaning "many," and *meros*, meaning "part."

A polypropylene molecule

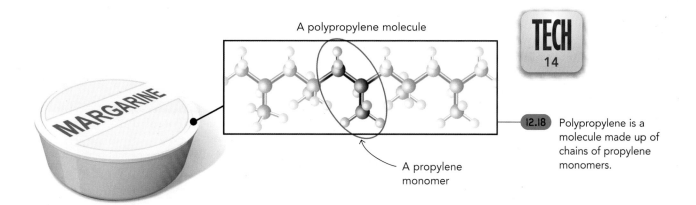

TECH 14

A propylene monomer

12.18 Polypropylene is a molecule made up of chains of propylene monomers.

Most plastics come from petroleum or natural gas. Monomers are extracted from these substances to make plastics. During processing, monomers are linked together through chemical reactions.

Other plastics are created by modifying natural polymers such as cellulose, which makes up the cell walls of plant. Celluloid, an example of a plastic made from cellulose, is used in the production of ping-pong balls.

▶ **PLASTIC is a manufactured material made of polymers.**

Plastics can be easily moulded and thus can be shaped into anything desired. Once moulded, plastics keep their new shape.

Plastics are divided into two categories: thermosetting plastics and thermoplastics.

- Thermosetting plastics harden permanently under the effect of an energy source such as heat, irradiation or a chemical reaction. The energy absorbed by the process provides the plastic with great rigidity.
- Thermoplastics soften when heated and harden when cooled. Thermoplastics can be reshaped when softened, maintaining their new shape when cooled.

1837
1920

John Wesley Hyatt

In the United States at the end of the 1800s, billiard balls were made of ivory. As ivory became increasingly rare, a contest was launched to find a replacement. John Wesley Hyatt received the grand-prize of $10 000 with his proposed use of celluloid.

This chapter focuses primarily on thermoplastics, which encompass three quarters of all plastic produced world–wide.

▶ THERMOPLASTIC is a plastic that, when heated, softens enough to be moulded or remoulded; when cooled, it hardens, retaining its new shape.

There are several principal types of thermoplastics. Table 12.19 identifies some of their properties and applications. Most are recyclable (where appropriate facilities exist) and thus carry the code for recycling.

12.19 PRINCIPAL TYPES OF THERMOPLASTICS

Type of thermoplastic	Recycling code	Properties	Applications
Polyethylene terephtalate	1 PETE	• Are impact-resistant • Are gas- and moisture-resistant • Are very heat-resistant	• Bottles (for soft drinks, sports drinks, etc.) • Containers (for peanut butter, jam, etc.) • Oven-proof packaging
Polyethylene	2 HDPE 4 LDPE	• Are flexible • Can be easily cut • Can be easily moulded • Are moisture resistant	• Collapsible squeeze bottles (for mustard, dish soap, etc.) • Garbage bags • Grocery bags • Plastic wrap (for packaging food) • Beach balls
Polyvinyl chloride (PVC)	3 V	• Are hard • Are resistant to grease, oil and other chemical products	• Medicine tubes • Patio furniture • CD cases • Construction materials (for piping, plumbing fittings, window frames)
Polypropylene	5 PP	• Are impact-resistant • Are heat-resistant • Are oil- and grease-resistant • Are waterproof	• Containers (for margarine, yogurt, etc.) • Water bottles • Automobile parts (bumpers) • Geotextiles
Polystyrene	6 PS	• Can be used in insulation • Can be used in foam or rigid plastic forms	• Slab insulation • Plastic dinnerware (for glasses, utensils, cups, plates, etc.) • Food packaging
Polyamide	Currently not recyclable	• Are elastic • Can absorb water	• Textiles (nylon fabrics) • Electrical components
Polymethyl methacrylate (also called *acrylic*)	Currently not recyclable	• Are very rigid • Can come in various colours	• Transparent bowls • Signs • Dental prostheses

Thermoplastics are used in a variety of fields, especially packaging. In addition to being easily moulded, thermoplastics also possess the following useful properties:

- They can be made in various colours.
- They are durable.
- They do not rust.
- They are lightweight.
- They are inexpensive.

3 BASIC MECHANICAL FUNCTIONS

CYCLE ONE
└ Basic mechanical functions (guiding, linking)

Technical objects are often composed of many parts. In such cases, the parts must be assembled so they can all work together, each one playing a specific role in the object's overall function. The role played by a part is its function.

The parts and fluids that have a function in a technical object are also called *components*.

> ▶ A technical object's COMPONENTS are the parts or fluids that have a mechanical function.

The function of a technical object can be studied in various ways. The role a component or mechanism plays in the function or assembly of a technical object is its basic mechanical function. A screw, for example, is the part that makes it possible to assemble other parts and prevent them from moving. Therefore, the screw fulfils a basic mechanical function.

> ▶ A BASIC MECHANICAL FUNCTION is the role played by a component or a group of components in the function or assembly of a technical object.

There are several basic mechanical functions. In the following pages, we'll take a look at two of them: guiding and linking.

3.1 GUIDING FUNCTION

Many technical objects possess one or more moving parts. The function of some components is to ensure that these moving parts perform a specific task. The components, therefore, ensure that the object's guiding function is carried out.

> ▶ GUIDING is the basic mechanical function of any component that controls the motion of one or several moving parts.

The components of a technical object that control the motion of the object's moving parts are called *guides*.

> ▶ **A GUIDE** is a component that has the basic mechanical function of guiding.

The principal guiding motions performed by technical objects are either rotational or translational motions.

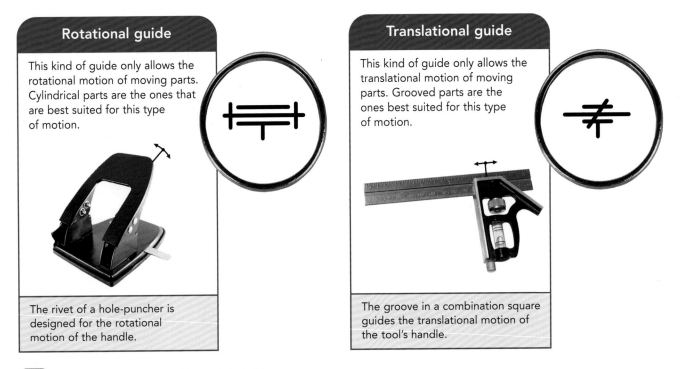

Rotational guide

This kind of guide only allows the rotational motion of moving parts. Cylindrical parts are the ones that are best suited for this type of motion.

The rivet of a hole-puncher is designed for the rotational motion of the handle.

Translational guide

This kind of guide only allows the translational motion of moving parts. Grooved parts are the ones best suited for this type of motion.

The groove in a combination square guides the translational motion of the tool's handle.

12.20 The principal guides used by technical objects

Some structures in the human body have guiding functions, such as the joints.

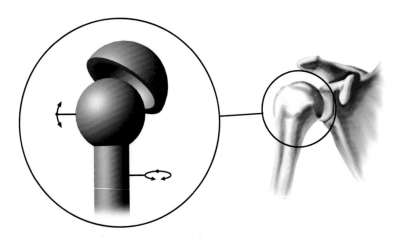

12.21 The bones that form a shoulder joint make it possible for the arm, not the torso, to make a rotational motion.

 For a guide to be effective, there must be some clearance between moving parts and the guiding component. In technology, clearance is the space between two parts. A certain amount of clearance is necessary for the moving parts to move easily; too little clearance makes movement difficult or even impossible.

3.2 LINKING FUNCTION

When a technical object is made up of more than one part, a *link* is needed to hold these parts together. A technical object can have more than one link.

> ▶ A LINK helps connect two or more parts of a technical object.

Components such as screws, bolts, nuts, nails, rivets and glue are sometimes needed to link parts. They perform a linking function and are referred to as *linking components*. In other cases, complementary components create a link on their own. For example, a pen and its cap are connected without a linking component.

> ▶ LINKING is the basic mechanical function provided by any component that links an object's parts.

> ▶ A LINKING COMPONENT is one that has the basic mechanical function of linking.

THE CHARACTERISTICS OF LINKS

Links are classified according to their characteristics. A link always has four characteristics, one for each of the following pairings: a direct or indirect link, a rigid or flexible link, a removable or non-removable link, a complete or partial link. Tables 12.23 to 12.26 present these four pairs of characteristics.

12.22 In this assembly, the linking components are nails, bolts and nuts.

THE FLIGHT OF PLANES ⓘ

Airplanes are machines with wings. Powered by motors, the propellers or turbines turn at high speeds because of a pivot mechanism. The propellers create a violent air current, which is projected backward, thus propelling the plane forward and creating an upward force beneath the wings. 📄

12.23 FIRST PAIR: DIRECT OR INDIRECT LINK

First pair of characteristics

● DIRECT LINK

A direct link exists when two parts can hold together without requiring a linking component.

◀ The link between the cover and the container is direct.

● INDIRECT LINK

An indirect link exists when the parts require a linking component to hold them together.

◀ The link between the street number and the siding is indirect. The link is created by the screws.

12.24 SECOND PAIR: RIGID OR ELASTIC LINKS

Second pair of characteristics

● RIGID LINK

A rigid link exists when the surfaces of the linked parts or the linking component are rigid.

◀ The link between the head of a hammer and its shank is rigid.

● FLEXIBLE LINK

A flexible link exists when the surfaces of the linked parts or the linking component can be deformed. Coils and rubber are often used to create flexible links.

◀ The link between the tire and wheel is flexible because the tire can be deformed.

12.25 THIRD PAIR: REMOVABLE OR NON-REMOVABLE LINKS

Third pair of characteristics

● REMOVABLE LINK

A removable link exists when linked parts can be separated without damaging them. Nuts and bolts form removable links.

◀ The link between the cap and the pen is removable because separating them does not damage either part.

● NON-REMOVABLE LINK

A non-removable link exists when separating the linked parts damages them or the linking component.

◀ The link between the ceramic tile and the floor is non-removable because separating them damages the ceramic tile.

12.26 FOURTH PAIR: COMPLETE OR PARTIAL LINKS

Fourth pair of characteristics

● COMPLETE LINK

There is a complete link when there is no movement between linked parts.

◀ The link between the skate blade and plate is complete because both parts are immobile.

● PARTIAL LINK

There is a partial link when at least one part is capable of motion with respect to the other.

◀ The link between the two parts of a clothespin is partial because each part can move with respect to the other.

Joints: what amazingly complex mechanisms!

The human body is a remarkable example of engineering. On close examination of the mechanisms that bring movement to the different parts of the human body, it is evident just how complex and ingenious it is.

The joints, which are the connecting structures between two bones, allow us to perform a variety of actions. Without joints, it would be impossible to jump, ski, run or dance with any ease, vigour or intensity.

We have to look after our bodies if we are to fully benefit from their marvellous mechanical parts. The key is to move them regularly.

Thirty minutes of moderate physical activity a day is recommended to maintain the strength and flexibility of our joints. This activity can come in many forms such as speed walking, biking or rollerblading.

It is always necessary to warm up our bodies before exercising them. A good warm-up helps increase muscle flexibility and enables the muscles to perform faster and more precise movements. A good warm-up also helps prevent injuries, cramps and heart strain.

In addition, we should stretch our muscles after exercise in order to relax the muscles and cardiovascular system, as well as prevent soreness the next day.

Joints make it possible for us to move in various ways and also to absorb impacts.

PRINCIPAL TYPES OF LINKS

Links are distinguished by the kind of motion made by their linked part. The principal types of links are:

- fixed links
- rotating links
- sliding links
- sliding rotating links
- spherical links
- helical links

TECH
16

With the exception of fixed links, one of the two linked parts always guides the other. The motion performed by the guided part determines its link type.

Fixed link

MOTION OF GUIDED PART

There is no movement between linked parts.

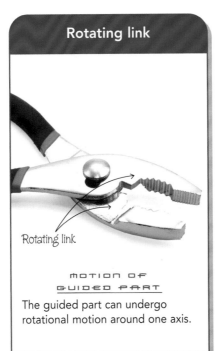

Rotating link

MOTION OF GUIDED PART

The guided part can undergo rotational motion around one axis.

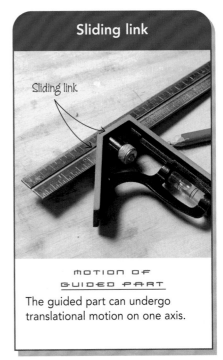

Sliding link

MOTION OF GUIDED PART

The guided part can undergo translational motion on one axis.

Sliding rotating link

MOTION OF GUIDED PART

The guided part can undergo rotational and translational motion on the same axis.

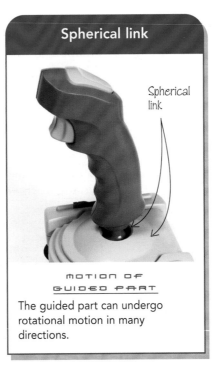

Spherical link

MOTION OF GUIDED PART

The guided part can undergo rotational motion in many directions.

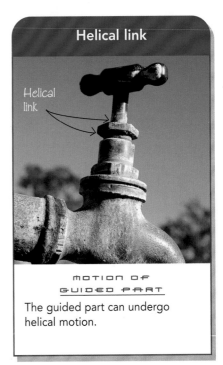

Helical link

MOTION OF GUIDED PART

The guided part can undergo helical motion.

12.27 Principal types of links

4. COMPLEX MECHANICAL FUNCTIONS

Many technical objects contain a group of pieces that play a common role. For example, in a bicycle, the sprocket linked to the crankset, the chain, as well as the sprocket linked to the rear wheel all share the function of transmitting motion from the crankset to the rear wheel. Since these three parts share the same function, they form a system.

▶ A SYSTEM is a set of components that share the same function.

A system performs a complex mechanical function when its role is to bring about a change in motion from one part to another in a technical object.

▶ A COMPLEX MECHANICAL FUNCTION is the role played by a set of components in transferring motion inside a technical object.

There are two principal complex mechanical functions: motion transmission and motion transformation. Figure 12.28 describes these two functions.

CYCLE ONE

- System (global function, inputs, processes, outputs, control)
- System components
- Mechanisms that transmit motion
- Mechanisms that transform motion

TECH 17

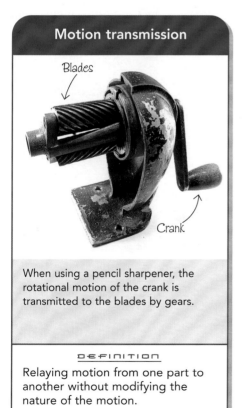

Motion transmission

Blades

Crank

When using a pencil sharpener, the rotational motion of the crank is transmitted to the blades by gears.

DEFINITION

Relaying motion from one part to another without modifying the nature of the motion.

Motion transformation

Crank

Cable

When using a winch, the rotational motion of the crank is transformed into the translational motion of the cable.

DEFINITION

Relaying motion from one part to another while at the same time modifying the nature of the motion.

12.28 Two principal complex mechanical functions

Human-like robots

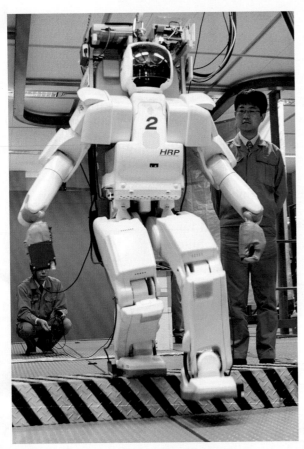

The HRP-2 (Humanoïd Robot Project) robot is quite advanced in its imitation of walking.

Engineers striving to create human-like robots have made amazing progress these last few years, as evidenced by the robots featured at this year's Robodex show in Japan.

Researchers have long since discovered just how difficult it is to replicate the process of walking, since it involves a variety of body parts. Balance, in which the inner ear, torso and arms play significant roles, is difficult to duplicate. The HRP-2 robot, however, which is the most sophisticated android at the show, can not only walk, but also stand up after a fall.

Another challenge facing engineers is that of endowing their creations with the ability to communicate. At Robodex, the HRP-2 robot demonstrated that it could decipher the human language. When told to "help me carry this table," the robot's cameras identified the table and its "grippers" picked it up.

One thing, however, that robots still can't do is emulate human emotion. That comes next!

Adapted from Cyril Fiévet, "Des robots sacrément humains," *Ordinateur individuel* 152 (July-August 2003), pp. 60-62.
[Translation]

All systems contain a driver, at least one driven component and possibly one or more intermediates. These three types of components are:

- The driver is at the root of the system's motion. It receives the power required to set the system in motion. In Figure 12.29, the system driver (the sprocket of the crankset) is highlighted in red. It is set in motion by the force from the cyclist's feet.

- The driven receives the motion and transmits it to another part. In Figure 12.29, the driven, which is the sprocket on the rear wheel, is highlighted in yellow. It transmits motion from the crankset to the rear wheel, making the bicycle move forward.

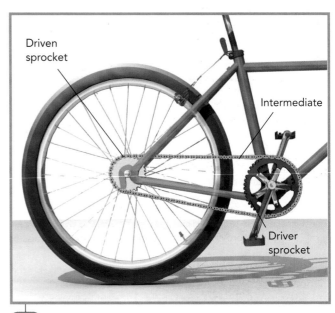

12.29 The motion transmission system of a bike's crankset

● The intermediate is located between the driver and the driven. A system can have one or more intermediates or even none at all. In Figure 12.29, the intermediate (the chain) is highlighted in green.

4.1 MOTION TRANSMISSION

Motion transmission systems make it possible for the complex mechanical function of motion transmission to take place. In such a system, the driver and the driven perform the same motion: the nature of the motion remains the same.

> ▶ A MOTION TRANSMISSION SYSTEM relays motion from one part to another without changing the nature of the motion.

In this section we'll take a look at five motion transmission systems:

● friction gear system
● simple gear system
● pulley and belt system
● chain and sprocket system
● worm and worm gear system

For each of these systems, we'll identify the function, the parts, the operation and their advantages and disadvantages. In addition, we'll provide examples of the various technical objects that use these systems.

A FRICTION GEAR SYSTEM

FUNCTION
Transmits rotational motion between two or more nearby parts.

COMPONENTS AND OPERATION
Has one or more wheels (without teeth) that roll together.

ADVANTAGES
● Is economical because it is easy to build.
● Is not very noisy.

DISADVANTAGE
● The wheels tend to slide one over the other, which is why the system does not always provide smooth continuous motion transmission.

EXAMPLES
● Turntables (for vinyl records)
● Audio cassette players
● Toys

A printing press

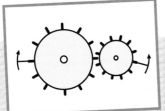

A SIMPLE GEAR SYSTEM

FUNCTION

Transmits rotational motion between two or more nearby parts.

A manual eggbeater

COMPONENTS AND OPERATION

Has two or more gears that come into contact; they mesh.

ADVANTAGES

- The action of the gears transmits motion constantly since the wheels do not slide.
- Transmits motion in tiny spaces, such as in a watchcase.
- Is highly effective since rotational speeds can be very high.

DISADVANTAGES

- Production of these systems requires great precision (for the teeth), which increases costs.
- A lubricant may be required during use.
- Is noisy when in operation.

EXAMPLES

- Watches
- Manual eggbeaters
- Salad spinners
- Hand drills

A PULLEY AND BELT SYSTEM

FUNCTION

Transmits rotational motion between parts that are relatively far apart from each other.

A pulley used in a merry-go-round

COMPONENTS AND OPERATION

Has belt slides on two or more wheels (referred to as pulleys). Pulleys must have a smooth surface for the belt not to break. They might also have raised edges (flanges) to keep the belt in place.

ADVANTAGES

- Does not require any lubrication.
- Makes high-speed motion transmission possible.

DISADVANTAGES

- The belt can slip, reducing the effectiveness of motion transmission.
- The belt can break and replacement is sometimes difficult.

EXAMPLES

- Band saw
- Car alternators
- Car fans
- Clothesline pulleys and line

A CHAIN AND SPROCKET SYSTEM

FUNCTION

Transmits rotational motion between parts that are relatively far apart from each other.

A bicycle

COMPONENTS AND OPERATION

Has two or more sprockets that do not touch, plus a chain.

ADVANTAGES

- The chain meshes with the wheel teeth to prevent slipping.
- A great force can be applied to the driving wheel to produce motion.

DISADVANTAGES

- Requires constant lubrication to prolong chain service life.
- Sprocket speeds are limited, since the chain has a tendency to derail when the mechanism spins too fast or the chain is not taut enough.

EXAMPLES

- Bicycle cranksets
- Industrial machinery
- Motor vehicles

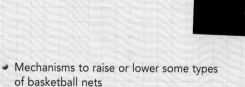

A WORM AND WORM GEAR SYSTEM

FUNCTION

Transmits rotational motion to non-parallel parts that are close to one another.

A guitar

COMPONENTS AND OPERATION

Has a worm and a worm gear. The teeth of the worm slide into the groove of the worm gear thread.

ADVANTAGES

- The system does not loosen when the worm gear is released (can maintain tightness).
- Can be adjusted precisely.

DISADVANTAGES

- Is difficult to build.
- Wears out quickly.

EXAMPLES

- Car gearboxes
- Stringed musical instruments
- Mechanisms to raise or lower some types of basketball nets

4.2 SPEED CHANGE

As we have seen, motion transmission is the relaying of motion from the driver to one or more driven components without modifying its nature. The speed of the motion being transmitted, however, can vary, as illustrated in Figure 12.30 on the next page.

TECH
18

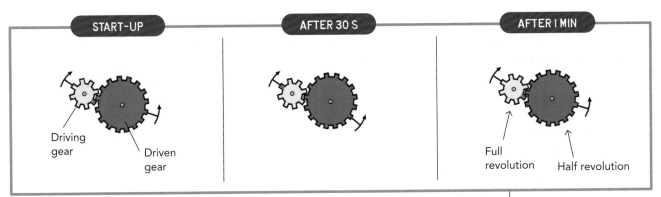

Driving gear

Driven gear

Full revolution   Half revolution

▶ There is a **SPEED CHANGE** in a motion transmission system when the driver does not turn at the same speed as the driven mechanism.

Now we'll take a look at how it is possible to vary rotational speed from one mechanism to another in the principal motion transmission systems.

FRICTION GEAR AND PULLEY AND BELT SYSTEMS

In a friction gear system or a pulley and belt system, rotational speed depends on the diameter of the wheels or pulleys.

In these systems:

- Rotational speed increases when motion is transmitted from a wheel or pulley to a wheel or pulley of smaller diameter.
- Rotational speed decreases when motion is transmitted from a wheel or pulley to a wheel or pulley of greater diameter.
- Rotational speed remains unchanged when motion is transmitted between two wheels or pulleys of the same diameter.

12.30 After one minute, the driving gear has made a full turn, or revolution, at a speed of 1 revolution/min. The driven gear has made a half revolution, at a speed of 0.5 revolution/min. The rotational motion has thus decreased speed during its transmission.

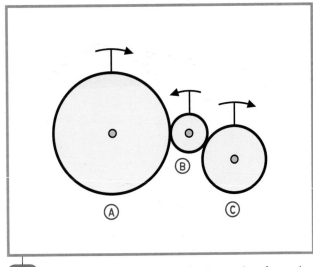

12.31 In this friction gear system, wheel A revolves faster due to its smaller diameter. Wheel A revolves at a slower speed due to its greater diameter.

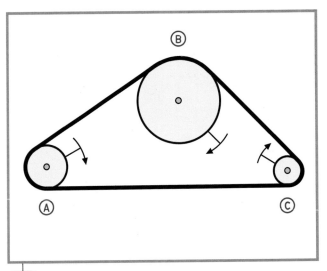

12.32 In this pulley and belt system, pulley C revolves faster due to its smaller diameter. Pulley B revolves at a slower speed due to its greater diameter.

Gears tend to slip in a friction gear system, just as the belt on a pulley tends to slip in pulley and belt systems. This is why speed ratios between the components in these two systems are not always consistent.

A GEAR TRAIN AND A CHAIN AND SPROCKET SYSTEM

In a gear train or a chain and sprocket system, contact between the various components is made with teeth. The teeth prevent slipping, making it possible to maintain speed ratio consistency in these systems.

In order for meshing between two or more components (gears or sprockets) to occur, the teeth must all have the same pitch point (the point of contact between two meshing components). This means the teeth must be the same size and the distance between the teeth must always be the same, otherwise the system will not function properly.

Consequently, the greater the diameter of the sprocket or gear, the more teeth the it has. The rotational speed of each component depends on the number of teeth.

In these systems:

- Rotational speed increases when motion is transmitted from one component to another with fewer teeth.
- Rotational speed decreases when motion is transmitted from one component to another with more teeth.
- Rotational speed remains unchanged when motion is transmitted between two components with the same number of teeth.

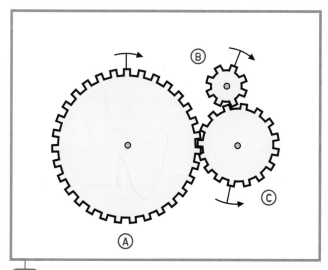

12.33 In this gear train, gear B revolves faster because it has fewer teeth. Gear A revolves at a slower speed because it has more teeth.

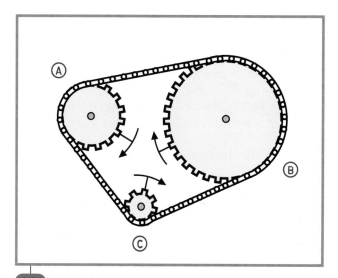

12.34 In this chain and sprocket system, sprocket C revolves faster because it has fewer teeth. Sprocket B revolves at a slower speed because it has more teeth.

WORM AND WORM GEAR SYSTEMS

A worm and worm gear system is used mostly in situations where a great decrease in rotational motion speed during its transmission is needed. For every full revolution of the worm, a worm gear only moves by one tooth, as illustrated in Figure 12.35. The speed variation between the worm and the worm gear depends on the number of teeth on the gear. The greater the number of teeth, the greater the decrease in speed will be.

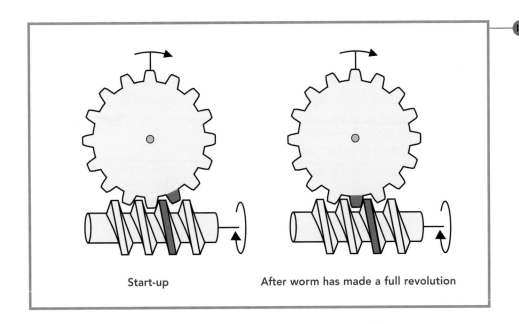

Start-up   **After worm has made a full revolution**

12.35 After the worm has completed a full revolution, the worm gear has only moved by one tooth. The rotational speed of the worm is greater than that of the worm gear.

4.3 MOTION TRANSFORMATION

So far, we have studied systems that transmit motion. There are also systems that transform motion. Let's take a look at this kind of system.

Motion transformation systems relay motion from the driver to the driven gear, while changing its nature, making it possible for the complex mechanical function of motion transformation to take place.

> ▶ A MOTION TRANSFORMATION SYSTEM transforms the nature of a motion as it is relayed from one part to another.

These are the motion-transformation systems that we'll examine:

- slider–crank system
- rack and pinion system
- cam and follower (also known as *cam follower*) system
- screw gear system

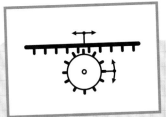

A SLIDER-CRANK SYSTEM

FUNCTION

Transforms a rotational motion into a translational motion or transforms a translational motion into a rotational motion.

COMPONENTS AND OPERATION

Has a connecting rod and crank. A connecting rod is rigid and is connected by rotary links at both ends. A crank is a part to which a rotational motion can be applied. The motion of the crank is transmitted to the connecting rod, which transforms it into a translational motion, before transmitting it to another part.

ADVANTAGE

- Can function at great speeds.

DISADVANTAGE

- Has many connecting parts and requires a great deal of lubrication.

EXAMPLES

- Gas engines
- Diesel engines
- Pumps

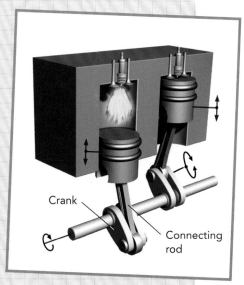

A slider-crank system in an internal combustion engine

Crank

Connecting rod

A RACK AND PINION SYSTEM

FUNCTION

Transforms a rotational motion into a translational motion or transforms a translational motion into a rotational motion.

COMPONENTS AND OPERATION

Has a straight rod with teeth called a *rack*, and a gear called a *pinion*. Sometimes the rack's surface is not entirely covered with teeth, so the mechanism can be blocked. The motion is transformed by the meshing of the teeth.

ADVANTAGE

- Transforms motion without any slipping.

DISADVANTAGE

- Because it involves a gear set, it requires a great deal of lubrication.

EXAMPLES

- Steering systems
- Net tensioners
- Adjustment mechanisms for some microscopes

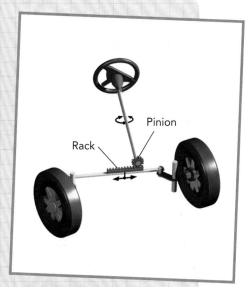

Pinion

Rack

A rack and pinion system in a car's steering system

A CAM AND FOLLOWER SYSTEM

FUNCTION

Transforms rotational motion into translational motion.

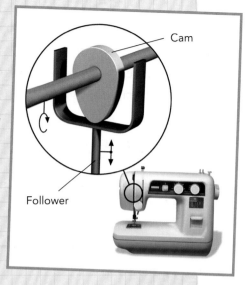

COMPONENTS AND OPERATION

An irregularly shaped disk (with an ovoid shape or uncentred pivot) called a *cam*, and a rod called a *follower*. The follower presses on the cam. When the cam turns, the follower makes a reciprocating translational motion: it goes up, then down. This is also referred to as a *back-and-forth* movement. The shape of the cam controls the motion of the follower. A spring usually makes it possible for the follower to return toward the cam.

ADVANTAGE

- Can configure the cam to modify the follower's change from translational motion to another type of motion.

DISADVANTAGE

- Has parts that wear out quickly.

EXAMPLES

- Mechanical toys
- Actuators for the opening and closing of car motor valves
- Sewing machines

A cam and follower system in a sewing machine

A SCREW GEAR SYSTEM

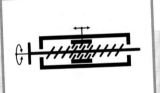

Driver: screw in rotational motion

Driven: nut in translation motion

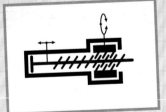

Driver: nut in rotational motion

Driven: screw in translational motion

FUNCTION

Transforms rotational motion into translational motion or transforms translational motion into rotational motion.

COMPONENTS AND OPERATION

At least one screw and at least one nut. In some systems, the nut is the driver and the screw transforms its rotational motion into translational motion. In some systems, the screw is the driver and the nut transforms its rotational motion into translational motion.

ADVANTAGE

- Can expend a great deal of force.

DISADVANTAGES

- Generates a great deal of friction.
- Is sometimes fragile, which can cause problems with the guide.

EXAMPLES

- Car jacks
- Cable tensioners

A screw gear system in a car jack

5 ELECTRICITY

Many technical objects only operate because of electricity. Portable digital players, lamps and refrigerators are just a few examples of technical objects that require an electric current in order to function. In this section, we'll learn exactly what an electric current is and how to control it.

5.1 ELECTRIC CURRENT

In order to understand what an electric current is, we must first understand the nature of the atom. Atoms are made up of positive and negative electrical charges. Since both types of charges are present in the same amount, most atoms are neutral.

As shown in Figure 12.36, the centre of an atom, also called the *nucleus*, primarily contains positive charges. The negative charge is carried by electrons, which orbit the nucleus.

Generally electrons rarely stray from their orbit around the nucleus. In some atoms, however, the more distant electrons break loose from the nucleus and become free electrons. When free electrons flow in the same direction, they produce an *electric current*.

▶ An **ELECTRIC CURRENT** is the orderly flow of negative charges carried by electrons.

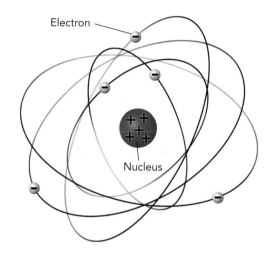

12.36 The nucleus of the atom is made up of positive charges, while the electrons orbiting around the nucleus carry negative charges.

There is no electric current because the free electrons are moving erratically.

There is an electric current because the free electrons are moving in the same direction.

12.37 An electric current is produced only if the free electrons are moving in the same direction.

There are two types of electric current: direct current and alternating current. The direction of electron flow determines the type of electric current present.

In direct current, free electrons always flow in the same direction. Batteries, for example, produce direct current. The electrons move from the battery's negative terminal to its positive terminal through conducting wires (Figure 12.39). The symbol for direct current is DC in English and CC in French, for *courant continu*.

> ▶ A **DIRECT CURRENT (DC)** is an electric current in which electrons always flow in the same direction.

In an alternating current, free electrons flow in one direction, then move in the reverse direction at regular intervals, thus they have a back-and-forth motion. This is the type of current that circulates in the electrical network of our homes. In North America, electrons flow in 60 back-and-forth motions per second. The symbol for alternating current is AC in English and CA in French, for *courant alternatif*.

> ▶ An **ALTERNATING CURRENT (AC)** is an electric current in which electrons flow in a back-and-forth motion.

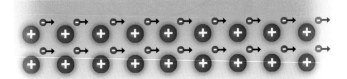

Direct current   Alternating current

12.38 In a direct current, all the electrons flow in the same direction, while in an alternating current, they flow in a back-and-forth motion.

5.2 ELECTRICAL FUNCTIONS

In a technical object, the electric current circulates through an electrical circuit. An electrical circuit contains a power source plus various components. Each component in an electrical circuit has a function.

> ▶ An **ELECTRICAL FUNCTION** is the role played by a component in the control or transformation of electric current.

In the following section, we'll take a look at various aspects of an electrical circuit: the power supply, the conduction, insulation and transformation of electrical energy, as well as control and protection. Any part of an electrical circuit that has an electrical function is called an *electrical component*.

HOW TO DRAW
A DIAGRAM
- SYMBOLS
- A CIRCUIT DIAGRAM

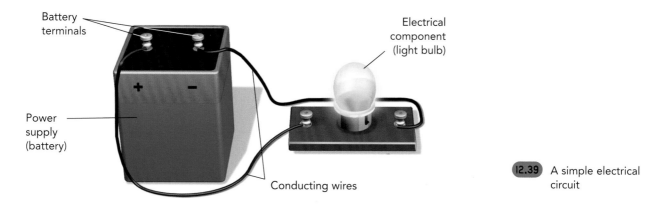

Battery terminals

Electrical component (light bulb)

Power supply (battery)

Conducting wires

12.39 A simple electrical circuit

Table 12.40 contains some electrical components that carry out the functions referred to above and below.

12.40 SOME ELECTRICAL COMPONENTS

Electrical function	Electrical components		
Power supply	Battery	Battery pack	Metal wiring
Conduction	Electric wire	Circuit board	Piece of metal
Insulation	Wire sheathing	Ceramic insulator on electric pylons	Porcelain lamp holder
Transformation of energy	Incandescent bulb	Refrigerator	Electric blender
Control	Dimmer switch	Push-button switch	Photoelectric cell
Protection	Socket fuse	Glass fuse	Circuit breaker

POWER SUPPLY

For a current to circulate in an electrical circuit, at least one component of the circuit must be a power source. Its function is to supply power.

> ▶ The **POWER SUPPLY** is the electrical component that produces or supplies electric current in a circuit.

CONDUCTION

Current flows in an electrical circuit through components called *conductors*. Any component that is able to transmit current from one part to another in an electrical circuit is a conductor. Metals make very good conductors.

> ▶ **CONDUCTION** is the function of any electrical component that can transmit an electric current from one part to another in an electrical circuit.

INSULATION

Components in an electrical circuit that prevent current from passing through them are called *insulators*. They carry out the function of insulation, a function opposite to that of conductors.

> ▶ **INSULATION** is the function of any electrical component able to block an electric current.

TRANSFORMATION OF ELECTRICAL ENERGY

Most electrical circuits are designed to transform electrical energy into another type of energy such as light energy, thermal energy or mechanical energy. In a flashlight, for example, the electrical energy contained in the batteries is transformed into light energy by the light bulb, which performs the function of energy transformation.

> ▶ **TRANSFORMATION OF ENERGY** is the function of any electrical component able to transform electrical energy into another type of energy.

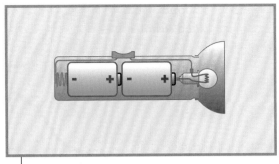

12.41 In a flashlight, the electrical cells of the battery provide the power source.

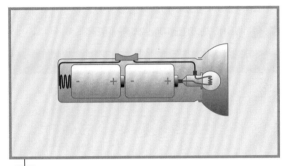

12.42 In a flashlight, the connecting wires and spring provide conduction.

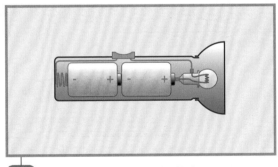

12.43 The plastic casing that covers the electrical circuit of the flashlight is the insulator. It is there to prevent a short circuit.

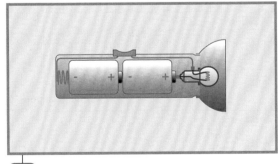

12.44 In a flashlight, the light bulb transforms electrical energy into light energy.

CONTROL

Devices that control current circulation in an electrical circuit are called *switches*. These devices carry out the control function.

> ◗ The CONTROL function is carried out by any electrical component that can open and close a circuit.

In the field of electricity, an electrical circuit is considered to be "open" when one part of the circuit is not connected to the power supply. The moment this occurs, current no longer flows. To turn off a ceiling light, for example, the circuit is usually opened by flipping "Off" a wall switch.

Conversely, when the circuit is closed, all components are once again connected to the power supply and the electric current can flow freely. So, once a wall switch is flipped "On," turning the ceiling light on, the electrical circuit is closed.

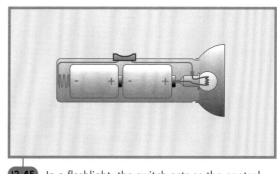

12.45 In a flashlight, the switch acts as the control.

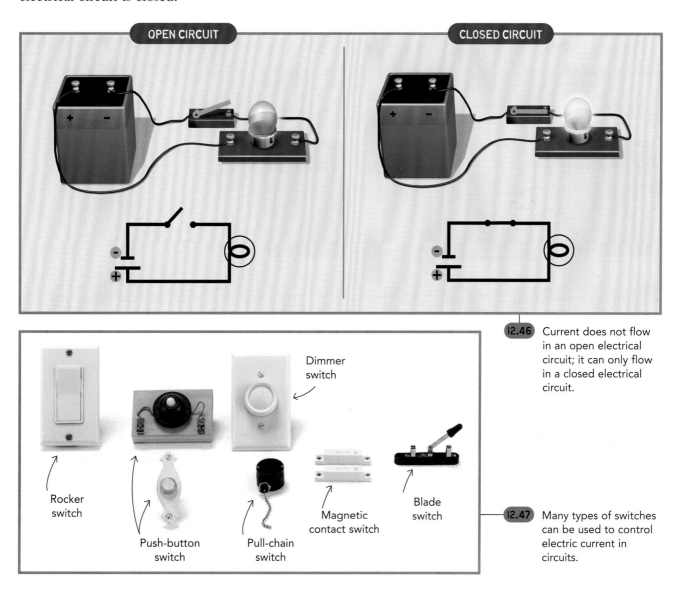

OPEN CIRCUIT

CLOSED CIRCUIT

12.46 Current does not flow in an open electrical circuit; it can only flow in a closed electrical circuit.

Rocker switch

Push-button switch

Pull-chain switch

Magnetic contact switch

Blade switch

Dimmer switch

12.47 Many types of switches can be used to control electric current in circuits.

PROTECTION

Protective devices can be inserted into electrical circuits to provide protection. Protective devices all function the same way: once current intensity goes beyond the tolerated limit, the device opens the circuit and the electric current immediately stops flowing.

> ◗ PROTECTION is the function performed by any electrical component that can automatically interrupt the flow of electric current in an abnormal situation.

A short circuit and a current overload are examples of abnormal situations that can occur in many electrical circuits, such as those found in households.

Conducting wires can overheat in a short circuit. This is very dangerous since the circuit could be damaged and start a fire. A short circuit may occur in the following situations:

● When two bare wires touch (Figure 12.48 **A**).

● When the terminals of a supply source are connected solely by a conducting wire without any other component between them (Figure 12.48 **B**).

Alessandro Volta

1745 / 1827

This Italian physicist is renowned for his work in the field of electricity. He developed the electrical cell in 1800. His invention revolutionized electricity since it was able to provide a safe and reliable current source.

12.48 Examples of short circuits

A current overload occurs when the intensity of the electric current flowing through the conducting wire(s) is too high. For example, when too many devices are plugged into the same electrical outlet, an overload may occur. The current intensity required for all the devices to function simultaneously is too high for the conducting wire to bear.

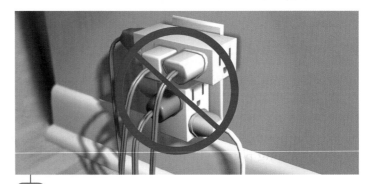

12.49 Plugging too many devices into the same electrical outlet may cause a current overload.

Current intensity is equal to the number of electrons that pass through a part of the conductor at any time, and is calculated in units called *amperes*. For example, an electric current of 1 ampere has 6.24×10^{18} electrons flowing per second. Current intensity increases according to the electrical consumption that a device requires to function. In the electrical circuit of a household, a 60-watt light bulb needs a current of 0.5 amperes to light up, and a 900-watt toaster requires 7.5 amperes to operate.

There are two types of protection devices: fuses and circuit breakers.

Fuses are components equipped with a small alloy conducting wire that melts when the current is too intense. If the fuse's wire melts, the circuit opens and current can no longer flow. The maximum intensity tolerated is indicated on the fuse.

> *Fuse* comes from the Latin word *fusilis*, meaning "melted."

Circuit breakers are switches that open automatically. They contain a device that cause a circuit to open automatically when current intensity exceeds the tolerated limit, normally identified on the circuit breaker itself.

Terminal boxes installed in residences are equipped with several circuit breakers that protect the various circuits in the house.

12.50 When current intensity exceeds the fuse's capacity, its wire melts and the current stops flowing.

6 THE MANUFACTURING PROCESS

So far, we have seen that technical objects are made from materials chosen for their mechanical properties. We have also learned that the various parts used to build technical objects can perform many functions, mechanical or electrical. Now, we will review the various manufacturing and assembly processes for components required to build technical objects.

A technical object is usually built following these three steps:

- measuring and marking the parts
- machining the parts
- assembling and finishing the parts

6.1 MEASURING AND MARKING

Before building a technical object, it is necessary to lay out the materials with cutting lines and drilling points. These markings represent the desired dimension and shape of the parts. *Measuring* determines the length of the line or the position of a drilling point, while *marking* consists of drawing a line or a drilling point on the material.

HOW TO MANUFACTURE AN OBJECT

> **MEASURING** involves identifying the size or the position of reference points on material.

> **MARKING** involves tracing lines or marking reference points on material.

Generally, the measurements and positioning of various reference points are indicated in the detail drawings, which are included with the engineering drawings of the object (Chapter 11, page 348).

12.51 Marking

6.2 MACHINING

The machining of parts begins once the marking process is completed. Various tools are used during this process to shape parts into their desired form.

> **MACHINING** is the action of forming parts into their desired shape with the necessary tools.

There are many different machining techniques, including:

- sawing
- drilling
- shearing
- bending
- moulding
- shaping
- forging
- rolling

12.52 Sawing

The machining process is followed by the verification and quality control of the process. These steps consist of:

- measuring each part to make sure its dimensions are accurate
- verifying that the drilling points are positioned correctly and the size of each hole is correct

12.53 Forging

- making sure the parts have no defects, such as bumps or sharp edges

Various techniques are used to modify parts that require adjusting, such as:

- grinding
- planing
- sanding

6.3 ASSEMBLING AND FINISHING

Following the machining and verification processes, the parts are put together to produce the object. This is called the *assembly process*.

12.54 Grinding

▶ The ASSEMBLY PROCESS involves a series of operations in which various parts are put together to produce a technical object.

There are many ways to assemble parts, for example:

- stamping
- nailing
- screwing
- bolting

- gluing
- stapling
- riveting
- welding

To manufacture more complex objects such as a bicycle, parts are put together to form various systems related to guiding, linking and motion transmission or transformation.

Finishing is the final step in the making of a technical object. Its purpose is to protect materials from weather and wear and tear, as well as to improve the object's appearance.

▶ FINISHING involves a series of operations required to complete the production of a technical object.

During finishing, parts may be:

- buffed
- polished
- painted

- stained
- varnished

Finishing usually follows assembly. However, when parts are hard to access once assembled, the finishing process precedes assembly.

12.55 Assembling

TECHNICAL OBJECTS
(pp. 368–369)

1. Which of the following are technical objects?

    A lake, a dog, a statue, an apple, a coin, a pair of pants

 MATERIALS (pp. 369–383)

2. Name the constraints placed on each of the following bones:

    a) the femur (the thigh bone), when standing up without moving

    b) the spine, when the back is curved

    c) the phalanges, when one finger is pulled

3. Wood is often used as flooring.

    a) Why are wood floorings seldom made of spruce or pine?

    b) What mechanical property makes wood flooring resistant to impact?

    c) Name at least three species of wood that are good to use as flooring.

4. Plywood is widely used in construction.

    a) What type of material is it?

    b) How are the sheets processed in the making of plywood?

    c) Name three other types of materials similar to plywood.

5. Name the mechanical property associated with each of the following statements.

    a) It is easy to flatten zinc without damaging it.

    b) Steel is very resistant to tension.

6. Name two mechanical properties that make it possible to use metal in electrical wires.

7. Which mechanical property makes it possible to manufacture coils? Explain your answer.

8. Today, stepstools and ladders are made of aluminum. Years ago, they were made of wood.

    a) Identify two benefits of using aluminum ladders instead of wooden ladders.

    b) What property does aluminum possess that explains why it is dangerous to use objects made of aluminum near electrical wires?

9. Explain the difference between a ferrous alloy and a non-ferrous alloy. Provide two examples for each type of alloy.

10. Plastics can be divided into two categories.

    a) Name the two categories.

    b) Which category contains plastic that cannot be remoulded after being heated?

11. The following statements are related to the properties of thermoplastics. Indicate whether they are true or false. Correct the statements that are false.

a) Polystyrene is a good electrical conductor.

b) A sealer must be applied to polyethylene surfaces because they rust easily.

c) Polyvinyl chloride is durable.

12. Look at the jar of honey in the picture below. What type of plastic was used to make the jar?

3 **BASIC MECHANICAL FUNCTIONS** (pp. 383–388)

13. Look at this jar and its cover.

a) Is it a technical object? Explain your answer.

b) How many components does this object contain?

c) Name the four link characteristics that describe the jar and its cover. Explain each of these characteristics.

d) Name the type of link.

14. Look at the bicycle in the picture below.

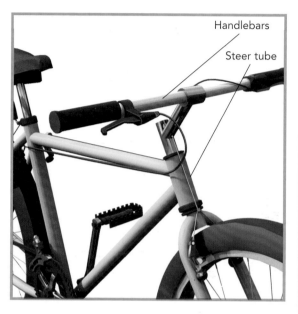

Handlebars

Steer tube

a) In a bicycle, part of the handlebars is inserted into the steer tube. The handlebars perform a rotational motion but not a translational one. What is the steep tube's basic mechanical function?

b) What type of link does this system have?

4 **COMPLEX MECHANICAL FUNCTIONS** (pp. 389–398)

15. Name the two types of complex mechanical functions. Provide four examples of each type.

16. Automobile engines contain a slider-crank system, among others. Why is it important to maintain the required oil levels? Answer by identifying the function of oil in car engines.

17. To activate the manual hand drill, the crank must be turned, which makes the mandrel turn as well.

Crank

Mandrel

a) Does this object contain a motion transmission system or motion transformation system? Explain your answer.

b) Name this object's system and draw a diagram of it.

18. Antiperspirant applicators contain a system that makes the antiperspirant stick move up and down.

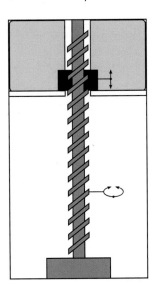

a) Does this object contain a motion transmission system or motion transformation system? Explain your answer.

b) Name this object's system.

19. An electric current is required to make many technical objects function.

a) What is an electric current?

b) For each of the photos below, indicate whether the current is alternating or direct.

①

②

③

20. The two electrical circuits described in the diagrams below contain an audible alarm device. When the current flows through the device, it emits a sound.

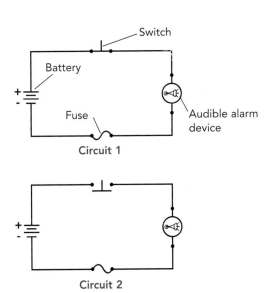

Switch

Battery

Fuse

Audible alarm device

Circuit 1

Circuit 2

a) For each electrical circuit, indicate whether the alarm will ring or not. If the alarm won't ring, explain why.

b) Identify the electrical function of each circuit component.

6 THE MANUFACTURING PROCESS (pp. 405–407)

21. Look at the five photos below. For each one, identify the manufacturing process used and the technique being shown.

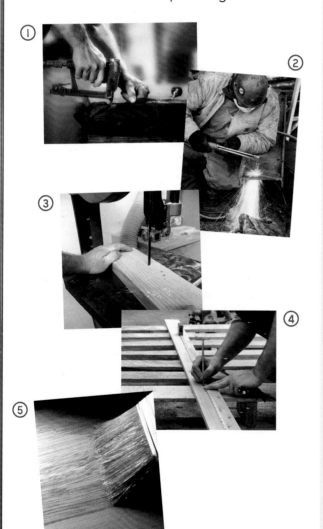

① ② ③ ④ ⑤

CONCEPT MAPS

HOW TO BUILD
A CONCEPT MAP

Prepare your own summary of Chapter 12 by building a concept map using the following terms:

- Alloys
- Basic mechanical functions
- Complex mechanical functions
- Electric current
- Electrical functions
- Electricity
- Forces
- Guide
- Guiding function
- Link
- Linking function
- Manufacturing process
- Materials
- Mechanical constraints
- Mechanical properties
- Metals
- Modified wood
- Motion transformation
- Motion transmission
- Plastics
- Technical objects
- Wood

DAILY SUPPORT FROM PROSTHESES AND ORTHOSES

We're all familiar with the peg legs and glass eyes worn by pirates, but what about modern prostheses and orthoses? Thanks to recent advances in technology and a bet-ter knowledge of materials and mechanical functions, prostheses and orthoses have evolved a great deal.

A prosthesis is an artificial device used to replace a sick, absent, defi-cient or mutilated limb. From a sim-ple dental prosthesis to an artificial heart, prostheses can be difficult to make. Materials used to build these devices must be compatible with human tissue, while at the same time they must achieve certain functions and specific movements. In addition, they need to resist wear and tear.

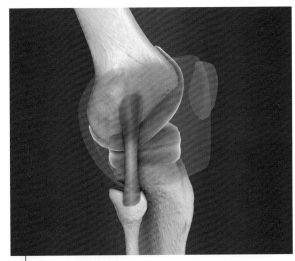
12.56 A knee implant

An orthosis, on the other hand, is an orthopedic apparatus designed to support a body part while providing mobility, correcting deformities or improving performance. Materials used to create orthoses are selected according to their function. For example, the plaster used to make casts for healing fractures should be strong enough to fully immobilize the part of the bone that needs to be rested. However, a knee orthosis must include a mechanism allowing it to support the knee and align its movements, while being light-weight enough for the knee to carry without strain.

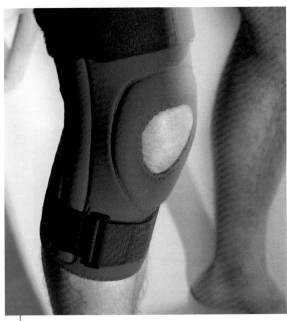
12.57 A knee orthosis

1. What is the difference between a prosthesis and orthosis?

2. A person moving around on crutches is using orthoses or prostheses? Explain your answer.

THOMAS SIMÉON

Thomas Siméon is a Montagnais living in the Mashteuiatsh Native Reserve. He loves telling stories and recounting the history of his people. He grew up in a family whose main activity is handicraft. He chose to carry on making crafts as a way of expressing his culture. His artwork focuses on sculpture; he has already created close to 500 pieces. His studies, observing his father's techniques and most importantly, the extensive research he carries out have helped him develop his own ways of working.

The materials Siméon uses are found in nature. They include stone, wood and even caribou antlers. Before creating a sculpture, he analyzes the properties of each material. Then, he chooses his tools and decides on the shape of his piece. If he selects a very hard material to work with, for example, he knows that a detailed carving will be impossible. He also knows he will be able to use only well-sharpened tools.

12.58 The Mishta Napeu people are characters featured in aboriginal legends. This sculpture demonstrates Thomas Siméon's perception of these characters.

NAME
Thomas Siméon

JOB
Artist-sculptor

AREA WHERE HE WORKS
Saguenay–Lac-Saint-Jean

EDUCATION
High school diploma, self-taught

PROUDEST ACHIEVEMENT
Created works of art representing the legends of the Montagnais people as well as his own family history

12.59 OCCUPATIONS CONNECTED TO SIMÉON'S WORK

Occupation	Education required	Length of study	Main tasks
Cabinetmaker	DEP in cabinetmaking	1650 hours	• Build wood or modified wood furniture
Mineralogy and geology technician	DCS in mineral exploration technology	3 years	• Ensure the extraction of ore and other geological materials
Art teacher	Bachelor's degree in visual arts	4 years	• Teach art-related techniques • Evaluate art work

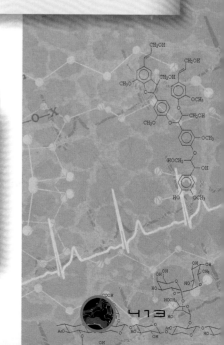

APPENDIXES

PROPERTIES OF COMMON SUBSTANCES

SUBSTANCES IN GASEOUS PHASE AT 20°C

Substance (chemical formula)	Description	Characteristics and applications	Dangers and precautions	Physical properties				Chemical properties
				MP (°C)	BP (°C)	ρ (g/mL at 20°C)	Solubility (g/L water at 20°C)	
Ammonia (NH_3)	• Colourless • Characteristic odour	• Manufacture of cleaning products and fertilizers • Refrigeration	• Highly toxic, irritating and corrosive • Can cause burns	-78	-33	0.00075	531	• Forms white smoke with hydrogen chloride • Extinguishes flame • Neutral litmus paper turns blue[1]
Carbon dioxide (CO_2)	• Colourless • Odourless • Does not exist in liquid form	• Product of combustion • Soft drinks • Dry ice (solid form)	• Causes greenhouse effect	-79[2]	N/A	0.00198	1.6	• Extinguishes flame • Turns limewater cloudy • Neutral litmus paper turns red[1]
Carbon monoxide (CO)	• Colourless • Odourless	• By-product of incomplete combustion	• Deadly if inhaled • Flammable	-207	-192	0.00125	0.26	• Produces bright-blue flame
Chlorine (Cl_2)	• Greenish-yellow • Suffocating odour	• Ingredient of disinfectants • Treatment of drinking water • Bleaching agent	• Highly toxic • Irritates respiratory tract, eyes and skin	-102	-35	0.00294	7.3	• Relights an incandescent ember
Helium (He)	• Colourless • Odourless	• Inflating balloons • Cryogenics • Welding • Refrigeration	• Generally non-toxic, but can cause asphyxia if inhaled in a large quantity	-272	-269	0.00018	0.0017	• Inert (does not react) • Extinguishes flame
Hydrogen (H_2)	• Colourless • Odourless	• Production of various substances (ammonia, hydrogenated vegetable oil) • Rocket fuel	• Explosive when near a flame • Can cause asphyxia	-259	-253	0.00009	0.002	• Explodes when exposed to flame

Substance	Appearance	Uses	Danger	MP	BP	ρ	Solubility[1]	Reactions/Properties
Hydrogen chloride (HCl)	• Colourless • Pungent odour	• Cleaning of metals • Treatment of rubber and cotton	• Highly toxic and highly corrosive • Can cause burns, coughing	-114	-85	0.00164	420	• Forms white smoke with ammonia • Extinguishes flame • Neutral litmus paper turns red[1]
Hydrogen sulphide (H_2S)	• Colourless • Characteristic rotten egg odour	• Protection of iron	• Toxic • Can damage sense of smell • Flammable	-83	-60	0.00154	4.13	• Turns lead acetate paper black • Explodes when exposed to flame
Methane or natural gas (CH_4)	• Colourless • Odourless	• Combustible	• Flammable	-183	-162	0.00072	0.025	• Explodes when exposed to flame
Nitrogen gas (N_2)	• Colourless • Odourless	• Constituent of air (78%) • Freezing of live cells (cryogenics)	• Generally non-toxic, but can cause asphyxia if inhaled in a large quantity	-210	-196	0.00125	0.02	• Extinguishes flame
Propane (C_3H_8)	• Colourless • Odourless	• Combustible fuel (barbecues)	• Flammable	-188	-42	0.00183	0.119	• Produces blue flame
Oxygen (O_2)	• Colourless • Odourless	• Constituent of air (21%) • Welding • Medicine	• Maintains combustion	-218	-183	0.00143	0.04	• Relights an incandescent ember
Ozone (O_3)	• Light-blue • Slight odour	• Protects Earth's inhabitants from UV rays at high altitude • Pollutant at low altitude	• Highly toxic if inhaled • Explosive	-193	-111	0.00214	0.57	• Relights an incandescent ember

MP: melting point   BP: boiling point   ρ: density   N/A: not applicable

1. This property is expressed when substance is dissolved in water.
2. Data corresponds to sublimation point.

SUBSTANCES IN LIQUID PHASE AT 20°C

Substance (chemical formula)	Description	Characteristics and applications	Dangers and precautions	MP (°C)	BP (°C)	ρ (g/mL)	EC	Solubility in water	Chemical properties
Acetic acid (CH_3COOH)	• Colourless • Characteristic vinegary odour	• Food (forms vinegar when diluted in water) • Antiseptic	• Corrosive • Irritating vapours • Can cause burns	17	118	1.05	Yes	Yes	• Neutral litmus paper turns red
Ethanol or ethyl alcohol (C_2H_6O)	• Colourless • Characteristic odour	• Product of sugar fermentation	• Can cause inebriation, nausea, vomiting • Harmful to eyes • Flammable	-114	78	0.79	No	Yes	• Produces light-blue flame
Ethylene glycol ($HOCH_2CH_2OH$)	• Colourless • Slightly sweet odour	• Antifreeze • Manufacture of vaccines	• Irritating vapours • Can cause vomiting and paralysis	-13	198	1.11	No	Yes	• Inflammable
Glycerin or glycerol ($C_3H_8O_3$)	• Colourless • Odourless • Viscous • Sweet taste	• Bubbly liquid • As humectant used in cosmetics and medications	• Explosive in certain conditions	18	290	1.26	No	Yes	• Explodes when exposed to certain substances
Mercury (Hg)	• Silvery-grey • Shiny	• Thermometers • Barometers • Mirrors • UV lamps	• Highly toxic • Can cause brain damage	-39	357	13.55	Yes	No	• Reacts with nitric acid (HNO_3) • Oxidizes into black solid
Methanol or methyl alcohol (CH_3OH)	• Colourless • Characteristic odour	• Antifreeze • Fuel • Solvent	• Toxic if ingested • Can be deadly • Dries out the skin • Can cause blindness • Flammable	-98	65	0.79	No	Yes	• Produces light-blue flame
Water (H_2O)	• Colourless • Odourless	• Essential to life • Food • Solvent	• None	0	100	1.00	No	N/A	• Cobalt chloride paper turns pink • Neutral litmus paper turns violet

MP: melting point   BP: boiling point   ρ: density   EC: electrical conductivity   N/A: not applicable

SUBSTANCES IN SOLID PHASE AT 20°C

| Substance (chemical formula) | Description | Characteristics and applications | Dangers and precautions | Physical properties | | | | Chemical properties |
				MP (°C)	BP (°C)	ρ (g/mL)	EC	Solubility (g/L water at 20°C)	
Aluminum (Al)	• Grey-white • Odourless • Shiny • Malleable	• Siding • Tin cans • Automobiles	• Toxic in large quantities	660	2467	2.7	Yes (good conductor)	0	• Oxidizes into white solid
Barium chloride (BaCl₂)	• White or colourless crystals • Odourless	• Fireworks • Manufacture of pigments	• Toxic if ingested • Avoid any contact with skin	963	1560	3.90	Yes[1]	360	• Produces yellowish-green flame
Barium Nitrate (Ba(NO₃)₂)	• White crystals • Odourless	• Fireworks • Manufacture of ceramics • Green traffic lights	• Highly toxic if inhaled or ingested	590	N/A[2]	3.24	Yes[1]	87	• Produces yellowish-green flame
Calcium carbonate (CaCO₃)	• White • Odourless	• Constituent of chalk • Constituent of marble	• Produces dust irritating to eyes and respiratory tract	N/A[2]	N/A	2.83	Yes[1]	0.0153	• Releases carbon dioxide when exposed to acid • Neutral litmus paper turns blue[1]
Calcium chloride (CaCl₂)	• White crystals • Odourless	• Food • De-icer for roads • Hardener for concrete	• Irritates eyes	772	1935	2.15	Yes[1]	425	• Produces orangey-red flame
Calcium hydroxide (Ca(OH)₂)	• White • Odourless	• Forms limewater when diluted in water	• Avoid any contact with eyes	N/A[2]	N/A	2.24	Yes[1]	1.59	• Neutral litmus paper turns blue[1]

MP: melting point   BP: boiling point   ρ: density   EC: electrical conductivity   N/A: not applicable

1. This property is expressed when substance is dissolved in water.
2. Not applicable because this substance decomposes before reaching melting or boiling point.

| Substance (chemical formula) | Description | Characteristics and applications | Dangers and precautions | Physical properties | | | | Chemical properties |
				MP (°C)	BP (°C)	ρ (g/mL)	EC	Solubility (g/L water at 20°C)	
Carbon (diamond) (C)	• Colourless crystals • Odourless	• Jewellery • Oil drilling	• N/A	3547	4200	3.52	Yes (but poor conductor)	0	• Oxidizes into carbon dioxide
Carbon (graphite) (C)	• Grey-black • Odourless	• Essential to life • Good fuel source • Pencil lead • Steel	• Produces a greenhouse gas if burned • Irritating dust	3652	4200	2.09	Yes (but poor conductor)	0	• Oxidizes into carbon dioxide
Copper (Cu)	• Red-brown • Odourless • Shiny	• Essential to life in small doses • Electrical wires • Piping for plumbing • Coins	• Produces dust irritating to eyes and stomach	1083	2595	8.94	Yes (excellent conductor)	0	• Oxidizes into greenish or black solid • Produces green flame
Copper oxide (CuO)	• Black powder • Odourless	• Pigments (green) • Fireworks	• Toxic if ingested	1446	N/A[2]	6.32	Yes[1]	0	• Reacts to certain metals • Produces blue-green flame
Copper sulphate (CuSO₄)	• Blue crystals • Odourless	• Fungicides • Bactericides • Pesticides • Food supplement for pigs	• Highly toxic • Avoid any contact with the skin	N/A[2]	N/A	3.60	Yes[1]	220	• Produces blue-green flame
Glucose (C₆H₂₂O₁₁)	• White • Slightly sweet odour • Sometimes sticky texture	• Produced by plants during photosynthesis • Food	• Dust irritating to eyes	146	N/A[2]	1.56	No	1000	• Turns golden colour when heated

Substance	Physical properties	Uses	Health hazards	MP	BP	ρ	EC	Solubility	Chemical reactions
Gold (Au)	• Golden • Odourless • Shiny • Soft	• Jewellery • Money • Electronic circuits	• N/A	1064	2807	19.32	Yes (good conductor)	0	• Does not oxidize • Reacts with ammonia
Iodine (I₂)	• Violet-black crystals • Acrid odour	• Essential to life in small doses • Antiseptic • Halogen lamps • Pharmaceutical products	• Emits toxic vapours	114	184	4.93	No	0.29	• Reacts when exposed to starch
Iron (Fe)	• Grey-white • Odourless • Shiny	• Essential to life • Steel • Construction • Automobiles • Magnetic tapes • Vitamin supplements	• Irritating dust	1535	3000	7.86	Yes (good conductor)	0	• Oxidizes into red-brown solid
Lead (Pb)	• Bluish-grey • Odourless • Very soft • Shiny	• Protects against radiation • Batteries	• Highly toxic if ingested • Causes brain damage	327	1740	11.34	Yes (good conductor)	0	• Oxidizes into black solid
Lithium chloride (LiCl)	• White powder • Odourless	• Fireworks • Refrigeration • Antidepressants	• Can cause long-term kidney problems	605	1360	2.07	Yes[1]	454	• Produces bright-red flame

MP: melting point   BP: boiling point ρ: density   EC: electrical conductivity   N/A: not applicable

1. This property is expressed when substance is dissolved in water.
2. Not applicable because this substance decomposes before reaching melting or boiling point.

Substance (chemical formula)	Description	Characteristics and applications	Dangers and precautions	Physical properties					Chemical properties
				MP (°C)	BP (°C)	ρ (g/mL)	EC	Solubility (g/L water at 20°C)	
Lithium nitrate ($LiNO_3$)	• White powder • Odourless	• Fireworks	• Toxic if ingested • Avoid any contact with skin	255	N/A[2]	2.38	Yes[1]	430	• Produces bright red flame
Magnesium (Mg)	• Grey-white • Odourless • Shiny	• Essential to life in small doses • Computer casings • Pharmaceutical products	• Flammable in small pieces	650	1100	1.74	Yes (good conductor)	0	• Oxidizes into white solid • Produces intensely white flame
Nickel (Ni)	• Grey-white • Odourless • Shiny	• Money • Stainless steel • Television screens	• Can cause lung cancer in high doses • Can irritate skin	1455	2730	8.90	Yes (good conductor)	0	• Oxidizes slightly into green solid
Nickel chloride ($NiCl_2$)	• Green crystals • Odourless	• Ink • Gas masks	• Irritant • Avoid any contact with skin	1001	N/A	3.55	Yes[1]	642	• Neutral litmus paper turns red[1] • Produces green flame
Para-Dichloro-benzene ($C_6H_4Cl_2$)	• White or colourless crystals • Characteristic odour	• Insecticides • Mothballs	• Vapours irritating to skin, throat and eyes	54	174	1.46	No	0.08	• Reacts with aluminum
Potassium chloride (KCl)	• White crystals • Odourless	• Photography • Electrical cells	• Toxic if ingested	774	1411	1.99	Yes[1]	344	• Produces violet flame
Potassium nitrate (KNO_3)	• White crystals • Odourless	• Fertilizer	• Toxic if ingested • Do not dispose of in sewers	334	N/A[2]	2.11	Yes[1]	357	• Produces violet flame
Sodium chloride (table salt) (NaCl)	• Cubic white crystals • Odourless	• Food • De-icer for roads	• Can cause hypertension	801	1413	2.17	Yes[1]	357	• Produces orangey-yellow flame

Substance	Physical properties	Uses	Safety precautions	MP (°C)	BP (°C)	ρ	EC	Solubility	Properties / reactions
Sodium hydroxide (NaOH)	• White crystals • Odourless	• Manufacture of plastic, detergent, soap	• Avoid any contact with skin • Corrosive	318	1390	2.13	Yes[1]	1111	• Neutral litmus paper turns blue[1]
Silver (Ag)	• Silvery-white • Odourless • Shiny • Malleable	• Jewellery • Photography • Electrical components	• Moderately toxic if ingested	961	2212	10.40	Yes (excellent conductor)	0	• Oxidizes into black solid • Produces silvery white flame
Strontium chloride (SrCl$_2$)	• White crystals • Odourless	• Fireworks	• Toxic if ingested • Avoid any contact with skin	875	1250	3.05	Yes[1]	538	• Produces red flame
Strontium nitrate (Sr(NO$_3$)$_2$)	• White crystals • Odourless	• Fireworks • Red traffic lights	• Toxic if ingested • Avoid any contact with skin	570	645	2.99	Yes[1]	700	• Produces red flame
Sulphur (S)	• Yellow • Characteristic odour	• Essential to life in small doses • Fungicides • Matches • Fireworks	• Causes acid rain • Irritates skin, eyes and respiratory tract	115	445	1.96	No	0	• Produces blue flame
Tungsten (W)	• Grey • Odourless • Shiny	• Light bulb filaments • Heating elements	• Can irritate respiratory tract	3410	5900	19.35	Yes (good conductor)	0	• Does not oxidize easily • Reacts with nitric acid

MP: melting point   BP: boiling point   ρ: density   EC: electrical conductivity   N/A: not applicable

1. This property is expressed when substance is dissolved in water.
2. Not applicable because this substance decomposes before reaching melting or boiling point.

THE NUTRITIONAL VALUE OF CERTAIN FOODS

Abbreviations and symbols

IU	International Unit (1 IU = 0.3 µg)	µg	Microgramme (1 µg = 0.001 g)
kJ	Kilojoule	N/A	Data not available
	(1 calorie = 4.184 kJ)	tr.	Trace (a very small quantity)

Useful metric unit equivalents

250 mL	1 cup (8 ounces)
125 mL	1/2 cup (4 ounces)
15 mL	1 tablespoon

BREAD, CEREAL, PASTA, RICE AND DERIVATIVES

Foods	Quantity[1]	Energy (kJ)	Proteins (g)	Carbohydrates (g)	Lipids (g)	Calcium (mg)	Iron (mg)	Zinc (mg)	Sodium (mg)	Potassium	Vitamin A (IU)	Vitamin C (mg)	Vitamin B6 (mg)	Folate or vitamin B9 (µg)	Thiamine or vitamin B1 (mg)	Riboflavin or vitamin B2 (mg)
Bagel	1/2	512	4.5	24	0.5	8	1.6	0.4	237	45	0	0	0.02	10	0.24	0.14
Bran cereal	30 g (107 mL)	311 (30 g)	3.4	22	0.9	26	4	1.8	270	314	0	0	0.18	29	0.6	0.06
Bran muffin	1	578	3	23	5	16	1.3	0.6	234	74	51	0	0.09	8	0.1	0.12
Butter croissant	1	970	5	26	12	21	1.2	0.4	424	67	307	tr.	0.03	16	0.22	0.14
Chocolate chip cookie	1	201	1	7	2	2	0.3	0.1	32	14	tr.	0	0.01	1	0.02	0.03
Corn flakes	30 g (288 mL)	505	2.4	28	tr.	1.2	4.2	0.1	306	35	0	0	0.19	19	0.62	0.85
Couscous, cooked	125 mL	342	3	17	tr.	6	0.3	0.2	4	42	0	0	0.04	11	0.05	0.02
Crusty bread, small	1	699	6	30	2	54	1.9	0.5	310	62	0	0	0.03	9	0.27	0.19
Granola bar	1	493	3	16	5	15	0.7	0.5	74	84	38	tr.	0.02	6	0.07	0.03
Granola bar with raisins	30 g (64 mL)	512	2.5	21	4	14	1	N/A	48	99	0	0	N/A	N/A	0.20	0.03
Hamburger or hot dog bun	1	514	4	22	2	60	1.4	0.3	241	61	0	0	0.02	12	0.21	0.13
Long grain white rice, cooked	125 mL	589	3	30	0.5	11	0.2	0.6	1	38	0	0	0.1	3	0.02	0.02
Oatmeal cookie	1	281	1	10	3	16	0.4	0.1	90	27	107	tr.	0.01	2	0.04	0.03
Pita bread, white	1	691	5	33	1	52	1.6	0.5	322	72	0	0	0.02	14	0.36	0.2

	Serving															
Plain donut	1	829	2	23	11	21	0.9	0.3	257	60	27	tr.	0.03	4	0.1	0.11
Plain waffle, frozen	1	410	2	15	3	86	1.7	0.2	292	48	500	0	0.37	19	0.18	0.2
Raisin bread	1 slice	298	2	14	1	17	0.8	0.2	101	59	1	tr.	0.02	9	0.09	0.1
Regular cream of wheat	175 mL	224	2	11	tr.	2	1.9	0.1	1	17	0	0	0.01	N/A	0.01	0.01
Rice cereal	250 mL (30 g)	460	2	24	tr.	4	3.8	0.5	297	34	0	0	0.17	17	0.57	0.01
Spaghetti, cooked	125 mL	436	3.5	21	0.5	5	1.1	0.4	0.7	23	N/A	0	0.03	5	0.15	0.7
White bread	1 slice	279	2	12	1	27	0.8	0.2	134	30	0	0	0.02	8	0.12	0.09
Whole wheat bread	1 slice	292	3	13	1	20	0.9	0.5	149	71	0	0	0.05	14	0.1	0.06
VEGETABLE AND VEGETABLE-BASED PRODUCTS																
Beans (green, yellow), boiled	125 mL	97	1	5	tr.	30	0.8	0.2	2	197	440	6	0.04	22	0.05	0.06
Broccoli, boiled	3 florets (125 mL)	130	3	6	tr.	51	0.9	0.4	29	324	1541	83	0.16	56	0.06	0.13
Carrots, boiled	125 mL	155	1	9	tr.	26	0.5	0.2	54	187	20237	2	0.2	11	0.03	0.05
Celery, raw	1 stick (125 mL)	27	tr.	1	tr.	16	0.2	0.1	35	115	54	3	0.03	11	0.02	0.02
Cucumbers, peeled, sliced	125 mL	29	0.5	1.5	tr.	7	0.2	0.1	1	79	118	3	0.03	7	0.02	0.01
Lettuce, chopped	250 mL	45	1	2	tr.	40	0.8	0.2	5	156	1124	11	0.03	29	0.03	0.05
Mushrooms, raw	6 medium (125 mL)	113	2	5	tr.	5	1.3	0.8	4	400	0	4	0.1	23	0.11	0.48
Potatoes, baked, skin and flesh	1 (200 g)	921	5	51	tr.	20	2.7	0.6	16	844	0	26	0.7	22	0.22	0.07
Potato, boiled	1 (135 g)	489	2	27	tr.	11	0.4	0.4	7	446	0	10	0.37	12	0.13	0.03
Potato, fried	10 french fries (50 g)	550	2	20	5	5	0.7	0.3	108	306	0	5	0.12	14	0.09	0.01
Vegetable juice, canned	125 mL	102	1	6	tr.	14	0.6	0.3	467	247	1496	36	0.18	27	0.06	0.03

1. The quantities of food indicated for each food group are based on servings listed in the *Canada Food Guide* (2007 version).

Abbreviations and symbols

IU	International Unit (1 IU = 0.3 µg)	µg	Microgram (1 µg = 0.001 g)
kJ	Kilojoule	N/A	Data not available
	(1 calorie = 4.184 kJ)	tr.	Trace (a very small quantity)

Useful metric unit equivalents

1 cup (8 ounces)	250 mL
1/2 cup (4 ounces)	125 mL
1 tablespoon	15 mL

Foods	Quantity¹	Energy (kJ)	Proteins (g)	Carbohydrates (g)	Lipids (g)	Calcium (mg)	Iron (mg)	Zinc (mg)	Sodium (mg)	Potassium	Vitamin A (IU)	Vitamin C (mg)	Vitamin B6 (mg)	Folate ou vitamine B9 (µg)	Thiamine or vitamin B1 (mg)	Riboflavin or vitamin B2 (mg)
Tomato, raw	1	108	1	6	tr.	6	0.6	0.1	11	273	766	23	0.1	18	0.07	0.06
Tomato juice, canned	125 mL	92	1	5.5	tr.	11.5	0.8	0.2	466	284	717	11	0.15	26	0.06	0.04
FRUITS AND FRUIT-BASED PRODUCTS																
Apple juice, with vitamin C	125 mL	258	tr.	16	tr.	9	0.5	0.05	4	156	1.5	54	0.04	tr.	0.03	0.02
Apple with skin, raw	1 medium	341	tr.	21	tr.	10	0.2	0.1	0	159	73	8	0.07	4	0.02	0.02
Banana, raw	1	441	1	27	1	7	0.4	0.2	1	454	93	10	0.66	22	0.05	0.11
Orange juice, refrigerated	125 mL	242	1	13	0.5	13	0.2	0.05	1.5	250	103	44	0.07	24	0.15	0.03
Orange, raw	1	258	1	15	tr.	52	0.1	0.1	0	237	269	70	0.08	40	0.11	0.05
Peach, raw	1	157	1	10	tr.	4	0.1	0.1	0	171	465	6	0.02	3	0.01	0.04
Pear with skin, raw	1	417	1	26	1	19	0.4	0.2	0	211	34	7	0.03	12	0.03	0.07
Pink or red grapefruit	1/2	154	1	9	tr.	14	0.1	0.1	0	159	319	47	0.05	15	0.04	0.02
Sliced pineapple, raw	1 slice (90 g)	185	tr.	11	tr.	6	0.3	0.1	1	102	21	14	0.08	10	0.08	0.03
Strawberries, raw	5 (60 g)	75	tr.	4	tr.	8	0.2	0.1	1	100	16	34	0.04	11	0.01	0.04

Food	Serving															
Watermelon, raw	1/2 slice (23 g)	308	1	16	1	18	0.4	0.2	5	267	22	0.33	22	5	0.18	0.05
MILK PRODUCTS																
Butter						(See fats)										
Melted thin-sliced cheddar cheese	4 slices (50 g)	571	8	3	10	239	0.3	1.2	664	116	380	0.06	0	3	0.01	0.18
Partially skimmed milk, 2%	250 mL	536	9	12	5	314	0.1	1	129	398	529	0.11	2	13	0.1	0.43
Whole milk, 3.25%	250 mL	663	8	12	9	308	0.1	1	126	391	325	0.11	2	13	0.1	0.42
Yogurt, fruit on the bottom, less than 1% fat	175 g	453	8	19	tr.	281	0.1	1.4	123	345	79	0.07	2	20	0.06	0.31
EGGS																
Fried egg, with salt	2	766	12	2	14	50	1.4	1	324	122	788	0.14	0	34	0.06	0.48
Hard boiled egg (or raw)	2	648	12	2	10	50	1.2	1	134	126	560	0.12	0	44	0.06	0.54
FISH, SHELL FISH AND SEAFOOD																
Atlantic salmon, roasted or grilled	1/2 fillet (75 g)	571	19	0	6	11	0.8	0.6	42	471	33	0.71	0	22	0.20	0.36
Bacon, pork	5 slices*	763	10	tr.	16	4	0.5	1	505	154	0	0.09	0	2	0.22	0.09
Beef strip loin, lean, grilled	1 serving (75 g)	672	23	0	7	6	1.8	4.1	46	295	0	0.34	0	6	0.07	0.15
Chicken breast, roasted	1/2 breast (75 g)	498	24	0	2	4	0.5	0.8	62	302	16	5.3	0	3	0.05	0.08
Cretons	30 mL*	238	3	1	4	19	0.2	0.4	96	73	22	0.07	tr.	2	0.14	0.15
Ground beef, medium, grilled	1 patty (75 g)	824	18	0	14	8	1.5	3.9	56	218	0	0.19	0	6	0.04	0.15
Lobster, boiled or steamed	125 mL (75 g)	314	16	1	tr.	47	0.3	2.2	291	270	67	0.06	0	7	0.01	0.05

1. With the exception of those with asterisks, the quantities of food indicated for each food group are based on servings listed in the *Canada Food Guide* (2007 version).

Abbreviations and symbols

IU	International Unit (1 IU = 0.3 µg)	µg	Microgram (1 µg = 0.001 g)
kJ	Kilojoule	N/A	Data not available
	(1 calorie = 4.184 kJ)	tr.	Trace (a very small quantity)

Useful metric unit equivalents

250 mL	1 cup (8 ounces)
125 mL	1/2 cup (4 ounces)
15 mL	1 tablespoon

Foods	Quantity[1]	Energy (kJ)	Proteins (g)	Carbohydrates (g)	Lipids (g)	Calcium (mg)	Iron (mg)	Zinc (mg)	Sodium (mg)	Potassium	Vitamin A (IU)	Vitamin C (mg)	Vitamin B6 (mg)	Folate or vitamin B9 (µg)	Thiamine or vitamin B1 (mg)	Riboflavin or vitamin B2 (mg)
MEAT, POULTRY AND CHARCUTERIE																
Pork loin fillet, lean, roasted	2 slices (75 g)	509	23	0	3	4	1.1	2	42	327	5	tr.	0.31	4	0.71	0.29
Scallops, boiled or steamed	3 large (75 g)	301	11	2	2	17	0.2	0.6	280	189	101	2	0.09	5	0.01	0.04
Shrimp, boiled or steamed	14 large (75 g)	319	17	0	1	29	2.4	1.3	172	140	168	1	0.08	7	0.03	0.03
Smoked chicken sausages	2 (75 g)	774	8	8	14	72	1.6	0.8	1028	64	98	0	0.24	4	0.04	0.08
Sole (whole fish), roasted or grilled	1 fillet (75 g)	373	19	0	1	14	0.2	0.4	80	262	29	0	0.18	7	0.06	0.08
Trout, roasted or grilled	1 fillet (75 g)	593	20	0	6	41	1.4	0.6	50	344	47	tr.	0.17	7	0.31	0.31
Veal cutlet, sautéed	1 (75 g)	478	23	0	2	4	1.5	2.3	33	269	N/A	N/A	0.39	13	0.06	0.22
Veal liver, sautéed	125 mL (75 g)	790	23	3	9	9	4.1	6.1	101	338	14475	17	0.7	246	0.19	2.59
LEGUMES, NUTS AND GRAINS																
Cashews, dry roasted, added salt	60 mL*	869	5	12	17	16	2.1	2	231	204	0	0	0.09	25	0.07	0.07
Peanut butter, natural	30 mL*	775	9	6	17	30	0.9	1.6	2	234	0	0	N/A	81	0.04	N/A

Food	Serving															
Peanuts, roasted in oil, added salt	60 mL	924	10	7	19	33	0.7	2.5	164	258	0	0	0.09	47	0.09	0.04
Tofu, regular	150 g	292	7	2	4	97	4.9	0.7	6	111	78	tr.	0.04	13	0.07	0.05
MIXED DISHES																
Cheese nachos	6 to 8*	1447	9	36	19	272	1.3	1.8	816	172	559	1	0.2	10	0.19	0.37
Chicken noodle soup	284 mL*	880	15	20	7	29	1.7	1.2	1020	130	1467	0	0.06	6	0.09	0.2
Pepperoni pizza (medium)	1/8* (75 g)	758	10	20	7	65	0.9	0.5	267	153	282	2	0.06	53	0.13	0.23
FATS, OILS AND DRESSINGS																
Butter	5 mL*	150	tr.	tr.	4	1	tr.	tr.	41	1	153	0	tr.	tr.	tr.	tr.
Italian dressing	15 mL*	389	tr.	1	10	1	tr.	tr.	235	3	12	0	tr.	1	tr.	tr.
Margarine (soft), canola oil and linseed oil	5 mL*	71	tr.	tr.	2	1	N/A	47	1	162	0	tr.	tr.	tr.	tr.	tr.
Mayonnaise	15 mL*	428	tr.	tr.	11	1	tr.	tr.	73	2	10	tr.	tr.	1	tr.	tr.
Olive oil	15 mL*	506	0	0	14	tr.	0.1	tr.	tr.	0	0	0	0	0	0	0
Peanut oil	15 mL*	506	0	0	14	tr.	tr.	tr.	tr.	tr.	0	0	0	0	0	0
SWEETS, CRACKERS, CHIPS AND OTHER TREATS																
Chocolate ice cream	125 mL*	630	3	20	8	76	0.6	0.4	53	174	290	N/A	0.04	11	0.03	0.14
Jam	15 mL*	205	tr.	13	tr.	4	0.1	tr.	8	16	2	N/A	tr.	7	0	tr.
Maple syrup	15 mL*	219	0	13	tr.	13	0.2	0.8	2	41	0	N/A	tr.	0	tr.	tr.
Plain chips	10*	451	1	10	7	4	0.3	0.3	107	266	0	12	0.06	9	0.03	0.01
Plain corn chips	10*	406	1	10	6	23	0.2	0.2	113	26	17	0	0.04	4	tr.	0.03
Plain popcorn	250 mL*	135	1	7	tr.	1	0.2	0.3	tr.	25	17	0	0.02	2	0.02	0.02
Sugar (refined white sugar)	15 mL*	205	0	13	0	tr.	tr.	tr.	tr.	tr.	0	N/A	0	0	0	tr.

1. With the exception of those with asterisks, the quantities of food indicated for each food group are based on servings listed in the *Canada Food Guide* (2007 version).

Abbreviations and symbols

IU	International Unit (1 IU = 0.3 µg)	µg	Microgram (1 µg = 0.001 g)
kJ	Kilojoule	N/A	Data not available
	(1 calorie = 4.184 kJ)	tr.	Trace (a very small quantity)

Useful metric unit equivalents

250 mL	1 cup (8 ounces)
125 mL	1/2 cup (4 ounces)
15 mL	1 tablespoon

Foods	Quantity[1]	Energy (kJ)	Proteins (g)	Carbohydrates (g)	Lipids (g)	Calcium (mg)	Iron (mg)	Zinc (mg)	Sodium (mg)	Potassium	Vitamin A (IU)	Vitamin C (mg)	Vitamin B6 (mg)	Folate or vitamin B9 (µg)	Thiamine or vitamin B1 (mg)	Riboflavin or vitamin B2 (mg)
Vanilla ice cream	125 mL*	585	2	16	8	89	0.1	0.5	56	139	285	N/A	0.03	3	0.03	0.17
Whole wheat crackers	4 crackers*	297	1	11	3	8	0.5	0.3	105	48	0	0	0.03	4	0.03	0.02
DRINKS																
Coffee (drip, black)	250 mL*	21	tr.	1	0	5	0.1	0.1	5	135	0	0	0	0	0	0
Coffee, (regular instant, dissolved in water, black)	250 mL*	21	tr.	1	0	8	0.1	0.1	8	91	0	0	0	0	0	tr.
Soft drink, cola	250 mL*	447	0	27	0	8	0.1	tr.	10	3	0	0	0	0	0	0
Tea, infused (black)	250 mL*	10	0	1	0	0	0.1	0.1	8	93	0	0	0	13	0	0.04
CONDIMENTS																
Ketchup	15 mL*	66	tr.	4	tr.	3	0.1	tr.	180	73	154	2	0.03	2	0.01	0.01
Prepared mustard	15 mL*	50	1	1	1	13	0.3	0.2	200	21	0	0	0.01	1	0	0
Salt	5 mL*	0	0	0	0	1	tr.	tr.	2373	tr.	0	0	0	0	0	0

1. With the exception of those with asterisks, the quantities of food indicated for each food group are based on servings listed in the *Canada Food Guide* (2007 version).

GLOSSARY

Definitions can also be found on the pages indicated in bold.

A

Absolute dating: method used to determine the age of fossils in years (p. **325**)

Absorption: passage of nutrients from the digestive tract into the blood or lymph (p. **171**)

Alloy: result of mixing a metal with one or more metallic or non-metallic substances (p. **379**)

Alternating current (AC): an electric current in which electrons flow in a back-and-forth motion (p. **400**)

Amplitude (of a wave): maximum distance travelled by a particle in a medium compared to its position at equilibrium (p. **94**)

Antibody: substance secreted by white blood cells to neutralize invaders (p. **189**)

Antigen: substance recognized as foreign by the body and that triggers the body's white blood cells to produce antibodies (p. **189**)

Artery: blood vessel that carries blood from the heart to other parts of the body (p. **183**)

Assembly process: series of operations in which various parts are put together to produce a technical object (p. **407**)

Assisted reproduction: all medical procedures used to help women become pregnant (p. 258)

Asteroid: celestial body of irregular shape, in orbit around the Sun (p. **283**)

Astronomical unit (AU): unit of measurement equal to about 150 million km, the average distance between Earth and the Sun (p. **281**)

Atmospheric pressure: pressure exerted by the atmosphere (p. **79**)

Atom: smallest particle of matter; it cannot be divided by chemical means (pp. **8, 36**)

B

Bacteria: unicellular organisms without nuclei (p. **236**)

Basic lines: lines whose appearance and meaning are determined by international agreements (p. **338**)

Basic mechanical function: role played by a component or a group of components in the function or assembly of a technical object (p. **383**)

Biotechnology: collection of technologies that are applied to living organisms or substances derived from living organisms in order to meet a need or a want (p. **236**)

Blood compatibility: fact that one person can receive blood from another person (p. **181**)

Blood transfusion: injection of blood into a person (p. **180**)

Bone: hard solid organ that forms part of the skeleton (p. **222**)

Brain: parts of the central nervous system located in the cranium (p. **206**)

Brain stem: control centre of internal stimuli as well as of involuntary movement (p. **211**)

C

Capillary: blood vessel with a small diameter and very thin walls in which exchanges between the blood and the cells of organs occur (p. **183**)

Celestial body: any natural objects in the Universe; synonym of celestial object (p. **283**)

Cell: basic unit of life (p. **126**)

Cell culture: laboratory technique that involves growing or culturing cells outside of their natural environment (p. **240**)

Cell division: process that is essential to the production of new cells for the purpose of growth, tissue repair and sexual reproduction (p. **131**)

Cellular respiration: process essential to life by which a cell produces energy through nutrient combustion, such as glucose (pp. 39, **172**)

Centrifugation: process that accelerates and amplifies the separation of components of a mixture using a centrifuge, a high-speed rotating machine (pp. 20, 177)

Cerebellum: centre of balance and movement coordination (p. **210**)

Cerebrum: control centre of voluntary movement, sensory interpretation and intelligence. It is also the centre of emotion (p. **208**)

Characteristic property: property that helps us identify a pure substance or the group to which the pure substance belongs (p. **23**)

Chemical change: change that transforms the nature and characteristic properties of matter (p. **50**)

Chemical energy: energy stored in the bonds of a molecule (p. **38**)

Chemical transformation (in digestive tract): process that breaks down the complex molecules of food into simpler molecules. These changes occur with the help of secretions from the digestive glands (p. **170**)

Circuit diagram: simplified drawing using symbols that shows how to connect the various parts (bulb, wire, battery, switch, etc.) of an electric circuit (p. **359**)

Cloning: process of producing a genetically identical copy of a living organism (p. **247**)

Colloid: homogeneous mixture in which at least two different substances can be distinguished under a magnifying instrument (p. **11**)

Comet: celestial body covered in ice that releases gas and ice debris as it passes the sun. The debris forms a tail that is lit up by the Sun (p. **283**)

Complex mechanical function: role played by a set of components in transferring motion inside a technical object (p. **389**)

Component: a part or fluid that has a mechanical function in a technical object (p. **383**)

Compound: pure substance that contains at least two types of atoms that have chemically combined; it can be separated into its constituent elements, using chemical separation techniques (p. **21**)

Compressible fluid: fluid whose volume can change. Gases are compressible fluids (p. **68**)

Concentration (of a solution): corresponds to the quantity of dissolved solute in a given quantity of solution (p. **13**)

Conditions essential for the emergence of life on Earth: conditions that made it possible for the synthesis of the first organic molecules and their development into living cells (p. **302**)

Conduction: function of any electrical component that can transmit an electric current from one part to another in an electrical circuit (p. **402**)

Control: function carried out by any electrical component able to open and close a circuit (p. **403**)

Cross section: section obtained by cutting transversely through an object, exposing its hidden details to view (p. **354**)

Culture medium: environment that contains all the necessary elements to promote cell growth in a culture (p. **242**)

Culturing cells: technique that results in an increase in the number of cells in a cell culture (p. **240**)

D

Decibel scale: relative scale that represents the perception of the intensity of sound by the human ear (p. **102**)

Decomposition: transformation of complex molecules into simpler molecules or into atoms (p. **55**)

Deformation: change that alters the shape of a material (p. **49**)

Density: mass of a substance per unit volume (p. **74**)

Design plan: simplified drawing that represents one or more aspects of the function of an object (p. **358**)

Detail drawing: engineering drawing that specifies all the details necessary to make a particular part of an object (p. **350**)

Diagram: simplified representation of an object, a part of an object or a system (p. **355**)

Diapedesis: process by which white blood cells exit the capillaries (p.**187**)

Diastole: phase during which blood fills the heart (p.**185**)

Diffuse reflection: reflection whereby parallel light rays hit an uneven surface and are reflected in all directions (p. **108**)

Diffusion: transport of molecules of a solute from a region of higher concentration to one of lower concentration (p. **175**)

Digestion: transformation of food into nutrients that can be used by the body (p. **168**)

Dilution: laboratory technique that involves decreasing the concentration of a solution by adding solvent (p. **15**)

Dimensioning: process of indicating the real dimensions of an object as well as the position of various elements of the object (p. **353**)

Direct current (DC): electric current in which electrons always flow in the same direction (p. **400**)

Dissolution: creation of a solution by a solute in a solvent (p. **46**)

Disturbance: localized and temporary change in the properties of a particular environment or medium (p. **92**)

DNA: molecule that is haped like a double helix and located inside the cell nucleus (pp. **128**, **236**)

Donor (blood): person who gives blood for the purpose of a transfusion (p. **180**)

Dwarf planet: celestial body of spherical shape that orbits a star and does not shine on its own; it shares its orbit with celestial bodies other than its own natural satellites (p. **283**)

E

Echolocation: process used by some animals to orient themselves, which involves the emitting of high-frequency sounds that are reflected back thus helping the animal to estimate the position of surrounding objects (p. **105**)

Ejaculation: expulsion of semen by the penis (p. **150**)

Electric current: orderly flow of negative charges carried by electrons (p. **399**)

Electrical function: role of a component in the control or transformation of electric current (p. **400**)

Electromagnetic spectrum: all electromagnetic waves organized according to their wavelength and their frequency (p. **97**)

Electromagnetic wave: wave that can travel in both a vacuum and a medium (p. **96**)

Element: pure substance that contains only one type of atom; it is impossible to separate an element into other substances, using chemical separation techniques (p. **21**)

Ellipses: closed curves that are oval-shaped (p. **340**)

Energy: capacity to do work or to produce change (p. **34**)

Energy transfer: movement of energy from one place to another (p. **41**)

Enzyme: molecule secreted by cells that accelerates chemical reactions in the organism (p. **236**)

Erection: increase in volume and rigidity of the penis as a result of sexual arousal (p. **150**)

Ethical standard: norm created to ensure that certain moral principles are being respected (p. **263**)

Evolution: very slow process that brings about changes in living organisms (p. **305**)

Excretion: elimination of a substance from inside a body (p. **190**)

Exploded view drawing: engineering drawing that shows the different parts, or features, of the object separately (p. **349**)

Extinction of a species: disappearance of all individuals belonging to that species. It is caused by the inability of the individuals to adapt to change(s) in their environment (p. **310**)

Extracellular fluid: clear liquid that surrounds our cells and contains water and other substances from blood plasma; also containing white blood cells (p. **187**)

F

Ferrous alloy: alloy whose main constituent is iron (p. **379**)

Fertilization: fusion of an ovum and a spermatozoan, resulting in one complete cell, the zygote, which contains the genetic material of both the father and the mother (p. **140**)

Finishing: series of operations required to complete the production of a technical object (p. **407**)

Fluid: substance that has the capacity to flow and assume the form of the container into which it has been poured (p. **66**)

Focal point: point where the refracted light rays actually meet (converging lens) or from where the refracted light rays appear to emanate (diverging lens) if the light rays travelling through the lens run parallel to the principal axis (p. **112**)

Focal point of a converging lens: real point where the refracted rays actually meet when the incident rays run parallel (p.**112**)

Focal point of a diverging lens: virtual point from which the refracted light rays appear to emanate when the incident rays run parallel (p. **113**)

Food: any substance that is ingested and sustains life (p. **160**)

Fossil: any remains or trace of an organism that has been preserved for a very long period of time in the Earth's crust (pp. **302**, **319**)

Frequency: number of cycles per unit of time (p. **95**)

G

Galaxy: massive cluster of stars and matter that orbits its (own) centre (p. **290**)

Gene: segment of DNA that contains the genetic information required to carry out a particular job (pp. **129**, 305)

General drawing: engineering drawing that shows the overall design of an object (p. **348**)

Genetic diversity: all possible genetic variations of a species (p. **130**)

Genetic transformation: modification of a species' genome either by removing or modifying one or more of its genes or by introducing genes from another species (p. **245**)

Genome: complete set of genetic information of an individual or species (p. **128**)

Geological time scale: tool that represents the main divisions in the history of Earth, based on the major events that have occurred in the history of life (p. **310**)

Geometric lines: figures that are composed according to the rules of geometry, the art of drafting lines and curves with a ruler and a compass (p. **340**)

GMO (genetically modified organism): living organism that has had its DNA modified through genetic transformation to provide it with traits it would not otherwise possess (p. **245**)

Guide: component that has the basic mechanical function of guiding (p. **384**)

Guiding: basic mechanical function provided by any component that controls the movement of one or several moving parts (p. **383**)

H

Heat: transfer of thermal energy from one place to another. Heat will always travel from the hotter place toward the colder place (p. **42**)

Heterogeneous mixture: mixture made up of at least two substances that can be distinguished with the naked eye (p. **10**)

Homogeneous mixture: mixture made up of at least two substances that cannot be distinguished with the naked eye (p. **11**)

Hormones: chemical messengers, which are transported by the blood and control the activity of one or more organs (p. **141**)

I

Immunity: capacity to resist a disease to which we have been exposed by being able to fight off the infectious agent that causes the disease (p. **253**)

Incompressible fluid: fluid whose volume cannot be varied. Liquids are incompressible fluids (p. **69**)

Indicator: substance that indicates the presence, absence or concentration of another substance or group of substances by the degree of reaction that occurs in its presence (p. **24**)

Insulation: function carried out by any electrical component able to block an electric current (p. **402**)

Isometric projection: perspective drawing of an object where the principal edges are arranged on three isometric axes (p. **347**)

J

Joint: junction between two or more bones (p. **223**)

L

Light: electromagnetic wave that is visible to the human eye (p. **106**)

Light year (ly): unit of measurement equal to the distance light travels in one year, which is about 9 500 billion kilometres (p. **282**)

Link: structure that helps connect two or more parts of a technical object (p. **385**)

Linking: basic mechanical function provided by any component that links an object's parts (p. **385**)

Linking component: component that has the basic mechanical function of linking (p. **385**)

Longitudinal wave: wave that propagates parallel to the motion of its medium (p. **93**)

Lymph: fluid derived from extracellular fluid as it circulates inside lymphatic vessels to evacuate cell waste (p. **187**)

M

Machining: action of forming parts into their desired shape with the necessary tools (p. **406**)

Marking: tracing lines or marking reference points on material (p. **406**)

Matter: anything that has volume and mass (p. **6**)

Measuring: identifying the size or the position of reference points on material (p. **406**)

Mechanical constraint: effect produced within a material by the external forces applied upon it (p. **369**)

Mechanical energy: energy that results from the speed of an object, its mass and its relationship to its surroundings (p. **39**)

Mechanical property: property that determines how a material will react when it is subjected to one or more mechanical constraints (p. **371**)

Mechanical transformation (during digestion): process of physically breaking down food into smaller substances in preparation for subsequent chemical transformation (p. **169**)

Mechanical wave: wave that requires a medium in order to propagate (p. **96**)

Meiosis: process of cell division in which male and female gametes are produced in order for sexual reproduction to take place (p. **135**)

Menstrual cycle: process encompasses all of the periodic changes in the uterine endometrium (p. **147**)

Metal: material extracted from an ore. Metals are usually shiny and are good conductors of electricity and heat (p. **378**)

Milky Way: galaxy we inhabit (p. **290**)

Mitosis: process of cell division in which cells multiply in order to ensure growth and tissue repair (p. **133**)

Mixture: consists of at least two different substances, that is, it contains at least two types of particles (p. **9**)

Modified wood: treated wood or materials made with wood that is mixed with other substances (p. **376**)

Molecule: group of two or more atoms held together by chemical bonds (pp. **8**, **36**)

Motion transformation system: system that transforms the nature of a motion while it is relayed form one part to another (p. **396**)

Motion transmission system: system that relays motion from one part to another without changing the nature of the motion (p. **391**)

Motor nerves: nerves that transmit impulses from the central nervous system to the muscles in order to produce voluntary and involuntary movements (p. **206**)

Multiview projection (or orthographic projection): two-dimensional representation of the different views of an object (p. **346**)

Muscle: organ with the ability to contract or to move (p. **226**)

N

Natural selection: process that occurs naturally within a species. It results in the reproduction of organisms with traits that allow them to survive better in their environment (p. **306**)

Nerve: structure that helps transmit information between the central nervous system and various regions of the body (p. **205**)

Nerve impulse: electrical signal transmitted by a neuron (p. **203**)

Nervous system: system that receives, processes, stores and transmits information that comes from various parts of the body and the external world (p. **203**)

Neuron: specialized nerve cell in the nervous system that receives and transmits messages (p. **203**)

Neurotransmitters: chemical substances secreted by axon terminals across the synapse between two neurons (p. **204**)

Non-ferrous alloy: alloy whose main constituent is a metal other than iron (p. **379**)

Nutrient: substance found in food that is used by the body to meet important needs (p. **161**)

Nutrients: foods that can be absorbed by the body (pp. **160, 170**)

O

Oblique projection: perspective drawing in which one of the object's sides is parallel to a sheet of paper, but its depth is represented by parallel straight lines drawn at an oblique angle (p. **348**)

Oogenesis: process of ovum production by meiosis (p. **144**)

Organ: structure composed of two or more tissue types performing one or more specific functions (p. **138**).

Orthogonal projection: projection in which all of the visual rays from the object are perpendicular to the surface of the sheet of paper (p. **345**)

Ovarian cycle: process whereby a single ovarian follicle matures (in order to release an ovum) and changes into a corpus luteum (in order to encourage the implantation of the ovum in the uterus) (p. **145**)

Oxidation: chemical reaction involving oxygen or a substance that has similar properties to oxygen (p. **57**)

P

Particle model: scientific model based on the idea that matter is made up of small particles (pp. **6, 44, 66**)

Pasteurization: process whereby food is heated for a time in order to destroy harmful microorganisms (p. **252**)

Pathogens: elements that are capable of producing disease (p. **19**)

Peripheral nervous system: system whose function is to connect different parts of the body to the central nervous system (p. **205**)

Perspective drawing: drawing that represents the three dimensions of an object in the same view (p. **347**)

Phagocytosis: mechanism whereby white blood cells ingest and destroy certain microorganisms (pp. **189, 253**)

Photosynthesis: process by which green plants and some microscopic algae transform energy from the Sun to produce their food (sugar) using carbon dioxide and water (p. **54**)

Physical changes: changes that do not affect the nature or the characteristic properties of matter (p. **43**)

Placenta: organ within the uterus that allows the passage of substances between the mother and foetus during pregnancy. It is eliminated once the mother gives birth (p.**146**)

Planet: celestial body of spherical shape that is not luminous, and revolves around a star. Only a planet's own satellites, and no other celestial bodies, share its orbit (p. **283**)

Plasmid: Ring-shaped DNA segment found in most bacteria and yeasts. Plasmids are very useful in biotechnology because new genes can be easily inserted into them (p. **236**)

Plastic: material made of polymers (p. **381**)

Power supply: function carried out by any electrical component able to produce or supply an electric current in a circuit (p. **402**)

Precipitate: substance formed by an excess of solute in a liquid solution (pp. **17, 52**)

Precipitation: formation of a solid that is less soluble, or not soluble, following the mixing of two solutions (p. **58**)

Pressure: result of a force applied in a perpendicular fashion to a surface (pp. 23, **70**)

Projection: representation of a three-dimensional object in two dimensions (p. **343**)

Protection: function performed by any electrical component that can automatically interrupt the flow of the electrical current in an abnormal situation (p. **404**)

Puberty: series of changes that prepare the human body for the ability to reproduce. This stage generally occurs between the ages of 10 and 14 years old (p. **141**)

Pure substance: substance containing only one type of particle (p. **9**)

R

Radioactive: of an element likely to change into another element by disintegration (p. **325**)

Radiation: energy contained in and transported by electromagnetic waves (p. **37**)

Real image: image produced at the real crossing of light rays (p. **109**)

Recipient (blood): person who receives blood from a transfusion (p. **180**)

Reflection: rebounding of light that occurs when a light ray hits a different medium and "bounces back" to the medium from which it came (p. **106**)

Reflex: rapid and involuntary reaction to a stimulus (p. **212**)

Reflex arc: path taken by a nerve impulse during a reflex (p. **212**)

Refraction: deviation of a light ray as it passes from one transparent medium to another (p. **110**)

Relative dating: method that helps establish the order in which fossils formed, without identifying their absolute age (p. **324**)

S

Satellite: celestial body in orbit around another celestial body that is not a star (p. **283**)

Saturated solution: solution that contains exactly the maximum amount of solute that can be dissolved in it (p. **17**)

Scale: relationship between the measurements of an object on a sheet of paper and the real measurements of the object in an engineering drawing (p. **352**)

Section: representation of a surface located in a cross-sectional view (p. **355**)

Sensory nerves: nerves that transmit information, in the form of nerve impulses from sensory receptors to the central nervous system (p. **206**)

Sensory receptor: structure that picks up stimuli and transforms the stimuli into nerve impulses (p. **205**)

Sketch: freehand drawing that respects, as much as possible, the conventions of drafting (p. **341**)

Small solar system body: any celestial body in orbit around the Sun that is neither a planet, nor a dwarf planet, e.g. asteroids and comets (p. **283**)

Solar system: system consisting of the Sun and all the celestial bodies travelling in its orbit (p. **285**)

Solubility: maximum amount of solute that can be dissolved in a given amount of solvent (p. **17**)

Solute: substance that dissolves in another substance (p. **12**)

Solution: homogeneous mixture in which it is impossible to distinguish its constituent parts, even under a magnifying instrument (p. **12**)

Solvent: substance that can dissolve a solute (p. **12**)

Sound: longitudinal mechanical wave produced by the vibration of an object and transmitted to the object's environment (p. **100**)

Specialized cell: cell that plays a specific role in the human body. When a specialized cell divides, it produces cells that have the same specialized functions as it does (pp. 136, **261**)

Speed change: change that occur in a motion transmission system when the driver does not turn at the same speed as the driven part or parts (p. **394**)

Specular reflection: reflection whereby parallel light rays hit a smooth surface producing parallel reflections, and thus a true mirror image (p. **108**)

Spermatogenesis: process of sperm production by meiosis (p. **149**)

Spinal cord: nervous system organ that carries information from various parts of the body to the brain. It is also the reflex centre (p. **211**)

Star: celestial body with a brilliance that comes from the energy it produces (p. **283**)

State change: transformation from one state (or phase) to another (p. **43**)

Stem cell: cell that does not play any particular role in the human organism. It has the capacity, however, to divide many times and to transform into a variety of specialized cells (p. **262**)

Sterile environment: an environment without any living microorganisms (p. **244**)

Stimulus: anything that can be perceived by a living organism and that can trigger a reaction. Sound, light, heat, electrical shocks, odours and hormones are examples of stimuli (p. **203**)

Stratigraphic layer: stratum of sedimentary rock that formed in the same time period (p. **323**)

Synapse: transition zone between two neurons that allows a nerve impulse to be transmitted (p. **204**)

Synthesis: formation of a complex molecule from atoms or simpler molecules (p. **53**)

System: group of organs and tissues working together to accomplish a common function (p. **139**); in technology, a set of components that share the same function (p. **389**).

Systole: phase during which the heart pushes the blood out (p. **185**)

T

Technical diagram: simplified diagram that contains information about the construction solutions for constructing an object or a system (p. **359**)

Technical drawings: drawings used in technology to communicate information about an object or a system (p. **337**)

Technical object: an object conceived of and manufactured by humans to meet one or morel needs or wants (p. **368**)

Technology: set of techniques used by humans to design, build and maintain objects and systems that we need or want (p. **337**)

Temperature: measure of the degree of agitation of atoms and molecules in a body or substance (p. **36**)

Thermal energy: energy resulting from the random motion of the particles that make up a substance (p. **36**)

Thermoplastic: plastic that, when heated, softens enough to be moulded or remoulded; when cooled, it hardens, retaining its new shape (p. **382**)

Tissue: group of similar cells that have a common function (p. **136**)

Tolerance: maximum variation of a specified dimension between a measurement on a plan and the real-life measurement (p. **353**)

Transformation of energy: changing of energy from one form to another (p. **41**)

Transformation of energy function: role carried out by any electrical component able to transform electrical energy into another type of energy (p. **402**)

Transverse wave: wave that propagates perpendicular to the motion of its medium (p. **93**)

U

Universal law of gravitation: law developed by Isaac Newton in the 17th century, which states that the gravitational attraction between two bodies increases with mass and decreases with distance (p. **276**)

V

Vaccine: prepared substance that is able to immunize an organism against one or several diseases (p. **254**)

Vein: blood vessel that carries blood back to the heart (p. **183**)

Villi *sing* **Villus:** folds in the small intestine that increase the surface area available for the absorption of nutrients (p. **171**)

Virtual image: image produced by the prolongation of reflected or refracted rays (p.**109**)

Virulence: capacity of an infectious agent to regain strength allowing it to multiply in the body and cause a disease (p. **257**)

Virus: entity that is unable to reproduce alone. Viruses enter living cells and use their structures to reproduce (p. **236**)

W

Wave: disturbance that travels through a medium. A wave transports energy; it does not transport matter (p. **92**)

Wavelength: length of a wave's complete cycle (p. **95**)

Wood: material that comes from cutting and processing of trees (p. **373**)

Y

Yeast: unicellular organism from the fungi family. Yeasts have a nucleus that contains their DNA (p. **236**)

Z

Zygote: diploid cell resulting from the fertilization between an ovum and a spermatozoan (p. **136**)

INDEX

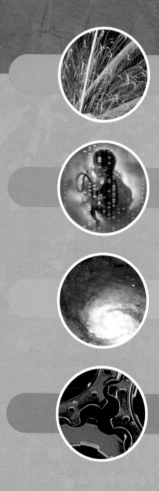

PHOTOGRAPHY CREDITS/SOURCES

ASE
p. 278 (9.15)
p. 279 (9.17): Medialab

ASSAAD EL-HAKIM
p. 138

CANADA SCIENCE AND TECHNOLOGY MUSEUM
p. 314

CCQ
p. 377 (middle, bottom): M. Élie

CENTRE D'INSÉMINATION ARTIFICIELLE DU QUÉBEC, SAINT-HYACINTHE
p. 248

CORBIS
p. 4: C. Savage
p. 25 (top): G. D. Orti
p. 29: C. Savage
p. 31 (1.38): Clouds Hill Imaging Ltd.
p. 34
p. 41 (2.13): T. Stewart
p. 42 (2.15): Japack Company
p. 42 (2.17): C. A. Purcell
p. 50 (2.36): Reuters
p. 52 (2.40): P. A. Souders
p. 53
p. 59 (middle, top): P. Giardino
p. 64 (bottom): B. Stormont
p. 84: J. L. Rotman
p. 87: B. Stormont
p. 88: R. Gomez
p. 90 (bottom): R. T. Nowitz
p. 97: Creasource
p. 98 (middle): C. O'Rear
p. 101 (4.17): Navy Visual News Service / Handout / N. Laird
p. 104: J. Craigmyle
p. 108 (4.28): Visuals Unlimited
p. 119 (bottom, right): R. T. Nowitz

p. 119 (top, left): K. Su
p. 129: B. Smith
p. 130: M. Pole
p. 156 (left): H. King
p. 163 (6.3) (lipids) (left): N. Benn
p. 163 (6.3) (vitamins) (left): J. Craigmyle
p. 164 (6.5): R. Faris
p. 166: M. Wong
p. 176: J. Luis Pelaez, Inc.
p. 186: M. Gamba
p. 188 (6.42): L. V. Bergman
p. 190 (6.46): J.-Y. Ruszniewski / TempSport
p. 209 (7.11) (middle, top): S. Westmorland
p. 209 (7.11) (middle): P. M. Fisher
p. 232 (7.56): Z. Smith
p. 238 (8.4) (top): J. Craigmyle
p. 238 (8.3): D. Fitzmaurice
p. 239 (8.6): K. Nomachi
p. 245 (8.15) (right): N. Fobes
p. 248 (8.17): C. McPherson
p. 250 (8.18) (middle): Envision
p. 250 (8.18) (right)
p. 250 (8.18) (left): LWA-JDC
p. 261: J. Luis Pelaez, Inc.
p. 275 (9.3): P. A. Souders
p. 276 (9.6): Agliolo / Sanford
p. 278-279: O. Rogge
p. 279 (9.12)
p. 280 (9.19): R. Messmeyer
p. 283 (9.22) (satellite): NASA
p. 308 (10.10) (protists): Clouds Hill Imaging Ltd.
p. 308 (10.10) (bacteria): Visuals Unlimited
p. 311 (10.14)
p. 319 (10.24): B. Gonzalez Riga / epa
p. 319 (10.25): J. L. Amos
p. 321 (10.28): K. Schafer
p. 321 (10.29): L. Psihoyos

p. 322 (10.30): Naturfoto Honal
p. 322 (10.31): F. Latreille
p. 322 (10.32): L. Kennedy
p. 323 (10.33): F. Muntada
p. 324 (10.34): C. Aurness
p. 328 (1): F. Muntada
p. 328 (2): T. Bean
p. 328 (3): T. Bean
p. 330 (10.37): D. Degnan
p. 334 (bottom): G. Brown
p. 366 (bottom): T. Stewart
p. 369 (12.2): D. Keaton
p. 369 (12.3): M. Pole
p. 370 (12.5) (shearing): D. Raymer
p. 371 (12.6) (top): L. Manning
p. 372 (12.7) (top, left): T. Street-Porter / Beateworks
p. 373 (12.8): D. Wilson
p. 376 (12.13): L. Kennedy
p. 386 (12.26) (right): M. Prince
p. 387: M. Chew
p. 391: D. Lees
p. 407 (12.55): J. Craigmyle
p. 407: L. Clarke
p. 411 (top, right): O. van der Wal

CORBIS / BETTMANN
p. 21
p. 26 (1.34)
p. 40
p. 179
p. 191
p. 251
p. 252
p. 276
p. 372 (12.7) (top, middle)

CORBIS / PHOTOCUISINE
p. 10 (1.9) (bottom, right): Maximilian Stock Ltd.
p. 10 (1.9) (top, right): Gaurier
p. 10 (1.9) (top, left): Bagros
p. 11 (1.12) (left): Maximilian Stock Ltd.

p. 30 (1.37): J. Riou
p. 160 (6.1): B. Lawton
p. 264 (6) (bottom):
    Maximilian Stock Ltd.
p. 264 (6) (top): Hall

CORBIS / REUTERS
p. 121 (4.46): C. Muschi
p. 121: S. Best
p. 180: T. Melville
p. 370 (12.5) (bending): J. Young
p. 390

CORBIS / SYGMA
p. 25 (bottom): L. Dan
p. 297: T. Jacques
p. 316 (10.20) (left, bottom):
    R. Bossu
p. 336 (11.1): P. Vauthey
p. 365 (11.40): C. Murray

CORBIS / ZEFA
p. 19 (1.24): B. Sporrer
p. 42 (2.16): P. Leonard
p. 59 (top): K. Zukowski
p. 66 (3.2): A. Inden
p. 67 (3.7): A. Inden
p. 67 (3.7): M. Kulka
p. 98 (right): M. Kulka
p. 157 (5.38): M. Kulka
p. 161 (6.2): Emely
p. 209 (7.11) (middle, bottom):
    I. Hatz
p. 228: S. Schuetz
p. 283 (9.22) (celestial body):
    J. Westrich
p. 325 (10.36): C. Collins
p. 368 (12.1): Newmann
p. 370 (12.5) (tension): A. Scott
p. 376: H. Sitton
p. 406 (12.51): L. Nelson /
    Stock Photo

CP IMAGES
p. 15 (1.17)
p. 32 (bottom)
p. 61
p. 193: R. Rycroft
p. 199 (6.52)
p. 208
p. 233 (7.58)
p. 378

CSA
p. 280 (9.19)
p. 280 (9.19)
p. 297 (9.39)

DORLING KINDERSLEY
p. 10 (1.9) (bottom, middle):
p. 11 (1.10)
p. 20 (1.27) (bottom, middle):
p. 20 (1.27) (bottom, left)
p. 20 (1.27) (top, right)
p. 70 (3.11)
p. 75 (3.20)

p. 167 (6.10)
p. 171 (6.17) (left)
p. 173 (6.20)
p. 173 (6.21)
p. 177 (6.25)
p. 177 (6.26)
p. 182 (6.32)
p. 188 (6.43)
p. 191 (6.47)
p. 202 (7.1)
p. 211 (7.15)
p. 213 (7.19)
p. 215 (7.24)
p. 217 (7.29)
p. 221 (7.38)
p. 222 (7.39)
p. 223 (7.42)
p. 226 (7.50)
p. 300 (10.1)
p. 307 (10.9)
p. 309 (10.10) (dinosaurs)
p. 314
p. 393 (top)
p. 405 (12.50)

ELEKTA
p. 156 (right)

ERPI PHOTO LIBRARY
p. 2
p. 4 (top)
p. 32 (top)
p. 49 (2.34)
p. 64 (top)
p. 66 (3.1)
p. 67 (3.3)
p. 76 (3.25)
p. 90 (top)
p. 106
p. 122 (top)
p. 124 (top)
p. 158 (bottom)
p. 158 (top)
p. 163 (6.3) (proteins) (right)
p. 163 (6.3) (carbohydrates) (right)
p. 169 (6.13)
p. 197
p. 200
p. 207
p. 231
p. 234
p. 254 (8.24)
p. 264 (5)
p. 267
p. 270
p. 272 (top)
p. 278 (9.8)
p. 282
p. 332
p. 334 (top)
p. 366 (top)
p. 374 (12.11)
p. 375 (12.12)
p. 386 (12.24) (right)

p. 398
p. 412 (12.57)

**FUNDAMENTAL
PHOTOGRAPHS, NYC**
p. 56 (2.51): R. Mathena

GETTY IMAGES
p. 67 (3.5): J. Spielman /
    Photographer's Choice
p. 98 (left): L. Lefkowitz / Taxi
p. 389 (12.28) (right): Photonica /
    Southern Stock
p. 411 (top): H. Sieplinga / Riser /
    HMS Images
p. 412 (12.56): 3D4 Medical.com

GETTY IMAGES / STONE
p. 86 (bottom, right): T. Flach
p. 94 (4.7): Dale & Newton
p. 163 (6.3) (vitamins) (right):
    Davies & Starr
p. 298: R. Wells
p. 329: R. Wells
p. 369 (12.4): M. Schreiber

GETTY IMAGES / THE IMAGE BANK
p. 73 (3.17): Z. Macaulay
p. 393 (bottom): P. LaCroix

INSTITUT ARMAND-FRAPPIER
p. 269

ISTOCKPHOTO
p. 10 (1.9) (bottom, left): A. Rohde
p. 10 (1.9) (top, middle):
    O. Shelego
p. 12 (1.3): O. Shelego
p. 15 (top): C. Silva
p. 19 (1.25): K. Cline
p. 19 (1.26): J. Blake
p. 39 (2.11): J. A. Snover
p. 42 (2.14)
p. 50 (2.35): S. Roberts
p. 56 (2.50) (right): C. Bishop
p. 57 (2.54): R. de Aguiar Campo
p. 58 (2.57): R. Adrian
p. 59 (middle, bottom): M. Lane
p. 67 (3.6): C. Balderas
p. 70 (3.10): Y.-F. Chen
p. 75 (3.22): M. Balcerzak
p. 76 (3.26): S. Nel
p. 77: D. Lewis
p. 92 (4.1): I. Tischenko
p. 96 (4.12)
p. 99 (middle): J. Steidl
p. 99 (left): J. Hunkele
p. 103 (4.21): L. Pastore
p. 105 (4.23): J. Maree
p. 105 (4.24): T. Gufler
p. 108 (4.30): E. Snow
p. 110 (4.33)
p. 111 (4.34): N. Chan
p. 124 (bottom): K. Russ
p. 155: K. Russ